PRENTICE HALL

Chemistry

Small-Scale Chemistry Laboratory Manual

TEACHER'S EDITION

Edward L. Waterman
Stephen Thompson

PEARSON

Prentice
Hall

Boston, Massachusetts
Upper Saddle River, New Jersey

ACKNOWLEDGMENTS

Many people contributed ideas and resource during the development and writing of this small-scale laboratory manual. Mrs. Jackie Resseguie prepared solutions, organized equipment, and provided other logistical support during the early stages of the experimental design. Peter Markow created the original formulation of the Thompson-Markow universal indicator and designed the first prototype of the small-scale balance, which has since been modified and refined over the years by chemistry students at Rocky Mountain High School. These same students provided uncounted suggestions about the manuscript and numerous modifications of the experiments as they worked through them over the years. Bill Cook and Karen Dixon were enthusiastic cheerleaders at the appropriate moments. John Knight and Nicki Miller provided thoughts and insights as they worked through the experiments with their own students. The US West Foundation and the Hach Scientific Foundation provided resources to make the most of the time spent preparing the manuscript. Finally, a special thanks goes to Mrs. Kathryn C. Hach for her unparalleled love for and commitment to laboratory chemistry and the students who study it.

Cover photograph: Image from Getty Images, Inc.

ISBN 0-13-190366-7

5 6 7 8 9 10   09 08 07 06

CONTENTS OF THE TEACHER'S EDITION

WHAT IS SMALL-SCALE CHEMISTRY?

Prentice Hall's *Small-Scale Chemistry Laboratory Manual* is designed to provide a complete laboratory program for a full-year course in first-year high school chemistry. Small-scale chemistry employs inexpensive, and for the most part, locally available plastic equipment, such as soda straws, cups, disposable pipets, and file protectors, to carry out surprisingly sophisticated and diverse chemical investigations on a small scale. Rather than using conventional glassware, such as beakers and test tubes, students perform qualitative experiments on hydrophobic plastic surfaces. Students also build, calibrate, and use quantitative instruments, such as balances, digital burets, spectroscopes, and pH meters.

This *Small-Scale Chemistry Laboratory Manual* contains both qualitative and quantitative studies of each of the major classes of chemical reactions as well as studies of chemical principles commonly covered in high school chemistry. Literally hundreds of chemical reactions are covered, including acid–base, precipitation, oxidation–reduction, organic, and biomolecule reactions. Those chemical reactions and principles are applied to solving many problems related to consumer and environmental chemistry.

Small-scale chemistry is designed to put the learning of chemistry into the hands of students. Students learn to do real experiments rather than just following recipes. Students participate in creative problem solving, invention, analytical thinking, effective writing, and descriptive chemistry while following the content of a standard high school chemistry curriculum.

Small-scale chemistry is designed to create a laboratory-based instructional chemistry program that fosters student creativity, invention, and problem solving. Small-scale was not developed simply to do better what traditional laboratory environments try to do. Small-scale does not, for example, miniaturize traditional experiments. Forty-one original small-scale experiments focus students' attention on concepts, thought processes, and invention. Students are given the freedom to design their own lab apparatus and procedures. Small-scale creates an environment where students make original discoveries, accumulate new knowledge, and participate in creating methods for investigating the chemical world.

Finally, small-scale chemistry solves some of the most burdensome problems of conventional chemistry laboratories. Historically, traditional labs have been designed around conventional pieces of equipment such as beakers, flasks, and Bunsen burners. By their very nature, these apparatus, developed in the nineteenth century, dictate experimental methodology, the types of experiments that can be performed, the time constraints, and the physical scale of experiments. By redefining the philosophy, the equipment, and the practice of the instructional chemistry laboratory, small-scale solves the problems of costly equipment and chemicals, safety and teacher liability, time constraints, class size, chemical waste disposal, and related environmental concerns.

WHY USE SMALL-SCALE CHEMISTRY?

Small-scale chemistry is relatively safe. Small-scale builds in safety at the design stage of an experiment rather than consigning teachers to try to control hazards at the execution stage. Hazardous reagents and procedures are eliminated as the experiments are designed. For example, solution concentrations are usually about $0.2M$, and concentrations never exceed $1.0M$. Plastic thin-stemmed pipets, originally designed for biomedical research, serve both as liquid-storage vessels and transfer devices. Each pipet delivers only about 20 microliters of dilute solution. The potential for major accidents in traditional labs is replaced by minor inconveniences in small-scale labs.

Small-scale chemistry is time-efficient. Setup is made easy for the teacher and the student. The experimental format does not rely on lengthy written instructions. Instead, the directions are easy to read and follow. Experimental results are immediate and obvious, and the time students take to set up, manipulate, and clean equipment is minimal. Teachers are available to spend their valuable time and energy interacting with students during the laboratory. The simplicity of the experiments also enhances learning outcomes. The simple organization under the reaction surface helps students accurately record, compare, and correlate their data. Students focus on what's happening rather than on what to do. The teacher decides and chooses which learning outcomes are best for the class.

Small-scale chemistry labs have less environmental impact than do conventional chemistry labs. Cleanup with a paper towel takes seconds, and the minute quantities of chemicals can be disposed of safely, usually in the waste bin. As many school districts trim budgets and tighten regulations on the use and disposal of school-laboratory chemicals, small-scale offers immediate solutions. The small amounts of common, relatively safe chemicals employed never become a waste-management problem.

Small-scale chemistry can be used as the central focus of a high school chemistry course. Teachers can build the conventional content around the lab where it seems to fit. For example, students write and balance only those chemical equations for reactions that they have carried out in the lab. Quantitative concepts, such as stoichiometry, are well suited for lab-centered teaching. Thus, teachers can bring the content of chemistry into the laboratory. Through small-scale, students can and do learn much more chemistry than they can through conventional labs. In addition, they learn to be creative and inventive with chemistry; to be good problem solvers; and to communicate effectively.

Small-scale is relatively safe, time-efficient, easy to set up, and environmentally sound. Small-scale enhances learning outcomes, provides for lab-practical evaluations, and teaches chemistry through direct, hands-on experience. Most important, small-scale creates an environment where students can do serious science. It is an environment where the teacher does not already know all the answers but forms partnerships with the students to devise methods of finding answers. Small-scale actively engages students in the processes of creativity and invention. Finally, small-scale teaches students and teachers to ask questions but not to be satisfied with the answers.

TEACHER'S GUIDE TO SAFETY WITH SMALL-SCALE CHEMISTRY

Handling chemicals of any kind in a high school lab setting always poses significant safety concerns. Though small-scale quantities and techniques are far safer than those used in conventional chemistry labs, and the experiments in this book were carefully constructed with safety in mind, some safety issues remain. The following suggestions should help minimize risk in your small-scale laboratory.

One of the largest potential problems is that students might use small-scale pipets as squirt guns. This misuse cannot be tolerated and

requires immediate action on your part at the first sign of such a problem. To show your resolve to curtail this behavior, consider removing from the laboratory area any student who uses small-scale pipets in unauthorized ways.

Hold students accountable not only for what they learn in the lab, but also for their behavior while learning it. Consider periodically giving students a safety grade based on how safe their behavior is in the laboratory. You may also want to give an "environmental" grade based on how environmentally sound their cleaning methods are. Be sure to stress cleaning the small-scale reaction surface in a way that the solutions touch only the paper towel and not the students' hands. Make available a container of liquid soap at every lab table, and insist that students wash their hands thoroughly when they finish cleaning up.

Solutions used in this book never exceed 1.0M and are usually 0.1M or 0.2M. Do not let students handle chemical solutions with a concentration greater than 1.0M. Always dilute concentrated acids yourself, by slowly and carefully adding them to water. In small-scale, it is unnecessary for high school students to conduct this very dangerous procedure. You may want to make up stock solutions of 3.0M acids and use these to prepare 1.0M solutions as you need them. This practice minimizes your own exposure to concentrated acids.

Keep your chemical storage area secure from students. Do not store chemicals alphabetically. Store chemicals by an approved method.

The National Electrical Code now requires that ground-fault-circuit-interrupter (GFCI) receptacles be installed in homes where an electrical outlet is within six feet of a kitchen or bathroom sink. Consider having your school install ground-fault-protected receptacles wherever electrical outlets are within six feet of a laboratory sink. This will greatly reduce the risk of death by electrocution if a student happens to come into simultaneous contact with a grounded metal plumbing fixture or a concrete floor and an electrical appliance such as a hot plate or light fixture. Be sure to inspect your electrical appliances on a regular basis, and replace faulty cords and equipment immediately.

Bunsen burners, alcohol burners, or open flames of any kind are not appropriate for small-scale because they provide sources of heat that are far too intense for small-scale quantities. Use hot plates only on their lowest settings for heating small-scale quantities. Keep in mind too that most commercial hot plates are not designed for small-scale quantities. They can become excessively hot! If you do not have access to low-temperature hot plates, the evaporations required in some of the experiments can be done overnight at room temperature.

Always model good safety practices for your students. Wear safety goggles when it is appropriate. If you do not have a sterilization procedure for safety goggles, consider requiring students to purchase and maintain their own safety goggles. This greatly reduces the risk of students transmitting skin diseases and eye infections.

HOW TO SET UP AND RUN A SMALL-SCALE CHEMISTRY LABORATORY

Efficient organization on the part of the teacher is a key to running a successful small-scale chemistry lab program. Here are some suggestions for the setup and day-to-day operations of a small-scale laboratory.

1. Assemble the following list of basic equipment. The quantities here assume you plan to convert your laboratory to small-scale chemistry entirely and further, that you will teach 5 to 6 sections of chemistry per day, with 24 students per section. You will need to adjust the numbers if you plan to use fewer small-scale labs your first year to augment your traditional program.

   4 boxes of thin-stemmed plastic disposable pipets (500 per box), to store and deliver liquids.

   50 plastic reagent bottles (250 mL), to store prepared solutions.

   10 plastic reagent bottles (1.0 L), to store prepared solutions.

   60 plastic screw-capped specimen jars (60 mL), to fill pipets.

   60 plastic cups (12 ounce), to store sets of pipets.

   120 plastic pill vials (30–60 mL), to store and dispense solid reagents.

   1 plastic "egg crate" light panel (2 feet × 4 feet, cut) to hold pipets for easy access.

   48 small-scale reaction surfaces (file protectors or overhead projection transparencies), to mix chemicals qualitatively.

   24 well plates (1 × 12), to calibrate pipets.

   12 pairs of scissors, to construct instruments.

   12 office hole punches (1/4-inch), to construct instruments.

   6 standard staplers, to construct instruments.

   150 plastic cups (1-ounce), for titrations and balance pans.

   150 plastic cups (3 1/2-ounce), for titrations and chromatography.

2. Prepare the reagent solutions on the Master Solutions List. Store each reagent solution in an appropriately sized plastic reagent bottle. Label each bottle with the concentration, the chemical formula of the contents, the number of grams of solute per volume of solution, and the date of preparation (e.g., $1M$ NaCl, 14.6 g per 250 mL, Jan. 20, 2006). When a reagent bottle is empty, simply make a new solution from the labeled directions and change the date. You do not have to make all the solutions at once; prepare the necessary solutions only for the first lab. Then as the year goes on, you can add solutions as you need them. By the end of your first year of small-scale chemistry, you will have a complete set that will need only occasional maintenance. Once a small-scale lab is set up, a teacher in charge of 5 sections of 24 students each should count on replenishing about 10 to 15 solutions a year.

3. Store each reagent bottle in a dedicated place. The storage area should be secure from students but easily accessible by a teacher during a laboratory period. The prepared solutions and solids in this manual require approximately 36 feet of shelf space.

4. For a classroom of 24 students, prepare and label 15 small-scale pipets and one 60-mL screw-capped plastic specimen jar (reagent-filling container) for each of the solutions listed on the Master Solutions List. Fill each set of pipets and store them stem-up in a labeled 12-ounce plastic cup on the shelf

along with the reagent bottle and plastic specimen jar. To save time, you may want to spend a few minutes in class having students pull pipets and tape labels on them. Use a computer to make labels or print the number of labels you need before you cut them out and tape them to the pipets.

5. Cut the egg-crate plastic light panel into small sections to use as pipet racks. Wear safety goggles and use a hacksaw. This is a job you have to do only once. Cut sections that are 3 squares by 10 squares, which will hold as many as 30 pipets.

6. When it is time to set up a lab, place one pipet of each of the reagents needed in the lab in 12 small-scale pipet racks. Distribute the reagent sets to your lab tables. Two students can share a set of reagents even if they are doing the lab individually. Leave three pipets of each solution in reserve in your storage area. Alternatively, you may want to set out the 12-ounce storage cups with sets of pipets in them. Let students be responsible for obtaining their own racks of pipets at the beginning of the lab and returning them at the end.

7. Fill empty pipets as students call your attention to them. Because students often need only one or two drops of each reagent, many pipets will not need filling until after several sections of students have done the lab. You may want to set out selected reagent bottles of chemicals when students need larger quantities, and teach them how to fill their own pipets, as described on page 8.

8. When the lab is finished, return the pipets to their storage cups. You may want to leave one or two sets out for another day or two to accommodate students who were absent during the lab.

9. For a classroom of 24 students, prepare and label plastic pill vials (30–60 mL) for each solid on the Master Solids list. Punch small holes in the lids and cover them with tape. To use the vials, students can remove the tape and carefully shake out the desired quantity. Store the solids in the plastic pill vials with the openings taped. You can store each set in a large plastic cup or in a standard plastic ice-cube tray.

HOW TO USE THIS BOOK

Prentice Hall's *Small-Scale Chemistry Laboratory Manual* is designed to be used in a variety of ways. Each experiment includes a reference to an appropriate section of the textbook, a set of Objectives, an Introduction, an Experimental Page or Experimental Procedure, an Experimental Data section, a Questions for Analyses section, and a Now It's Your Turn section.

The Experimental Page is designed to give students the instructions they need to carry out the basic experiment. In many labs, students place the Experimental Page under a plastic reaction surface and do the experiment on top of the page, following the directions that show through the plastic. Often the Experimental Page is marked with black X's where students are to place drops of solutions. These X's provide both black and white backgrounds against which students can observe reaction mixtures. In the labs where the Experimental Page is not used under a reaction surface, the heading Experimental Procedure indicates this difference.

The Experimental Data section follows the Experimental Page. Here students record their data as they do the experiment. You may choose to have students write their experimental results directly into a lab notebook. In this case, they would use the printed Experimental Data table(s) as an example and construct a similar table(s) in their notebooks.

The Questions for Analyses section allows students to think about and write about the main points of each experiment. You may want to have students work on these questions as they do the lab, assign the questions as homework, or ask students to answer the questions in their laboratory notebooks for future reference.

The Now It's Your Turn section suggests some extended experiments that ask students to apply what they learned in the basic experiment. Specific instructions are not always given; students are left to decide for themselves what to do based on what they have learned in the basic experiment. Depending on the time you want to spend and the depth at which you want to cover the material, you may want to assign one item or all the items in this section. Some of the Now It's Your Turn items could be used for lab-practical exams. Students may suggest other experiments to try. Be open to their ideas and let them try other experiments that you consider to be appropriate and safe.

EVALUATION OF STUDENT LEARNING THROUGH SMALL-SCALE CHEMISTRY

The following list provides some suggestions for how you could evaluate what your students learn from doing small-scale chemistry laboratories.

1. **Lab notebook:** Rather than having students write lab reports or hand in data sheets, you may want to have them keep a laboratory notebook. The lab notebook is a real-time, permanent, handwritten record of all of a student's laboratory experiences, including dates, titles, experimental procedures, data, conclusions, and further research and investigations. Pick the lab notebooks up periodically, and grade them for completeness rather than for specific details. With only a quick glance you can verify that a student has kept his or her work up to date. You may be less interested in format than in how well students can use their own lab records to solve problems. In this case, look for signs of creativity, invention, problem solving, and good thought processes. Tell students beforehand what you are looking for. You may want to give extra credit for evidence of creativity or invention. For example, students might discover interesting new questions or ways to solve problems, or a student might choose to write the lab procedure in cartoon format.

2. **Open-lab-notebook tests:** To check for details and understanding, you may want to give students regular lab tests and allow them to use their own handwritten notes to answer the questions. Try to balance the range of questions from knowledge-level questions to those that evaluate comprehension, analysis, synthesis, evaluation, and creativity. Students soon learn that to score well on these exams, they must not only bring to class a well-written lab book, but they must be able to use it to interpret their results and to suggest new questions and experiments.

3. **Closed-book tests:** Some skills learned in the lab need to be internalized by any student of chemistry. Use closed-book tests to evaluate how well students have learned these skills. For example, test students' abilities to write and balance equations.

4. **Laboratory-practical exams:** Small-scale chemistry lends itself well to the direct hands-on evaluation of problem solving using both qualitative and quantitative analysis. Variations of the unknowns in Small-Scale Experiments 22 and 23 provide good examples. Quantitative titrations of unknowns in Small-Scale Experiments 18 and 19 provide others. The various items in the Now It's Your Turn sections provide still other possibilities for lab-practical exams.

5. **Writing essays:** Consider having students write short essays on their conclusions of various labs. Try to assign essays that bring creativity and original thought out of students. For example, upon measuring vitamin C in various fruit juices in Small-Scale Experiment 39, you might assign this: "Write a letter to the editor of the local newspaper telling him or her of your findings and recommendations," or "Write to a scientist explaining your results, and ask him for additional information on vitamin C."

MASTER MATERIALS LIST

The following lists give all chemicals necessary to do all the experiments in Prentice Hall's *Small-Scale Chemistry Laboratory Manual*. The first is an alphabetical list of chemical solutions. Indicator solutions follow in a separate alphabetical list. The last two lists are the Master Solids List and the Master Household Products List.

MASTER SOLUTIONS LIST

The most efficient way to organize your small-scale lab is to make up the appropriate aqueous solutions and use and replace them as needed. Store each solution in a plastic reagent bottle. Depending on the labs you do, some solutions will have to be replaced several times during the year, and others will last the entire year. Most solutions are 0.1M or 0.2M. In no case is any solution in greater concentration that 1.0M. Also, in no case are there two different concentrations of the same chemical. For example, all the experiments that use sodium hydroxide use 0.5M NaOH. All salts are anhydrous unless the hydrated formula is given.

Label each reagent bottle with the chemical formula, the concentration, the number of grams of solute per volume of solution, and the date. When the bottle is empty, simply replenish it by following the directions on the label, and change the date. When making dilute acid solutions from concentrated acids, remember always to add acid to water slowly and carefully. **Be sure to make up all solutions with the quantities given to a volume of 250 mL, unless one liter or 50 mL is specified.**

Chemical	Quantity	Concentration	Experiments
ethanoic acid, CH_3COOH	Use commercial vinegar.	0.8M (5%)	8, 14, 15, 16, 18, 19, 25, 31, 32, 33
aluminum chloride hexahydrate, $AlCl_3 \cdot 6H_2O$	12.1 g	0.2M	10, 25, 26
ammonia, NH_3	67 mL conc. in 1.0 L	1.0M	2, 14, 15, 17, 22, 23, 24, 25, 29, 31, 32, 33
ammonium chloride, NH_4Cl	13.4 g	1.0M	12, 21, 26, 32, 33
boric acid, H_3BO_3	7.8 g	0.5M	30, 32
calcium chloride, $CaCl_2$	14.2 g	0.5M	2, 10, 12, 17, 19, 22, 23, 25, 26
calcium hydroxide, $Ca(OH)_2$	1.0 g, then filter	saturated	12, 15, 32
citric acid, $C_6H_8O_7$	9.6 g	0.2M	30, 32
copper(II) sulfate pentahydrate, $CuSO_4 \cdot 5H_2O$	12.5 g	0.2M	2, 10, 12, 17, 22, 23, 25, 26, 29, 34, 35, 36, 40
ethylenediamine tetraacetic acid, EDTA, $(C_{10}H_{16}N_2O_2)$	0.744 g in 1.0 L	0.002M	25
hydrochloric acid, HCl	82 mL of 12M in 1.0 L	1.0M	2, 14, 15, 17, 18, 19, 20, 21, 22, 23, 24, 25, 28, 29, 31, 33, 35, 41
hydrogen peroxide, H_2O_2	Use commercial.	3%	17, 21, 25, 28
iron(III) chloride, hexahydrate, $FeCl_3 \cdot 6H_2O$	6.8 g in 250 mL of 0.1M NaCl	0.1M	10, 12, 17, 22, 23, 24, 25, 26, 28, 29, 35, 37
iron(II) sulfate, $FeSO_4$	3.8 g in 50 mL 1.0M H_2SO_4, enough water to make 250 mL		33

Chemical	Quantity	Concentration	Experiments
lead(II) nitrate, $Pb(NO_3)_2$	16.6 g	0.2M	2, 12, 17, 19, 22, 23, 28, 29, 36
magnesium sulfate, $MgSO_4$	6.0 g	0.2M	10, 12, 26, 36
nickel(II) sulfate, $NiSO_4$	2.94 g	0.2M	10
nitric acid, HNO_3	63 mL 15.8M in 10. L	1.0M	14, 15, 18, 19, 21, 22, 23, 25, 29, 31, 32
phosphoric acid, H_3PO_4	67.5 mL 14.8M in 1.0 L	1.0M	14, 25, 30, 31, 33
potassium bromide, KBr	6.0 g	0.2M	12, 17
potassium chloride, KCl	7.5 g	0.4M	17, 33
potassium dichromate, $K_2Cr_2O_7$	7.3 g	0.1M	35
potassium fluoride, KF	5.8 g	0.4M	12, 17
potassium hydroxide, KOH	2.8 g	0.2M	15, 24, 25, 37
potassium iodate, KIO_3	5.35 g	0.1M	17, 28, 35, 38, 39
potassium iodide, KI	4.2 g	0.1M	1, 2, 12, 16, 17, 21, 22, 23, 26, 28, 33, 35, 38, 39, 40
potassium permanganate, $KMnO_4$	0.16 g	0.02M	21, 35
potassium thiocyanate, KSCN	2.4 g	0.1M	29
silver nitrate, $AgNO_3$	2.1 g	0.05M	2, 10, 12, 17, 19, 22, 23, 26, 29, 34, 36
sodium ethanoate, CH_3COONa	10.3 g	0.5M	12, 14, 32, 33
sodium carbonate, Na_2CO_3	26.3 g	1.0M	2, 10, 12, 14, 19, 22, 23, 25, 26, 29
sodium chloride, NaCl	14.6 g	1.0M	10, 11, 12, 26
sodium dihydrogen phosphate, NaH_2PO_4	17.2 g	0.50M	12, 14, 32, 33
sodium hydrogen carbonate, $NaHCO_3$	21 g	1.0M	2, 12, 14, 21, 25, 28, 32, 33
sodium hydrogen phosphate, Na_2HPO_4	7.1 g	0.2M	12, 14, 32
sodium hydrogen sulfate $NaHSO_4$	34.5 g	1.0M	2, 14, 25, 32
sodium hydrogen sulfite, $NaHSO_3$	2.6 g	0.1M	14, 21, 32, 35
sodium hydroxide, NaOH	20.0 g in 1.0 L	0.5M	2, 10, 12, 14, 18, 19, 21, 22, 23, 25, 26, 29, 31, 33, 40
sodium hypochlorite, NaClO	Dilute 50 mL household bleach with 200 mL water.	1.0%	1, 2, 17, 21, 28, 35, 40
sodium nitrate, $NaNO_3$	4.26 g	0.2M	26, 36
sodium nitrite, $NaNO_2$	6.9 g	0.4M	12, 21, 32, 35
sodium phosphate, dodecahydrate, $Na_3PO_4 \cdot 12H_2O$	9.5 g	0.1M	10, 12, 14, 22, 23, 25, 26, 32
sodium sulfate, Na_2SO_4	7.1 g	0.2M	26
sodium thiosulfate pentahydrate, $Na_2S_2O_3 \cdot 5H_2O$	24.8 g	0.1M	16, 17, 28, 29, 35

Chemical	Quantity	Concentration	Experiments
starch	Dilute 50 mL liquid household starch with 200 mL water.	20%	2, 17, 21, 35, 38, 39, 40
sulfuric acid, H_2SO_4	56 mL 18M in 1.0 L	1.0M	14, 15, 18, 19, 21, 22, 23, 25, 28, 32
tin(IV) chloride pentahydrate, $SnCl_4 \cdot 5H_2O$	17.6 g	0.2M	12
zinc chloride, $ZnCl_2$	6.8 g	0.2M	25, 26, 34, 36

MASTER INDICATOR SOLUTIONS LIST

Indicator	Quantity	Concentration	Experiments
alizarine yellow R, AYR	50 mg	0.02%	14, 30
blue dye	15 drops blue food coloring		
bromcresol green, BCG*	100 mg in 14.3 mL 0.01M NaOH	0.04%	14
bromphenol blue, BPB*	100 mg in 14.9 mL 0.01M NaOH	0.04%	14, 15, 17, 19, 21, 24, 29, 32
bromthymol blue, BTB*†	100 mg in 16.0 mL 0.01M NaOH	0.04%	14, 15
FD&C blue #1‡	50 mg in 50 mL water	0.1%	2, 11
FD&C blue #2	50 mg in 50 mL water	0.1%	11
FD&C green #3	50 mg in 50 mL water	0.1%	11
FD&C blue #3	50 mg in 50 mL water	0.1%	11
FD&C red #40	50 mg in 50 mL water	0.1%	11
FD&C yellow #5	50 mg in 50 mL water	0.1%	11
FD&C yellow #6	50 mg in 50 mL water	0.1%	11
meta cresol purple, MCP*	100 mg in 26.2 mL 0.01M NaOH	0.04%	14
methyl orange, MO	125 mg	0.05%	14
methyl red, MR	50 mg in 250 mL 70% 2-propanol	0.02%	14, 15, 18
phenolphthalein, phen	250 mg in 250 mL 70% 2-propanol	0.10%	2, 14, 15, 18, 19, 21, 41
Sudan III	50 mg in 50 mL rubbing alcohol	0.1%	40
thymol blue, TB*	100 mg in 21.5 mL 0.01M NaOH	0.04%	14
universal indicator, UI	See formulation directions for UI in the Teaching Suggestions for Small-Scale Experiment 31.		19, 30, 31, 32, 33

*If this indicator is available as the sodium salt, dissolve directly in 250 mL of deionized or distilled water.

†The final solution of bromthymol blue should be green. If it is yellow, add 0.01M NaOH drop by drop with stirring until it is green. If it is blue, add 0.01M HCl drop by drop with stirring until it is green.

‡FD&C dyes are used in consumer products as colorants and are certified by the FDA. The set used in this text is available from Rainbow Colors, 286 Baxter St., Tolland, CT 06084.

MASTER SOLIDS LIST

Fill six 30 to 60 mL plastic pill vials with each solid. Use a 1/4-inch office hole punch to make a hole in each plastic lid. Cover the hole with plastic tape. Label each vial and store each set of six in plastic ice cube trays. When a laboratory calls for a solid, distribute the set of six vials among 24 students.

Solid	Experiments
ammonium chloride, NH_4Cl	24, 28
calcium carbonate, $CaCO_3$ (granular)	28
calcium chloride, $CaCl_2$	24
chalk	13
copper, Cu	34, 36
eriochrome black-T, Ero-T*	25
fluorite	13
glass marble	13
hematite	13
iron, Fe (granular)	34
lead, Pb	36
magnesium, Mg (turnings)	28, 32, 34, 36, 41
polystyrene peanut	13
potassium chloride, KCl	24
silver, Ag	34, 36
sodium carbonate, Na_2CO_3	1, 24
sodium chloride, NaCl (rock salt)	24
sodium chloride, NaCl (table salt)	11, 13, 24, 25
sucrose, $C_{12}H_{22}O_{11}$	13, 24, 40
zinc, Zn (granular)	28, 36

* Mix 0.1 g of erinochrome black -T with 100 g of sodium chloride (table salt), thoroughly.

MASTER HOUSEHOLD PRODUCTS LIST

Obtain one container of each of the following household products. Store liquids in their original containers. When a laboratory lists a household product, place it where it is accessible to students working in the lab.

Household Product	Experiments
ammonia	14, 15, 30
antacid (tablets)	14, 15, 24, 30, 33
aspirin	14, 30, 33
baking powder	14, 24, 30, 33
baking soda	2, 14, 30, 33
beans, dry	2, 6, 40
bleach, liquid containing NaClO	2, 14, 16, 21, 28, 35, 40
cabbage juice	14, 16, 30
cola	14, 24, 30, 40
copper polish	34
cream of tartar	14, 30, 33
grape juice	14, 16, 30
glass cleaner, liquid	2, 14, 30, 33
laundry detergent, powdered	2, 14, 30
lemon juice	14, 15, 30
milk, powdered	14, 30, 40
orange juice, canned, frozen, fresh	11, 14, 30, 39
oven cleaner (Bicarbonate based. Do not use products containing lye.)	2, 14, 30
peas, dry	2, 6, 40
pens, colored felt-tipped	2, 16, 30
popcorn, dry unpopped	2, 6, 40
rubbing alcohol, 70% 2-propanol	11, 24
rubbing alcohol, 70% ethanol	11, 24
salt, iodized	2
salt, noniodized	2, 11, 24, 30
sidewalk de-icer ($CaCl_2$ or KCl)	2
silver polish	34
soft-drink mixes, dry (Kool-Aid)	2, 11, 14, 16, 30
starch, liquid	2, 16, 21, 30, 35, 40
toilet-bowl cleaner containing HCl	2, 14, 18, 19, 30

Household Product	Experiments
toilet-bowl cleaner containing $NaHSO_4$	2, 14, 24, 30
vinegar	14, 15, 18, 30
vitamin C tablets (100 mg)	14, 30, 38

MASTER EQUIPMENT LIST

All equipment quantities in the Teaching Suggestions for each experiment are given per student unless otherwise indicated. The Common Equipment, mentioned in the Teaching Suggestions, is to be shared among students.

Equipment	Experiments
acid resin ion exchanger	25
adhesive label	3, 4, 5, 7
alcohol thermometer	27
atomic emission tubes and sources	8
boxes, various shapes and sizes	7
candle	8
chromatography paper	11
clothespins	21
colored construction paper	8
colored plastic light filters	8
conductivity/electrolysis apparatus	24, 32
cotton swab	15, 18
diffraction grating	7
dimes	5, 36
electronic balance (optional)	4, 7, 13, 19, 20, 25, 38, 39
filter paper disks (9 cm)	36
glass slide	15, 16, 24, 40
graph paper, tenth inch	3
hand lens	1
mineral oil	1
nails, galvanized and iron	7
nickels	4, 5, 36
paper clips, jumbo	3
paper clips, standard	3, 4, 20
paper, various kinds	11
paper towels, brands with price tags	20

Equipment	Experiments
pennies	4, 5, 36
pennies, set of 10 from 1978–1987	5
pin, extra-long (1 1/4-inch)	3
plastic cup, 1-ounce	3, 18, 19, 27, 28, 38, 39, 41
plastic cup, 3 1/2-ounce	3, 6, 20
plastic cup, clear	8, 11, 21
plastic light rod (clear plastic picnic knife)	7
plastic spoon	13
polystyrene coffee cup	27
poster board	7, 11, 20
river rock, rounded	1
rubber bands	7
ruler	7
silverware	34
small-scale pipet	2, 5, 12, 14, 15, 22, 23, 26, 29, 30, 31, 32, 38, 40
small-scale pipet rack	2, 5, 12, 14, 15, 22, 23, 26, 29, 30, 31, 32, 38, 40
small-scale reaction surface	1, 2, 10, 12, 14, 15, 16, 21, 22, 23, 24, 26, 28, 29, 30, 31, 32, 33, 34, 35, 36, 38, 40
soda straws, long and short	3, 4, 29
toothpicks	40
typing paper	11, 40
washers, zinc-plated	34
well plate, 1×12	18, 37
wood blocks, drilled	3
zipper-locking plastic bag	4, 37

Common Equipment	Experiments
batteries (dry cells), various, 4 each	36
brass or steel wire, 24-gauge, 1 spool	3, 4
cellophane tape, 6 rolls	3, 7
colored marking pens, 12 sets	11
hot plates, 6	15, 24, 40
model sets, 12 as follows: 6 one-inch polystyrene spheres 12 pop beads 3 black pipe cleaners (30 cm $\times$ 3 mm) 3 white pipe cleaners (30 cm $\times$ 3 mm)	37
hole punches, 1/4-inch, 6	3, 4, 20
scissors, 12 pairs	3, 4, 7, 11, 24, 36, 40
standard staples	4
standard weights, 5 mg	3
staplers, 6	4, 11
teacher-built spectroscope	7
thread, 1 spool	3
volt meters, 12	36
watches or clocks, 12	41

TEACHING SUGGESTIONS FOR SMALL-SCALE EXPERIMENTS

For many of the small-scale labs, students will use the following equipment: a small-scale reaction surface, an empty pipet for stirring, and pipet racks for storing small-scale pipets.

 ## MAKING OBSERVATIONS OF MATTER

Small-Scale Experiment for text Section 1.3

Estimated Class Time: One 50-minute period.
Estimated Teacher Preparation Time: 20 minutes.

OVERVIEW

Students practice making observations and explaining their observations in terms of the behavior of particles at the atomic level.

MATERIALS

Solid sodium chloride, NaCl
Small-scale pipets containing the following:
water
mineral oil
potassium iodide, KI
sodium hypochlorite, NaClO

EQUIPMENT

Hand lens, rounded river rock, conductivity testing device

TEACHING SUGGESTIONS

This lab allows students to become familiar with the use of small-scale equipment and to do qualitative analysis on samples early in the year. You can use file protectors, overhead transparencies, or plastic wrap for the reaction surface.

This lab is designed to get students acting and thinking like scientists. Emphasize the importance of making good observations and using them to solve problems. The intent in this experiment is to convince students that chemical observations can be useful to them in exploring their world.

Although the procedure and observations are relatively simple, because of their lack of experience, your students might find answering the questions difficult. Consider using a class discussion to walk students through each question and answer in the Questions for Analyses section. It is important to focus on the processes of observing and making hypotheses, not on the actual explanations for the changes observed in Experiment 1. At relevant points in the course, you might revisit this experiment and have students offer more complete explanations for what they observed.

A classroom set of a dozen or so golf ball-sized rounded rocks make good instruments for breaking solids. Baby oil can be substituted for mineral oil.

 ## A STUDY OF CHEMICAL CHANGES

Small-Scale Experiment for text Section 2.4

Estimated Class Time: One to three 50-minute periods, depending on how many household products are used in Now It's Your Turn
Estimated Teacher Preparation Time: 20 minutes, after stock solutions are prepared.

OVERVIEW

Students mix solutions and observe a variety of clues to chemical changes (color, bubbles, precipitation). Students learn to recognize distinctive changes and to use them to identify specific substances in household products.

MATERIALS

Small-scale pipets of the following solutions:

sodium hydrogen
  carbonate
  ($NaHCO_3$)
FD&C Blue No. 1
potassium iodide (KI)
calcium chloride
  ($CaCl_2$)
sodium carbonate
  (Na_2CO_3)
sodium hydroxide
  (NaOH)
ammonia (NH_3)
starch

hydrochloric acid
  (HCl)
sodium hypochlorite
  (NaClO)
lead(II) nitrate
  ($Pb(NO_3)_2$)
sodium hydrogen
  sulfate ($NaHSO_4$)
phenolphthalein
silver nitrate ($AgNO_3$)
copper(II) sulfate
  ($CuSO_4$)

HOUSEHOLD PRODUCTS

Baking soda; iodized table salt; cereal, bread, crackers, potato chips, or similar foods containing starch; dishwasher liquid containing NaClO.

TEACHING SUGGESTIONS

Provide each student with an Experimental Page to be placed under the reaction surface. Tell students that the black X's on the Experimental Page serve as contrasting backgrounds for viewing the reactions in the drops of aqueous solutions. Tell them to view their mixtures against both the white and black backgrounds the X's provide.

You may want to emphasize the importance of designing experiments. Even in the first few weeks of a chemistry class, students can design their own experiments. You may want to assign only a portion of Now It's Your Turn, depending on the time you have and the household products available. Place the household products in their original containers in a reagent area common to students. Students should sample them, using clean soda straws. Solids are sampled by making small-scale spatulas as described in "Safe and Efficient Techniques for Using Small-Scale Equipment," and liquids are sampled by dipping the tip of a clean soda straw into the liquid, holding a finger over the open end, and removing a drop to be placed on the reaction surface.

Good lab-practical problems include having students distinguish between iodized and non-iodized salt and between carbonate-based and noncarbonate-based laundry detergents.

3 DESIGN AND CONSTRUCTION OF A SMALL-SCALE BALANCE

Small-Scale Experiment for text Section 3.2

Estimated Class Time: Two 50-minute periods.
Estimated Teacher Preparation Time: 20 minutes, after materials are organized.

OVERVIEW

Students learn that using a balance is the fundamental method of measuring mass. Students practice invention by designing and constructing their own milligram balances, which they use to investigate macroscopic matter.

EQUIPMENT

6 soda straws, extra-long pin (1 1/4-inch), 2 paper clips, adhesive label, drilled wood block, 4 square centimeters of tenth-inch graph paper, plastic cup (1-ounce or 3 1/2-ounce).

COMMON EQUIPMENT

12 pairs of scissors, 1 spool of thread, 1 spool of wire, six 1/4-inch hole punches, 6 rolls of cellophane tape, 36 longer soda straws, standard 5 mg masses.

TEACHING SUGGESTIONS

To prepare for the lab, you need to drill balance bases made from square pieces of 1 × 4's or 2 × 4's. Drill 1/4-inch holes halfway through the wood at the places marked on the diagram on page 32. Each hole should be 3/4 inch from the center.

If the soda straws do not fit snugly in the holes, wrap tape around the ends of the straws. Purchase extra-long straws and plastic cups from a restaurant-supply store or a membership warehouse store. You can buy extra long pins (1 1/4 inch) from a fabric store.

Using the Introduction, go over the basic principles of an operating balance, especially sensitivity, capacity, and the critical parts of a balance, with students. Then let them begin to build the basic balance, as shown in Figure 3.1. As they build it, encourage them to invent and create as they try to improve the major features: a light beam, a frictionless fulcrum, and square angles. Some students will build only the basic balance, but others will make innovations that you will want to share with the rest of the class.

Most students need to be reminded that a freely swinging beam is most important. If students build the basic balance shown in Figure 3.1, they will have a functional instrument that will serve them well if the beam swings freely and without friction.

The pencil holes that hold the pin fulcrum should be made so the head of the pin slips through them easily. After mounting the beam-fulcrum assembly, gently press the posts together to keep the pin from falling out. Do not squeeze so tightly that the ends of the pin touch the insides of the straws. The aim here is to get the beam to swing freely without having the pin fall out.

Some students will choose to build high balances with long pointers so that a small movement in the beam will produce a large movement of the pointer. Discuss with them the trade-off between structural stability problems of high balances versus the greater sensitivity they produce. Students will solve these problems if they are given the time and encouragement to do so. Other students will think they have a better way to design the superstructure and spend their time being creative with it. A few students will want to work on building a better beam-fulcrum assembly. Still other students may want to try a magnetic levitation of the beam by simple electromagnets or permanent magnets. The possibilities for invention are many.

 DESIGN AND CONSTRUCTION OF A SET OF STANDARDIZED MASSES

Small-Scale Experiment for text Section 3.2

Estimated Class Time: One or two 50-minute periods, depending on how much time you allow for invention.

Estimated Teacher Preparation Time: 20 minutes, after purchase of materials.

OVERVIEW

Students learn about calibration and make sets of masses to use with their balances. Invention is the key!

EQUIPMENT

Half-page of graph paper that is divided into tenth-inch squares, standard paper clip, jumbo paper clip, penny, nickel, zipper-locking plastic bag.

COMMON EQUIPMENT

36 soda straws, 12 pairs of scissors, 6 staplers with standard staples, 36 small adhesive labels, six 1/4-inch hole punches, *spool of 24-gauge brass or steel wire.

TEACHING SUGGESTIONS

Standard staples are 33 mg each, one square inch of standard 20-pound paper has a mass of 50 mg, and 1/4-inch disks punched from soda straws are 5 mg each. Photocopied graph paper that is divided in tenths of inches works well, but you can make your own by drawing a grid of square

inches on a standard 8 1/2" × 11" sheet of paper and photocopying it. Because staples are more precisely made than paper, students do best if they use more staples and less paper. Students who make the following mass set will get good results.

5 mg to 30 mg: Use the appropriate number of 1/4-inch soda straw disks.

50 mg: 1 square inch of photocopied graph paper.

100 mg: 2 square inches of photocopied graph paper.

300 mg: 2 square inches of photocopied graph paper + 6 staples.

Masses of 500 mg and larger will not be exactly 500 mg or 1000 mg, but their exact mass can be determined by using the smaller masses. Here are some approximations:

500 mg: One standard paper clip with an adhesive label (1/2" × 3/4")

1500 mg: One jumbo paper clip with an adhesive label (1/2" × 3/4")

2550 mg: One penny (post-1982) with an adhesive label (1/2" × 3/4")

5050 mg: One nickel with an adhesive label (1/2" × 3/4")

If there is an accurate milligram balance in the lab, allow students to check their smaller masses (50–300 mg) against the accurate balance and make the necessary corrections by adding pieces of adhesive labels or cutting off corners. Then they can use the small masses with their small-scale balance to calibrate the larger masses. If an accurate balance is not available, experience has shown that if students are careful, their smaller masses (50–300 mg) are rarely in error by more than a few milligrams. Emphasize the importance of recycling all the materials students do not use.

Given the time and encouragement, students can invent many different kinds of masses. Highly reproducible small objects make the most reliable masses. Stainless-steel or brass wire (28-gauge) can be massed on an analytical or electronic milligram balance and the length of wire needed to make a certain mass can be calculated. The same method works with a soda straw, measuring the straw and cutting an appropriate length. If you have an accurate balance in the lab, students can have fun exploring the precision of all kinds of objects to see which are suitable to use as reliable masses.

*Equipment for Now It's Your Turn.

5 · MASSING ACTIVITIES FOR A SMALL-SCALE BALANCE

Small-Scale Experiment for text Sections 3.1, 3.2, and 3.3

Estimated Class Time: One or two 50-minute periods, depending on how much time you allow for Now It's Your Turn.

Estimated Teacher Preparation Time: 20 minutes, after purchase of materials.

OVERVIEW

Students use their balances to solve a variety of problems associated with matter at the macroscopic level.

EQUIPMENT

Penny, nickel, dime, and enough adhesive labels to attach to them; small-scale balance; small-scale pipet filled with water; *a set of ten pennies representing each year from 1978 to 1987.

TEACHING SUGGESTIONS

This is a good opportunity for students to practice using their balances, test the accuracies of their masses, and solve any problems. If the percent error exceeds 5%, have the student adjust the fulcrum for a frictionless, freely swinging beam, and try again. Students can also check and adjust their masses on an analytical or milligram balance.

Label 48 pennies and find the mass of each on an accurate balance before class so students can know the "accurate" mass. Do not tell them the accurate mass until they have determined the mass using their balances. The experiment is a good blind test of their balances and masses. Once they consistently get the "right" answer, they grow confident in the accuracies of their own balances. Post-1982 pennies have a mass of about 2550 mg with an adhesive label (1/2" × 3/4"). Nickels have a mass of about 5050 mg with labels, and dimes have a mass of about 2250 mg.

Most small-scale pipets deliver around 50 drops per mL (1000 mg) of water. All pipets are different, however, and they often vary ±10 drops per mL. The angle and the air bubble affect the results.

*Equipment for Now It's Your Turn.

For item 1 of Now It's Your Turn, make up sets of ten pennies: one each for the dates 1978 through 1987. Place each set of ten pennies in a zipper-locking plastic bag and label it for easy identification. Some of the 1982 pennies are copper and some are zinc, so students will get varying answers, depending on what sets they have.

6 · ISOTOPES AND ATOMIC MASS

Small-Scale Experiment for text Section 4.3

Estimated Class Time: One 50-minute period.
Estimated Teacher Preparation Time: 15 minutes.

OVERVIEW

Students find the mass of sample mixtures of peas, beans, and corn and use their data to calculate the average mass of all the particles. They relate this to the concept of atomic mass.

EQUIPMENT

A sample of vegium in a plastic cup, balance.

TEACHING SUGGESTIONS

For a class of 24 students, thoroughly mix 1-pound bags each of: dried kidney or pinto beans, dried split peas, and unpopped popcorn. Mass-produce enough samples for your class by dipping out a level 1-ounce plastic cup full of vegium, and place each sample in a 3 1/2-ounce plastic cup to distribute to each student.

When students find the mass of the various kinds of vegium particles, they will encounter some technical problems. For example, the sample of beans might be too large to mass on their balances. Suggest that they solve this problem by making more masses or by using a larger mass on the balance. This approach increases the capacity of the balance. (Remind students that it also results in a heavier beam, which reduces the sensitivity of the balance; there are always trade-offs when designing experiments.) Alternatively, you may want to suggest that they mass a portion of their vegium, say half, and then multiply the result by 2 (or a fifth and multiply by 5). The beans are of various sizes, so if a student masses just one bean and multiplies by the number of beans to get the total mass of beans, a significant error might result.

Emphasize that it is important to mass a large enough sample to get a good estimation of the average mass of a bean.

Although the calculations and concepts are the same for each student, each sample will he slightly different and will yield a slightly different atomic mass. You may want to pursue item 2 of Now It's Your Turn with students. Emphasize the importance of sampling techniques and the size of samples. Larger samples give more homogeneous results. Relate this to the number of atoms in even a very small mass and students should get the idea that it's easier to obtain more consistent samples of atoms than of vegium.

7 DESIGN AND CONSTRUCTION OF A QUANTITATIVE SPECTROSCOPE

Small-Scale Experiment for text Section 5.2

Estimated Class Time: One 50-minute period.

Estimated Teacher Preparation Time: 20 minutes, once materials are purchased.

OVERVIEW

Students build their own small-scale spectroscopes. Students use them to study the interaction of light with matter.

EQUIPMENT

diffraction grating, cut 28-cm × 23.7-cm poster board, 3 rubber bands, plastic light rod, adhesive label.

COMMON EQUIPMENT (per 6 students)

teacher-built spectroscope, 3 rulers, three 2-cm guide strips, 3 pairs of scissors, roll of tape, 3 nails. *Various boxes such as shoe boxes, safety-goggles boxes, toothpaste boxes, pizza boxes, or cereal boxes

TEACHING SUGGESTIONS

Build a few spectroscopes (without diffraction gratings) as examples, and have them available in the lab as students work through the Experimental Page. This exercise will help the students understand how to build their own spectroscopes.

*Equipment for Now It's Your Turn.

The poster board should be a dark color. Black, dark blue, red, or green work equally well. You will need four or five 22-inch × 28-inch (56 cm × 71 cm) standard poster boards for a class of 24 students. To save time and waste, you can precut each standard board to make six equal 23.7-cm × 28-cm pieces.

Cut with a paper cutter several 2-cm × 28-cm guide strips for students to use to trace their borders. This saves them the time of measuring.

Cut the diffraction grating material into 1-cm × 2-cm rectangles with the diffraction lines parallel to the 2-cm side. An 8 1/2-inch × 11-inch piece of diffraction grating material will make about 270 gratings.

The plastic light rods can be made from clear plastic drink stirrers or clear plastic picnic knives. Score each light rod by placing it over the template or a piece of tenth-inch graph paper and carefully making straight parallel scratches every 1/10 inch.

Boxes are good alternatives to poster board. Shoe boxes, safety-goggles boxes, cracker boxes, cereal boxes, and pizza boxes work well. Experiment with sizes and designs.

8 VISIBLE SPECTRA AND THE NATURE OF LIGHT AND COLOR

Small-Scale Experiment for text Section 5.3

Estimated Class Time: One or two 50-minute periods, depending on how much of the Now It's Your Turn you assign.

Estimated Teacher Preparation Time: 20 minutes

OVERVIEW

Using their spectroscopes, students find that there is important chemical information linked to light. They examine emission, reflection, transmission, and absorption.

EQUIPMENT (per 24 students)

Small-scale spectroscope, 4 to 6 fluorescent and incandescent light sources. *4 candles, *4 pieces of colored construction paper (red, blue, green, and yellow), *4 sets of colored plastic filters (red, green, blue, and yellow), *3 to 4 atomic emission tubes and sources, *set of food dye (red, green, blue, and yellow), *16 clear plastic cups.

TEACHING SUGGESTIONS

For light sources, students can use overhead incandescent or fluorescent lights. They can use the incandescent light in an overhead projector if you cover it with white paper and do not let students look directly into it. They can even use its reflection off a white screen.

For reflectance spectra, tape various colors of construction paper to a wall or screen, and shine an overhead projector on them. If students use colored plastic films for absorption, have them cover only half the slit with the colored film so they can simultaneously compare a white light spectrum with an absorption spectrum. Place a drop of food dye in a clear plastic cup, add some water, set it in front of a light source, and students can explore the absorption spectra of various colored solutions.

You can set up one or more discharge tubes around the room for students to examine. Hydrogen, neon, and mercury work well. You may also wish to demonstrate flame tests to students. **Caution:** Do not let students use Bunsen burners!

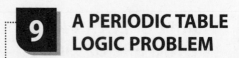

9 A PERIODIC TABLE LOGIC PROBLEM

Small-Scale Experiment for text Section 6.3

Estimated Class Time: One 50-minute period.
Estimated Teacher Preparation Time: 5 minutes.

OVERVIEW

Students learn to apply their knowledge of electron configurations and periodic trends to solve a periodic table logic problem.

EQUIPMENT

Sharpened pencil.

TEACHING SUGGESTIONS

Remind students that the 26 elements represented in this activity exclude the fourth period transition elements, atomic numbers 21–30. Students may want to place atomic numbers in the proper boxes before they begin. Remind students that the clues for some elements contain sufficient information for students to place them with no other

information. Other clues give only a general idea where to place elements, and those clues must be logically combined to solve the puzzle.

10 ELECTRONIC CONFIGURATIONS OF ATOMS AND IONS

Small-Scale Experiment for text Sections 7.1 and 7.2

Estimated class time: One 50-minute period.
Estimated Teacher Preparation Time: 20 minutes.

OVERVIEW

Students observe the colors of various metal salt solutions and practice writing electron configurations of common metals and metal ions. They learn that the presence of color in a salt solution is usually characteristic of a transition metal ion having an electron configuration with partially filled d orbitals.

MATERIALS

Small-scale pipets of the following solutions:

sodium chloride (NaCl)

magnesium sulfate ($MgSO_4$)

aluminum chloride ($AlCl_3$)

copper(II) sulfate ($CuSO_4$)

silver nitrate ($AgNO_3$)

sodium hydroxide (NaOH)

iron(III) chloride ($FeCl_3$)

calcium chloride ($CaCl_2$)

nickel(II) sulfate ($NiSO_4$)

sodium carbonate (Na_2CO_3)

sodium phosphate (Na_3PO_4)

EQUIPMENT

Small-scale reaction surface.

TEACHING SUGGESTIONS

Explain to students that this activity is an exercise in observing solutions and practicing writing electron configurations of the ions in those solutions. The chemical reactions that they carry out are observational in this lab. However, you may want to illustrate how to write double-replacement equations for each reaction or you may wish to save this topic for Chapter 11.

PAPER CHROMATOGRAPHY

Small-Scale Experiment for text Section 8.3

Estimated Class Time: One or two 50-minute periods.
Estimated Teacher Preparation Time: 20 minutes.

OVERVIEW

Students learn about paper chromatography and use it to separate and identify dyes in inks.

EQUIPMENT (per 24 students)

48 pieces of chromatography paper, 24 template cards, 48 clear plastic cups, 6 small bottles of solvent (0.1% NaCl in water), 6 sets of FD&C dyes in 1×12 well strips, 6 pieces of typing paper. *Various other papers such as coffee filters and tablet paper, various solvents such as rubbing alcohol, various colored food, candy, soft drinks, and food coloring.

COMMON EQUIPMENT

12 pairs of scissors, 12 sets of colored marking pens, 6 staplers.

TEACHING SUGGESTIONS

To make 0.1% aqueous sodium chloride solution, dissolve one gram NaCl in one liter of water. Rubbing alcohol (70% isopropyl alcohol) straight from the bottle works well also, but it takes three to five times as long to elute a chromatogram. The aqueous solvent needs no cover cup.

Prepare a classroom set (12 to 24) 10-cm × 5-cm template cards from poster board marked exactly like the one in Figure 11.1. Students simply trace the card on chromatography paper, then cut out and mark the paper. Consider using a paper cutter to cut strips of chromatography paper 5 cm wide. This saves even more time and paper.

Make a 0.1% solution of each FD&C dye (50 mg of dye in 50 mL of water) and store it in a small, plastic dropping bottle. Make up six sets of dyes for student use in 1×8 or 1×12 well strips. Tape each to a 3-inch × 5-inch index card, and label each dye

*Equipment for Now It's Your Turn.

by writing its identity next to its well. Replenish the wells periodically by dropping in the correct dyes. Consider making up sets of soft drink, food coloring, and other samples in this way.

Remind students to use typing paper triangles and not chromatography paper when spotting dyes. Plastic and wood toothpicks also work for spotting samples, but they are more expensive.

For a lab practical, consider mixing several dyes and having students identify the components of the mixture. Alternatively, you can select some colors of a brand of pens that students have not analyzed and have them identify the dyes.

CHEMICAL NAMES AND FORMULAS

Small-Scale Experiment for text Section 9.2

Estimated Class Time: One 50-minute period.
Estimated Teacher Preparation Time: 30 minutes.

OVERVIEW

Students observe small-scale samples of ionic compounds and learn to name them and to write their formulas. Students use aqueous solutions to synthesize new compounds and explore their names and formulas. Students learn that chemical formulas are symbolic representations of submicroscopic matter.

MATERIALS (per pair of students)

Small-scale reaction surface where 1 drop of each of the following solutions has been allowed to evaporate in its place as indicated on the Experimental Page:

potassium iodide (KI)

sodium chloride (NaCl)

magnesium sulfate ($MgSO_4$)

copper(II) sulfate ($CuSO_4$)

sodium hydrogen carbonate ($NaHCO_3$)

silver nitrate ($AgNO_3$)

sodium nitrite ($NaNO_2$)

potassium fluoride (KF)

sodium carbonate (Na_2CO_3)

lead(II) nitrate ($Pb(NO_3)_2$)

*iron(III) chloride ($FeCl_3$)

*potassium iodide (KI)

*sodium hydroxide (NaOH)

*sodium carbonate (Na_2CO_3)

sodium ethanoate

ammonium chloride (NH_4Cl)

sodium phosphate (Na_3PO_4)

calcium hydroxide ($Ca[OH]_2$)

tin(IV) chloride ($SnCl_4$)

potassium bromide (KBr)

calcium chloride ($CaCl_2$)

iron(III) chloride ($FeCl_3$)

sodium hydrogen phosphate (Na_2HPO_4)

sodium dihydrogen phosphate (NaH_2PO_4)

*silver nitrate ($AgNO_3$)

*lead(II) nitrate ($Pb(NO_3)_2$)

*copper(II) sulfate ($CuSO_4$)

*magnesium sulfate ($MgSO_4$)

TEACHING SUGGESTIONS

The day before the lab (or an hour before), place 1 drop of each indicated compound on a small-scale reaction surface on top of the Experimental Page and allow the water to evaporate. Make up one reaction surface for each pair of students. Keep these sets to use from class to class throughout the day. Alternatively, have students do this at the beginning of the period. As they name the compounds and write the formulas, the solutions will evaporate and the solid compounds will appear. In this case, have students clean the file protector as usual.

This lab is designed to get students to name and write formulas of compounds they are likely to encounter in the rest of the course. As a start, suggest to students that they memorize the names and formulas of a few monatomic and polyatomic ions. They can master the system of naming and writing formulas without becoming overloaded with information.

Now It's Your Turn provides an excellent prechemical-reaction exercise. Tell students that these kinds of chemical reactions and their products will be studied in Chapter 10.

13 MEASURING MASS: A MEANS OF COUNTING

Small-Scale Experiment for text Section 10.2

Estimated Class Time: One 50-minute period.

Estimated Teacher Preparation Time: 15 minutes.

OVERVIEW

Students measure the mass of common chemicals and calculate moles, molecules and atoms from their data. Students also find the mass of common objects and investigate their quantitative compositions, using the chemical quantities of mass, moles, and atoms.

MATERIALS (per student)

Solids: one teaspoon of sodium chloride, one teaspoon of sucrose, glass slide, piece of chalk, polystyrene peanut, one piece each of sulfur, fluorite, and hematite. You may substitute any other minerals you have on hand.

*A nickel coin, and pieces of the following mineral samples: gypsum ($CaSO_4 \cdot 2H_2O$); graphite, C; barite ($BaSO_4$); calcite ($CaCO_3$); pyrite (FeS_2); and galena (PbS_2).

EQUIPMENT

Plastic spoons, balance.

TEACHING SUGGESTIONS

Assign as many or as few of the substances as time permits. The calculations are given to the students in dimensional-analysis form, so they can focus on the fact that the experimental data (the masses) are the keys to counting atoms. Students can learn how to construct their own solutions to problems, using dimensional analysis from the text.

A possible lab-practical problem would be to give students objects of known composition, with masses known only to the teacher, and have the students determine their masses and calculate chemical quantities.

Make classroom sets of materials and place them in zipper-locking plastic bags. One set of materials should consist of one piece each of sulfur, fluorite, and hematite; a piece of chalk; a

*Equipment for Now It's Your Turn.

marble; a polystyrene peanut; and a plastic spoon. Sugar and salt can be placed in containers on the lab benches. You can substitute other minerals.

14 CHEMICAL EQUATIONS

Small-Scale Experiment for text Section 11.1

For your course planning, you may not want to use this lab until Chapter 19.

Estimated Class Time: One 50-minute period.

Estimated Teacher Preparation Time: 20 minutes, after stock solutions are prepared.

OVERVIEW

Students observe color changes in indicators and learn how to write single-replacement chemical equations to describe them. Students classify solutions as acids or bases based on the color changes.

MATERIALS

Small-scale pipets of the following solutions:

sodium hydrogen carbonate ($NaHCO_3$)

ethanoic acid

hydrochloric acid (HCl)

sodium carbonate (Na_2CO_3)

sulfuric acid (H_2SO_4)

sodium ethanoate

sodium hydroxide (NaOH)

nitric acid (HNO_3)

sodium hydrogen sulfate ($NaHSO_4$)

ammonia (NH_3)

phosphoric acid (H_3PO_4)

sodium dihydrogen phosphate (NaH_2PO_4)

sodium hydrogen phosphate (Na_2HPO_4)

sodium phosphate (Na_3PO_4)

sodium hydrogen sulfite ($NaHSO_3$)

bromthymol blue (BPB)

phenolphthalein

bromphenyl blue (BTB)

*methyl red (MR)

*bromcresol green (BCG)

*phenol red

*alizarine yellow R (AYR)

*thymol blue (TB)

*meta cresol purple (MCP)

Household Products: Baking soda, vinegar, cola, ammonia cleaner, laundry detergent, grape juice, cabbage juice, food dyes, flower petals, vegetable juices, fabric dyes, and water-soluble pen inks.

TEACHING SUGGESTIONS

Small-Scale Experiments 14, 15, 19, and 20 use acid–base concepts to illustrate both qualitative and quantitative properties of chemical reactions. Acid–base reactions were chosen because of their simplicity, the colorful chemistry they produce in the presence of indicators, and the availability and low toxicity of the reagents. Small-Scale Experiment 14 uses simple acid–base reactions and the color changes they impart to indicators to introduce simple chemical reactions and the chemical equations that represent them. Small-Scale Experiment 15 uses acid–base neutralization reactions as examples of how chemical equations are balanced. Small-Scale Experiment 20 also uses neutralization reactions and titrations of acids and bases to apply the mole concept in the laboratory. You may want to leave these labs for later in your course or refer to them during your students' formal study of acids and bases in Chapter 19.

15 BALANCING CHEMICAL EQUATIONS

Small-Scale Experiment for text Section 11.2

For your course planning, you may not want to use this lab until Chapter 19.

Estimated Class Time: One 50-minute period.

Estimated Teacher Preparation Time: 20 minutes, after stock solutions are prepared.

OVERVIEW

Students carry out reactions between acids and bases and use indicators to detect the reactions. Students learn to balance the chemical equations that describe the reactions. Students learn to recognize chemical equations as symbolic interpretations of submicroscopic chemical reactions.

*Equipment for Now It's Your Turn.

MATERIALS

Small-scale pipets of the following solutions:

bromthymol blue (BTB)

sodium hydroxide (NaOH)

potassium hydroxide (KOH)

calcium hydroxide ($Ca[OH]_2$)

ammonia (NH_3)

hydrochloric acid (HCl)

nitric acid (HNO_3)

sulfuric acid (H_2SO_4)

ethanoic acid (CH_3COOH)

phosphoric acid (H_3PO_4)

*phenolphthalein

*bromphenyl blue (BPB)

*methyl red (MR)

*Household Products: Vinegar, lemon juice, ammonia cleaner, antacid tablets.

EQUIPMENT

Glass slide, cotton swab.

COMMON EQUIPMENT

6 hot plates.

TEACHING SUGGESTIONS

Emphasize to students that the given examples reveal a pattern for how to balance the equations. Stress that the coefficients they use indicate the number of formula units and the number of moles of each reactant and product.

The chemical equations the students balance are more concrete to them when they can see or smell evidence of chemical change beyond the indicator changes. Point out that a salt is formed in each reaction and that when students evaporate mixtures, they can see the salts. Extinction of the ammonia smell by HCl brings meaning to the word *neutralization*.

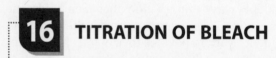 **16 TITRATION OF BLEACH**

Small-Scale Experiment for text Section 11.3

For your course planning, you may not want to use this lab until Chapter 19.

Estimated Class Time: One 50-minute period.

Estimated Teacher Preparation Time: 20 minutes.

OVERVIEW

Students use the chemistry of several nonmetal compounds to determine quantitatively the amount of sodium hypochlorite and other oxidizing agents in household products such as bleach.

MATERIALS

Small-scale pipets of the following solutions:

sodium hypochlorite (NaClO)

potassium iodide (KI)

ethanoic acid (CH_3COOH)

starch

*FD&C dyes

sodium thiosulfate ($Na_2S_2O_3$)

household bleach (diluted, 20 mL bleach + 80 mL H_2O)

*Household Products: Colored marking pens, dishwasher liquid, powdered cleansers.

EQUIPMENT

Plastic cup, 1×12 well plates.

TEACHING SUGGESTIONS

Part A of the Experimental Procedure is designed to help students understand the complicated chemistry of the titration and the end point. You can have students do the titration by calibrating their burets, using well strips, as described in Part B of the Experimental Procedure. Alternatively, consider having them calibrate a buret, using a balance or doing a mass titration, as described in Now It's Your Turn and in Small-Scale Experiment 20.

Make up fresh NaClO solution by diluting 20 mL of household bleach with 80 mL of water. Use this solution for the NaClO and for the household bleach solution the students titrate. Explain that the dilution factor used in the calculation is due to the fact that the bleach was diluted by one fifth before students titrated it. **Caution:** Do not use full-strength household bleach: It is noxious and irritating to the skin, eyes, and nose.

*Equipment for Now It's Your Turn.

17 HALOGEN IONS IN SOLUTION

Small-Scale Experiment for text Section 11.3

Estimated Class Time: One 50-minute period.

Estimated Teacher Preparation Time: 20 minutes, once materials are purchased.

OVERVIEW

Students investigate the aqueous reactions of the halides and learn to identify them by their different chemical properties.

MATERIALS

Small-scale pipets of the following solutions:

calcium chloride ($CaCl_2$)

lead(II) nitrate ($Pb[NO_3]_2$)

silver nitrate ($AgNO_3$)

sodium hypochlorite (NaClO)

ammonia (NH_3)

potassium fluoride (KF)

potassium chloride (KCl)

potassium bromide (KBr)

potassium iodide (KI)

starch

sodium thiosulfate ($Na_2S_2O_3$)

hydrochloric acid (HCl)

bromthymol blue (BTB)

hydrogen peroxide (H_2O_2)

FD&C blue #1, blue dye

copper(II) sulfate ($CuSO_4$)

iron(III) chloride ($FeCl_3$)

*Household Products: Baby oil.

EQUIPMENT

3 1/2-ounce clear plastic cup, *glass slide.

TEACHING SUGGESTIONS

Emphasize that the reactions students observe are typical of the halide anions across the top of the Experimental Page and the cations of the compounds down the left side (except hypochlorite (OCl^-). Therefore, the precipitates all contain a halide ion.

Be sure to use freshly prepared NaClO (20 mL household bleach + 80 mL water) because an old solution will give poor results. The bromine produced in the NaClO + KBr reaction is sometimes slow to form. Tell students to be patient.

*Equipment for Now It's Your Turn.

Remind students that Step 2 requires the reaction surface to be very clean.

You may want to have students use net ionic equations in this lab, as they are easier to write than the balanced equations that include all of the spectator ions.

18 TITRATION: DETERMINING HOW MUCH ACID IS IN A SOLUTION

Small-Scale Experiment for text Section 12.2

For your course planning, you may not want to use this lab until Chapter 19.

Estimated Class Time: Two 50-minute periods.

Estimated Teacher Preparation Time: 20 minutes, after stock solutions are prepared.

OVERVIEW

Students use the technique of titration to measure the concentration of various acids in solution. Students learn to calibrate small-scale pipets and analyze errors associated with quantitative determinations.

MATERIALS

Small-scale pipets of the following solutions:

hydrochloric acid (HCl)

sodium hydroxide (NaOH)

phenolphthalein

nitric acid (HNO_3)

ethanoic acid (CH_3COOH)

sulfuric acid (H_2SO_4)

*Household Products: Vinegar and toilet-bowl cleaner (containing HCl).

EQUIPMENT

Plastic cup, 1×12 well plate, cotton swabs.

TEACHING SUGGESTIONS

This experiment is set up in a way that not only gives students procedures to follow but also allows them to invent procedures and concepts as they go along. For example, students invent their own methods for calibrating small-scale pipets. Most students prefer to expel the air bubble first and count drops while holding the pipet vertically. It does not matter what criteria the students use to define a full well as long as students are consistent.

Point out the difference between qualitative and quantitative analysis in this lab. In a lab-practical exam, you may want to have each student identify three unknown acids. He or she might also titrate each and calculate the molar concentration of each.

Give students the algorithm (in the Experimental Data section) for calculating the molarity of the acid, and let them work with it before you explain it. Once they have used the equation, they are ready to understand where it comes from and why it works.

Students are challenged to analyze their errors and make necessary adjustments in procedures and the experimental design to minimize error. As a result, students learn about the limitations of experimental designs. For example, the difference in the end point and the equivalence point is as much as one drop. Therefore, a larger number of drops for a sample size will make the relative error smaller. Point out that larger sample errors from other factors come into play. There is no right or wrong answer. Students must trust their own results on the basis of precision rather than comparing them to some "known" value.

Finally, students learn to apply what they have learned to real samples of household products with real problems (highly colored, high concentration).

MATERIALS

Small-scale pipets of the following solutions:

phenolphthalein	*universal indicator
sodium hydroxide (NaOH)	*sodium carbonate (Na_2CO_3)
nitric acid (HNO_3)	*lead(II) nitrate ($Pb(NO_3)_2$)
sulfuric acid (H_2SO_4)	
ethanoic acid	*silver nitrate ($AgNO_3$)
hydrochloric acid (HCl)	*calcium chloride ($CaCl_2$)
*bromthymol blue (BTB)	

*Household Products: Vinegar and toilet-bowl cleaner (containing HCl).

EQUIPMENT

Balance, plastic cup.

TEACHING SUGGESTIONS

Emphasize that finding the mass of samples can be more accurate than counting drops because sample sizes are larger and relative errors are smaller. Students should use two small-scale balance pans, one for the titrations and one for finding the mass of the NaOH pipets. As in Small-Scale Experiment 18, point out that the stoichiometry of the $NaOH/H_2SO_4$ reaction is 2:1, so the equation used to calculate the molarity of the acid must have a factor of 2 in the denominator.

---

19 MASS TITRATIONS: MEASURING MOLAR CONCENTRATIONS

Small-Scale Experiment for text Section 12.2

For your course planning, you may not want to use this lab until Chapter 19.

Estimated Class Time: One 50-minute period.

Estimated Teacher Preparation Time: 20 minutes, after stock solutions are prepared.

OVERVIEW

Students use balances to carry out mass titrations of acids and bases.

---

20 ABSORPTION OF WATER BY PAPER TOWELS: A CONSUMER LAB

Small-Scale Experiment for text Section 13.2

Estimated Class Time: One 50-minute period.

Estimated Teacher Preparation Time: 20 minutes, once materials are purchased.

OVERVIEW

Students compare some properties of different brands of paper towels. Students find that there are quantitative answers for consumers.

*Equipment for Now It's Your Turn.

EQUIPMENT (per 24 students)

twelve 5-cm × 10-cm poster-board cards; several brands of paper towels, one roll each with their labels, including price tag; balance; 24 plastic cups; water, 24 soda straws; 50 clothespins.

COMMON EQUIPMENT

12 pairs of scissors, six 1/4-inch hole punches.

TEACHING SUGGESTIONS

Cut a classroom set of 5-cm × 10-cm poster-board templates to save students' time measuring. Students use them to trace out equal-sized pieces of paper towels. These are the same templates you will use for Small-Scale Experiment 24.

One roll of each brand of paper towels is more than sufficient for many sections of 24 students. The day before the experiment, suggest to students that they bring from home two or three sheets of paper towels along with their labels. This gives the students ownership in the experiment.

Encourage students to invent different ways to test wet strength. For example, they could stack pennies on a stretched wet towel. In Part C, be sure students use 1-cm × 10-cm strips of towels.

21 SYNTHESIS AND QUALITATIVE ANALYSIS OF GASES

Small-Scale Experiment for text Section 14.4

Estimated Class Time: One 50-minute period.

Estimated Teacher Preparation Time: 20 minutes, once materials are purchased.

OVERVIEW

Students carry out chemical reactions that produce gases. Students use indicators to identify the gases.

MATERIALS

Small-scale pipets of the following solutions:

potassium iodide (KI)

starch

bromthymol blue (BTB)

hydrochloric acid (HCl)

sodium hypochlorite (NaClO)

sodium hydrogen sulfite (NaHSO$_3$)

sodium nitrite (NaNO$_2$)

sodium hydroxide (NaOH)

sodium hydrogen carbonate (NaHCO$_3$)

hydrogen peroxide (H$_2$O$_2$)

potassium permanganate (KMnO$_4$)

ammonium chloride (NH$_4$Cl)

*ethanoic acid (CH$_3$COOH)

*phenolphthalein

*sulfuric acid (H$_2$SO$_4$)

*nitric acid (HNO$_3$)

EQUIPMENT

2 clear plastic cups.

TEACHING SUGGESTIONS

Because stray gases from other experiments can affect results, tell students to do only two of the experiments on the Experimental Page at a time. Remind students of the importance of cleaning the cup between experiments with a dry paper towel to absorb stray gases. Emphasize that some of the reactions do not happen immediately and that they have to watch patiently for several minutes for some of the indicators to change color.

Use freshly prepared solutions of NaHSO$_3$ (4.1 g in 250 mL), NaNO$_2$ (6.9 g in 250 mL), and KMnO$_4$ (a few grains in 100 mL of 0.1M H$_2$SO$_4$). The NaHSO$_3$ and NaNO$_2$ solutions degrade over time, and the KMnO$_4$ solution forms an insoluble brown MnO$_2$ precipitate over time.

The word equations in the Questions for Analyses section are designed to give students valuable experience writing and balancing chemical equations. Point out the relationships between the equations they write and the observations they made in Table 20.1.

*Equipment for Now It's Your Turn.

Identifying the six unknowns in Now It's Your Turn provides a good lab-practical exam. For convenience, label the unknown pipets with numbers and keep a key of the identities. You might want to use the other Now It's Your Turn item as a lab practical.

22 REACTIONS OF AQUEOUS IONIC COMPOUNDS

Small-Scale Experiment for text Section 15.2

Estimated Class Time: One or two 50-minute periods.

Estimated Teacher Preparation Time: 20 minutes, once solutions are prepared.

OVERVIEW

Students carry out many mixings of ionic compounds and learn to organize large amounts of information in ways that will help them to solve problems logically.

MATERIALS

Small-scale pipets of the following solutions:

lead(II) nitrate
  ($Pb(NO_3)_2$)
ammonia (NH_3)
iron(III) chloride
  ($FeCl_3$)
sodium carbonate
  (Na_2CO_3)
nitric acid (HNO_3)
calcium chloride
  ($CaCl_2$)
silver nitrate ($AgNO_3$)

sodium hydroxide
  ($NaOH$)
sulfuric acid (H_2SO_4)
copper(II) sulfate
  ($CuSO_4$)
potassium iodide (KI)
sodium phosphate
  (Na_3PO_4)
hydrochloric acid
  (HCl)

TEACHING SUGGESTIONS

Set up one set of chemicals for each two students. They can share chemicals and still do their own work.

To save time, consider having students copy Table 22.1 in their notebooks as homework the day before the lab. Emphasize to students the right way to use and read Table 22.1. The most common mistake with students is to make their

mixings in the wrong places, and they are often off by just one line. Having them do all the lead nitrate reactions first is often enough to get them started correctly.

Have students play the games on the smaller grids in the Now It's Your Turn until they become proficient at using chemical reactions to identify unknown chemicals. These types of exercises provide good lab practical exams. The equation writing provides review and practice in writing equations for precipitation reactions and for the reactions of acids with carbonates.

23 IDENTIFICATION OF EIGHT UNKNOWN SOLUTIONS

Small-Scale Experiment for text Section 15.2

Estimated Class Time: One 50-minute period.

Estimated Teacher Preparation Time: 20 minutes, once solutions are prepared.

OVERVIEW

Students use what they learned in Small-Scale Experiment 21 to work out the identities of unknown solutions by various methods.

MATERIALS

Small-scale pipets of the following solutions:

lead(II) nitrate
  ($Pb(NO_3)_2$)
ammonia (NH_3)
iron(III) chloride
  ($FeCl_3$)
sodium carbonate
  (Na_2CO_3)
nitric acid (HNO_3)
calcium chloride
  ($CaCl_2$)
silver nitrate ($AgNO_3$)

sodium hydroxide
  ($NaOH$)
sulfuric acid (H_2SO_4)
copper(II) sulfate
  ($CuSO_4$)
potassium iodide (KI)
sodium phosphate
  (Na_3PO_4)
hydrochloric acid
  (HCl)

Eight small-scale pipets per student containing unknown solutions labeled with different numbers.

TEACHING SUGGESTIONS

Prepare 15 small-scale pipets of each of the 13 solutions in Small-Scale Experiment 23. Label each of these 195 pipets with a number, and record the numbers on a master list for your reference for refilling, grading, and helping students identify their unknowns. For a class of 24 students, use the 195 pipets to make up 24 sets of 8 different unknowns (24 × 8 = 192 pipets). Place each set of eight in a plastic cup to be handed out to students. Any combination of solutions is solvable using known solutions as probes. If time permits, have them do more than one combination.

Keep in mind that for a given set of unknowns to be identifiable by the approach used in Now It's Your Turn (no known chemicals can be used), it must contain eight distinctly different chemicals. Furthermore, the acids are distinguished from each other only if each is accompanied by a specific solution. An unknown set containing sulfuric acid must also contain calcium chloride; hydrochloric acid must be accompanied by silver nitrate; and nitric acid must have lead nitrate with it.

Consider coding the unknowns by assigning each of the 13 solutions with a number between 3 and 16. Use a four-digit number for each unknown. The sum of the middle two digits identifies the unknown. For example, assign calcium chloride the number 3. The following numbers, then, identify an unknown as calcium chloride: 1123, 8301, 4215, and 9031. (The sum of the middle two digits in each case is 3.) If you use a code, don't tell students that it even exists. It is surprising how easily students break any code, once they know one exists!

Once you have the original 24 sets made up, you can keep them labeled for several years. All you need to do is refill them and mix and match the numbers to make a large number of unknown sets.

24 ELECTROLYTES

Small-Scale Experiment for text Section 15.2

Estimated Class Time: One 50-minute period.
Estimated Teacher Preparation Time: 20 minutes, once conductivity devices are constructed.

OVERVIEW

Students discover that matter is electrical. They investigate the conductivity of aqueous solutions and draw conclusions about electrolytes and nonelectrolytes.

MATERIALS

Small-scale pipets of the following solutions:

calcium chloride ($CaCl_2$)

sodium hydrogen sulfate ($NaHSO_4$)

sodium hydroxide ($NaOH$)

sodium phosphate (Na_3PO_4)

sodium hydrogen carbonate ($NaHCO_3$)

iron(III) chloride ($FeCl_3$)

copper(II) sulfate ($CuSO_4$)

aluminum chloride ($AlCl_3$)

zinc chloride ($ZnCl_2$)

sodium carbonate (Na_2CO_3)

water

ethanol (CH_3CH_2OH)

2-propanol

methanol (CH_3OH)

hydrogen peroxide (H_2O_2)

*hydrochloric acid (HCl)

*nitric acid (HNO_3)

*sulfuric acid (H_2SO_4)

*phosphoric acid (H_3PO_4)

*ethanoic acid (CH_3COOH)

*ammonia (NH_3)

*potassium hydroxide (KOH)

Solids:

sodium chloride ($NaCl$)

potassium chloride (KCl)

potassium iodide (KI)

calcium chloride ($CaCl_2$)

sodium carbonate (Na_2CO_3)

sucrose ($C_{12}H_{22}O_{12}$)

*Household Products: Soft drink, orange juice, pickle brine, coffee, seltzer tablets, solid toilet-bowl cleaner, baking powder, plaster of Paris.

EQUIPMENT

Glass slide, conductivity apparatus.

COMMON EQUIPMENT

6 hot plates.

*Equipment for Now It's Your Turn.

TEACHING SUGGESTIONS

Make a classroom set of electrolysis/conductivity devices (see lab Figure 24.1). The materials needed are: 9-volt battery, 9-volt battery clip, small light-emitting diode (any color), 330-ohm 1/4-watt resistor, 4 micro clips (for 0.042-inch holes), 1-inch × 4-inch piece of punched perfboard (0.042-inch-hole diameter, 0.100-inch × 0.100-inch spacing), 1/2 inch of fabric adhesive or similar fastener, 2 nickel-plated sewing pins.

Cut the perfboard from 6-inch × 8-inch or larger pieces, using a hacksaw or band saw. Place the micro clips and other components in the locations shown in the diagram, and solder the components together with a soldering iron. Fix the battery in place with the fabric adhesive or a similar fastener. The exact arrangement is not critical. The wire leads should be about 1/2 cm apart and extend about 1 to 2 cm from the edge of the perfboard. The light-emitting diode (LED) is polarized, so be sure to connect the positive (red) lead of the battery clip to the positive (long) lead of the LED, and the negative (black) lead of the battery clip to the negative (short) lead of the LED.

Remind students to keep the hot plates on a low setting. As an alternative to a hot plate, try a heat gun or a hair dryer on a low setting, or consider having students store their glass slides overnight at room temperature. **Caution:** Do not use Bunsen burners, as they are dangerous and produce far too much heat to be appropriate for a small-scale experiment.

This is a good place to introduce net ionic equations. Consider reviewing the chemical reactions studied so far in terms of net ionic equations. Small-Scale Experiment 25 then naturally follows.

25 HARD AND SOFT WATER

Small-Scale Experiment for text Section 15.3

Estimated Class Time: Two 50-minute periods.
Estimated Teacher Preparation Time: 30 minutes.

OVERVIEW

Students titrate various water samples for hardness and learn how to soften water.

MATERIALS

Small-scale pipets of the following liquids:

various water samples

deionized water

ammonia/ammonium chloride $(NH_3)/(NH_4Cl)$

ethylenediamine tetraacetic acid ((EDTA) $(C_{10},H_{16}N_2O_2$

*hydrochloric acid (HCl)

*bromthymol blue (BTB)

*potassium hydroxide (KOH)

Solids: Eriochrome black T indicator.

EQUIPMENT

Balance, extra small-scale balance pan.

COMMON EQUIPMENT

*Acid resin ion exchanger.

TEACHING SUGGESTIONS

The end point of this titration is difficult for students to see. As they titrate, the color gradually changes from wine-red through reddish-blue to blue. Tell the students to adjust the amount of Ero-T until they see the change from wine-red to blue with the last drop.

Make the Ero-T indicator by mixing 0.1 g Ero-T with 100 g solid NaCl. Place in plastic-topped vials, and punch holes in the plastic tops so each vial functions like a salt shaker.

If you do not want to collect actual water samples, you can make hard water. To prepare a stock solution of 1000 ppm $CaCO_3$, dissolve 1.22 g $CaCl_2$ in 1100 mL of deionized water. Add 5 drops of $0.2M$ $MgSO_4$ solution. Dilute the stock solution with tap water in ratios 1:1, 1:2, 1:3 and 1:4. Place the hard water in small-scale pipets labeled "water sample 1," "water sample 2," etc. Prepare the buffer by dissolving 9.2 g NH_4Cl and 67 mL concentrated NH_3 in 1 L of deionized water.

26 SOLUBILITY RULES

Small-Scale Experiment for text Section 16.1

Estimated Class Time: One 50-minute period.
Estimated Teacher Preparation Time: 20 minutes.

*Equipment for Now It's Your Turn.

OVERVIEW

Students investigate precipitation reactions and correlate large amounts of data to generalize about solubility rules.

MATERIALS

Small-scale pipets of the following solutions:

aluminum chloride (AlCl$_3$)

ammonium chloride (NH$_4$Cl)

calcium chloride (CaCl$_2$)

copper(II) sulfate (CuSO$_4$)

sodium chloride (NaCl)

iron(III) chloride (FeCl$_3$)

lead(II) nitrate (Pb(NO$_3$)$_2$)

magnesium sulfate (MgSO$_4$)

potassium iodide (KI)

silver nitrate (AgNO$_3$)

zinc chloride (ZnCl$_2$)

sodium carbonate (Na$_2$CO$_3$)

sodium chloride (NaCl)

sodium hydroxide (NaOH)

sodium nitrate (NaNO$_3$)

sodium phosphate (Na$_3$PO$_4$)

sodium sulfate (Na$_2$SO$_4$)

TEACHING SUGGESTIONS

Students can derive general solubility rules easily from this colorful experiment. You may want to break this experiment into two shorter sessions and discuss the results with students as they proceed. Point out to students that the Experimental Page is set up to allow them to readily find the right reagents (the complete formula is given) and to easily write the net ionic equations. Emphasize that all of the 2$^+$ cations will yield similar net ionic equations, as will all the 1$^+$ cations and 3$^+$ cations.

27 HEAT OF FUSION OF ICE

Small-Scale Experiment for text Section 17.3

Estimated Class Time: One 50-minute period.

Estimated Teacher Preparation Time: 10 minutes.

OVERVIEW

Students use the technique of calorimetry to measure the heat of fusion of ice.

MATERIALS

hot water from the tap, crushed ice

EQUIPMENT

Balance, polystyrene coffee cup, one-ounce plastic cup, alcohol thermometer.

TEACHING SUGGESTIONS

Discuss with students the importance of heat losses to the surroundings and their relationship to errors. Point out that larger samples of hot water and ice will probably involve greater heat losses to the environment. The sample data given for Trial 3 in Table 27.2 is good evidence that larger samples produce greater errors. (Compare Trials 1 and 2 with Trial 3.) The ideal final temperature to achieve is room temperature (about 25°C).

Emphasize that melting ice absorbs much more heat than simply changing the temperature of liquid water. It requires only one calorie to change the temperature of 1 gram of liquid water by 1 Celsius degree and 80 calories to melt one gram of ice. Ice cools drinks by melting, not by changing temperature.

28 FACTORS AFFECTING THE RATE OF A CHEMICAL REACTION

Small-Scale Experiment for text Section 18.1

Estimated Class Time: One 50-minute period.

Estimated Teacher Preparation Time: 15 minutes.

OVERVIEW

Students study the effects of concentration, temperature, and surface area on the rates of chemical reactions.

MATERIALS

Small-scale pipets of the following solutions:

hydrochloric acid (HCl)

*lead nitrate (Pb[NO$_3$]$_2$)

sodium hydrogen carbonate (NaHCO$_3$)

*potassium iodide (KI)

*sulfuric acid (H$_2$SO$_4$)

water

*calcium chloride (CaCl$_2$)

Solids: Magnesium, calcium carbonate.

EQUIPMENT

Ice, hot water, 2 plastic cups.

TEACHING SUGGESTIONS

Magnesium turnings and split-pea-sized CaCO$_3$ chips work well. Use plastic jars or large plastic vials to serve as recycling containers. Wash the recycled magnesium turnings and calcium carbonate chips with water and dry them. They can be used again for another lab.

Hot water from the tap is sufficient. Have students equilibrate their pipets in both ice water and hot water long enough to see a difference. You may have to review the chemical equations with students, especially the reaction of magnesium with acid if they have not seen it before. Clean Mg works best. Use steel wool to clean Mg ribbon. Clean turnings by dipping them briefly in 1M HCl. Wash with water and dry thoroughly.

29 LE CHÂTELIER'S PRINCIPLE AND CHEMICAL EQUILIBRIUM

Small-Scale Experiment for text Section 18.2

Estimated Class Time: One 50-minute period.
Estimated Teacher Preparation Time: 15 minutes.

OVERVIEW

Students investigate chemical systems at equilibrium by disturbing the equilibrium and then explaining the observable changes in terms of Le Châtelier's principle.

MATERIALS

Small-scale pipets of the following solutions:

bromthymol blue (BTB)

sodium thiosulfate (Na$_2$S$_2$O$_3$)

hydrochloric acid (HCl)

sodium phosphate (Na$_3$PO$_4$)

sodium hydroxide (NaOH)

*phenolphthalein

ammonia (NH$_3$)

*bromphenyl blue (BPB)

copper(II) sulfate (CuSO$_4$)

*methyl red (MR)

lead(II) nitrate (Pb(NO$_3$)$_2$)

*alizarine yellow R (AYR)

potassium iodide (KI)

*iron(III) chloride (FeCl$_3$)

nitric acid (HNO$_3$)

silver nitrate (AgNO$_3$)

*potassium thiocyanate (KSCN)

sodium carbonate (Na$_2$CO$_3$)

EQUIPMENT

*Small (4-inch) pieces of soda straws.

TEACHING SUGGESTIONS

Be sure to remind students to stir each mixture thoroughly; stirring is critical. Use small pieces of soda straws to separate the FeCl$_3$/KSCN mixture in Now It's Your Turn. Simply place the end of the straw into the mixture and drag it across the reaction surface. Some of the mixture will move, while the bulk of it will stay behind. Suggest that students invent efficient ways to move liquids from place to place on the reaction surface without contamination.

30 A SMALL-SCALE COLORIMETRIC pH METER

Small-Scale Experiment for text Section 19.2

Estimated Class Time: One 50-minute period.
Estimated Teacher Preparation Time: 45 minutes to make up fresh buffer solutions.

OVERVIEW

Students build a colorimetric pH meter and measure the pH's of various laboratory and household chemicals.

*Equipment for Now It's Your Turn.

MATERIALS

Small-scale pipets of the following solutions:

universal indicator

buffer solutions, pH 1–12

Household Products: Baking soda, vinegar, window cleaner, baking powder, lemon juice, tea, soft drink, laundry detergent, milk, orange juice, *red cabbage or juice, *flower petals, *grape or berry juice, *common indicators.

TEACHING SUGGESTIONS

To make up the universal indicator solution, add the following to 1000 mL of water:

150 mg phenolphthalein (disodium salt)

150 mg bromthymol blue (sodium salt)

113 mg methyl orange (sodium salt)

225 mg alizarine yellow R (sodium salt)

75 mg bromcresol green (sodium salt)

150 mg meta cresol purple

Store indefinitely in a plastic bottle. This amount should last 2 or 3 years, assuming 125 students a year.

Make the following stock solutions and prepare fresh buffer solutions each year from these stock solutions:

Solution A: Dissolve 0.5 g thymol, 14.9 g boric acid (H_3BO_3), and 12.6 g citric acid ($C_6H_8O_7$) in 1200 mL deionized or distilled water.

Solution B: Dissolve 0.5 g thymol and 45.6 g sodium phosphate (Na_3PO_4) in 1200 mL of water.

Prepare the buffer solutions, pH 1–12 by mixing the stock solutions according to the following table. (Use 1.0M phosphoric acid for pH 1.)

pH	mL of Solution A	mL of Solution B
2	195	5
3	176	24
4	155	45
5	134	66
6	118	82
7	99	101
8	85	115
9	69	131
10	54	146
11	44	156
12	17	183

Be sure students add the buffer to the universal indicator and not vice versa. This helps to stir the indicator into the buffer. Students should then stir with an empty pipet. Each integer pH should have a unique and distinguishing color. If not, tell students to add more buffer.

Have students sample solid household products by using soda straw spatulas. Have students sample liquid products by inserting the end of a straw 1 to 2 cm into the liquid and withdrawing it while they hold a finger on the other end. A student can then immediately place a few drops on his or her reaction surface.

31 TITRATION CURVES

Small-Scale Experiment for text Section 19.4

Estimated Class Time: One 50-minute period.
Estimated Teacher Preparation Time: 15 minutes.

OVERVIEW

Students carry out titrations of strong and weak acids and bases. Students observe how the pH changes with added titrant and plot their data.

MATERIALS

Small-scale pipets of the following solutions:

universal indicator

buffer solutions, pH 1–12

hydrochloric acid (HCl)

sodium hydroxide (NaOH)

ethanoic acid (CH_3COOH)

*nitric acid (HNO_3)

*sulfuric acid (H_2SO_4)

*phosphoric acid (H_3PO_4)

*sodium carbonate (Na_2CO_3)

*ammonia (NH_3)

EQUIPMENT

Plastic cup.

TEACHING SUGGESTIONS

The initial experiment on the reaction surface is designed to get students to visualize each step of the entire titration simultaneously. Be sure to have students stir each mixture thoroughly. Depending on how carefully they add the drops, they will get varying results. Some will see a distinct pH jump between two drops, while others will have an intermediate drop between

*Equipment for Now It's Your Turn.

the pH inflection. A few students who have been less careful adding drops will see a sharp increase, followed by a decrease and then another increase as the pH jumps. Once the students have visualized the effect, they should do all the rest of the titrations in a cup, as described in Step 3.

32 STRONG AND WEAK ACIDS AND BASES

Small-Scale Experiment for text Section 19.5

Estimated Class Time: One 50-minute period.
Estimated Teacher Preparation Time: 20 minutes.

OVERVIEW

Students carry out tests to distinguish between strong and weak acids and bases. Students learn to write hydrogen–ion transfer equations to enhance their understanding of Brønsted-Lowry theory.

MATERIALS

Small-scale pipets of the following solutions:

hydrochloric acid (HCl)

nitric acid (HNO_3)

sulfuric acid (H_2SO_4)

ethanoic acid (CH_3COOH)

citric acid ($C_6H_8O_7$)

boric acid (H_3BO_3)

bromthymol blue (BTB)

universal indicator

sodium carbonate (Na_2CO_3)

sodium hydrogen sulfate ($NaHSO_4$)

sodium hydroxide (NaOH)

sodium dihydrogen phosphate (NaH_2PO_4)

sodium monohydrogen phosphate (Na_2HPO_4)

potassium hydroxide (KOH)

sodium hydrogen carbonate ($NaHCO_3$)

sodium hydrogen sulfite ($NaHSO_3$)

calcium hydroxide ($Ca(OH)_2$)

sodium ethanoate (CH_3COONa)

sodium phosphate (Na_3PO_4)

ammonia (NH_3)

ammonium chloride (NH_4Cl)

*buffer solutions, pH 1–12

*Solids: Magnesium.

*Equipment for Now It's Your Turn.

EQUIPMENT (per 24 students)

12 conductivity devices.

TEACHING SUGGESTIONS

Remind students of the single-replacement chemical equations they wrote in Small-Scale Experiment 14. Part B of this experiment is essentially the same thing except now the universal indicator helps students to refine their concept of acids and bases in terms of their strengths. Remind students that they can approximate the pH of any solution from the color it imparts to universal indicator. The following rule of thumb is helpful. The colors of the visible spectrum, ROY G BIV, when imparted to universal indicator, approximately correlate with the pH's 1, 3, 5, 7, 9, 11, and 12, respectively. Alternately, students can set up the same pH meter with the universal indicator and buffers from Small-Scale Experiment 30. Remind students to clean the leads of the conductivity apparatus before each test.

33 BUFFERS

Small-Scale Experiment for text Section 19.5

Estimated Class Time: One 50-minute period.
Estimated Teacher Preparation Time: 15 minutes.

OVERVIEW

Students make various buffer solutions and test them for pH and buffer capacity.

MATERIALS

Small-scale pipets of the following solutions:

universal indicator

buffer solutions, pH 1–12

water

sodium hydroxide (NaOH)

hydrochloric acid (HCl)

ethanoic acid (CH_3COOH)

sodium ethanoate (CH_3COONa)

phosphoric acid (H_3PO_4)

sodium dihydrogen phosphate (NaH_2PO_4)

sodium hydrogen carbonate ($NaHCO_3$)

sodium carbonate
(Na$_2$CO$_3$)

sodium nitrate
(NaNO$_3$)

ammonium chloride
(NH$_4$Cl)

sodium sulfate
(Na$_2$SO$_4$)

ammonia (NH$_3$)

potassium iodide (KI)

sodium chloride
(NaCl)

*Household Products: Seltzer tablets, baking soda, baking powder, vitamin C.

EQUIPMENT

3 plastic cups.

TEACHING SUGGESTIONS

This experiment becomes more meaningful if students can make buffers from common household products. A solution of an effervescent tablet is an especially good buffer. Others include solutions of baking powder and mixtures of baking soda and cream of tartar or citric acid. Make these items available for student experimentation.

DETERMINATION OF AN ACTIVITY SERIES

Small-Scale Experiment for text Section 20.1

Estimated Class Time: One 50-minute period.
Estimated Teacher Preparation Time: 20 minutes.

OVERVIEW

Students learn that metals and metal ions in aqueous solution have different tendencies to gain and lose electrons. Students construct an activity series from experimental data.

MATERIALS

Small-scale pipets of the following solutions:

copper(II) sulfate
(CuSO$_4$)

magnesium sulfate
(MgSO$_4$)

iron(II) sulfate
(FeSO$_4$)

silver nitrate (AgNO$_3$)

zinc chloride (ZnCl$_2$)

Solids: Zinc, magnesium, iron, copper, silver.

*Household Products: Zinc-plated washers, silverware, staples, pennies.

EQUIPMENT

*Galvanized nails, pennies, staples, zinc-plated washers.

TEACHING SUGGESTIONS

As in the last lab, look for alternatives to pure-metal pieces like staples (Fe) and galvanized nails (Zn). Because silver does not react, consider using reusable silver coins or pieces of old plated silverware. Set up recycling containers for all the metals. Students should wash and dry each metal thoroughly after use.

35 OXIDATION–REDUCTION REACTIONS

Small-Scale Experiment for text Section 20.3

Estimated Class Time: One 50-minute period.
Estimated Teacher Preparation Time: 20 minutes.

OVERVIEW

Students explore the redox reactions of common ions in solution and learn to write and balance their half-reactions and equations. Students recognize common oxidizing and reducing agents.

MATERIALS

Small-scale pipets of the following solutions:

potassium iodide (KI)

copper(II) sulfate
(CuSO$_4$)

sodium hypochlorite
(NaClO)

iron(III) chloride
(FeCl$_3$)

potassium permanganate
(KMnO$_4$)

starch solution

hydrogen peroxide
(H$_2$O$_2$)

hydrochloric acid
(HCl)

potassium iodate
(KIO$_3$)

sodium hydrogen sulfite (NaHSO$_3$)

potassium dichromate
(K$_2$Cr$_2$O$_7$)

*sodium thiosulfate
(Na$_2$S$_2$O$_3$)

sodium nitrite
(NaNO$_2$)

sodium hydrogen sulfate (NaHSO$_4$)

*Equipment for Now It's Your Turn.

TEACHING SUGGESTIONS

The Experimental Page gives students the reactants and products of each redox equation in ionic form. From these, students can determine oxidation numbers and write half-reactions for each oxidation and reduction. You may want to have students balance only the half-reactions or add them to write the entire equation as described in Section 20.3.

36 SMALL-SCALE VOLTAIC CELLS

Small-Scale Experiment for text Section 21.1

Estimated Class Time: One 50-minute period.
Estimated Teacher Preparation Time: 20 minutes.

OVERVIEW

Students explore the nature of the voltaic cell and then make and test many variations.

MATERIALS

Small-scale pipets of the following solutions:

copper(II) sulfate ($CuSO_4$)

silver nitrate ($AgNO_3$)

zinc chloride ($ZnCl_2$)

lead(II) nitrate ($Pb(NO_3)_2$)

sodium nitrate ($NaNO_3$)

magnesium sulfate ($MgSO_4$)

Solids: Copper, zinc, silver, lead, magnesium.

EQUIPMENT (per 24 students)

24 filter paper disks (9 cm), *dimes, nickels, nails, galvanized nails, washers.

COMMON EQUIPMENT

12 volt meters, 4 each of various commercial batteries (dry cells), 12 pairs of scissors.

TEACHING SUGGESTIONS

Have students practice using the volt meters on different batteries of each type: carbon, heavy-duty carbon, alkaline, and rechargeable. You may want to have students bring batteries from home. "Dead" batteries work fine, as they usually still have measurable voltages. Steps 1 and 2 are

*Equipment for Now It's Your Turn.

designed to allow students to get an idea of the concept before they do the more complicated Step 3.

37 MOLECULAR STRUCTURE OF HYDROCARBONS

Small-Scale Experiment for text Section 22.3

Estimated Class Time: One 50-minute period.
Estimated Teacher Preparation Time: 10 minutes.

OVERVIEW

Students use pipe cleaners, pop beads, and polystyrene spheres to construct models of hydrocarbons. Students invent other ways to accurately depict structures.

COMMON EQUIPMENT

12 zipper-locking plastic bags containing model sets consisting of: six 1-inch polystyrene spheres, 12 pop beads, 3 black and 3 white pipe cleaners (30 cm × 3 mm), 12 pairs of scissors, 12 rulers.

TEACHING SUGGESTIONS

Store student sets of materials in zipper-locking plastic bags for reuse. Have extra pipe cleaners for students to use as replacements in their sets as needed. Each carbon-hydrogen bond is represented by a 2-cm piece of pipe cleaner, so consider having students cut all the white pipe cleaners into 2-cm pieces before they begin. Each carbon-carbon bond is represented by a 5-cm piece of black pipe cleaner, so students can also cut these to 5-cm lengths before they begin. For the line-angle models in Now It's Your Turn, students will need five 4-cm pieces of white pipe cleaner and black pipe cleaners cut in 5-cm and 10-cm lengths.

38 VITAMIN C IN TABLETS

Small-Scale Experiment for text Section 23.3

Estimated Class Time: One 50-minute period.
Estimated Teacher Preparation Time: 20 minutes.

OVERVIEW

Students measure the amount of the important organic compound, vitamin C, in various vitamin tablets.

MATERIALS

Small-scale pipets of the following solutions:

0.1M potassium iodate (KIO_3)

potassium iodide (KI)

hydrochloric acid (HCl)

starch

ascorbic acid (vitamin C)

Household Products: 48 vitamin C tablets (100 mg), *vitamin C tablets (250 mg, 500 mg, or 1000 mg).

EQUIPMENT

Plastic cup, balance.

TEACHING SUGGESTIONS

Be sure to put away any 0.1M KIO_3 pipets at the end of this lab so students do not use them by mistake in Small-Scale Experiment 39.

Part A of the Experimental Procedure is designed to help students to understand the chemistry of the titration and the end point. Students can do the mass titration given in the procedure, or they can calibrate their pipets using a 12-well plate or the balance and then count drops.

Make a fresh vitamin C solution for Part A. Dissolve 3.5 g of ascorbic acid in 100 mL water.

You will need two 100-mg vitamin C tablets per student. If 100-mg tablets are not available, students can use 250-mg or 500-mg tablets. These larger tablets will make counting drops tedious because of the large amount of KIO_3 needed for the titration. It is better to do a mass titration for larger amounts of vitamin C. Alternatively, students can find the mass of a tablet, crush it, and then find the mass and titrate only a portion of it and make the correction in their calculations. For example, if a tablet's mass is 300 mg and a student titrates a 100-mg portion of the tablet, the student needs to multiply the experimental result by 3 to obtain the amount of vitamin C in the whole tablet.

39 VITAMIN C IN DRINKS

Small-Scale Experiment for text Section 23.3

Estimated Class Time: One 50-minute period.
Estimated Teacher Preparation Time: 20 minutes.

OVERVIEW

Students try to find the answer to the question, "What's the best source of vitamin C?" by titrating various drinks for vitamin C.

MATERIALS

Small-scale pipets of the following solutions:

potassium iodide (KI)

hydrochloric acid (HCl)

0.01M potassium iodate (KIO_3)

starch

*Household Products: Various samples of fruit juices and fruit drinks, powdered fruit drinks, fresh vegetables.

EQUIPMENT

Plastic cup, balance.

TEACHING SUGGESTIONS

The potassium iodate solution in this experiment is 0.01M (one tenth the concentration of the KIO_3 used in Small-Scale Experiment 38) because of the low concentration of vitamin C usually found in fruit drinks and juices. Be sure not to have the students use the 0.1M solution you prepared for Small-Scale Experiment 38.

Prepare the 0.01M KIO_3 by diluting 50 mL of 0.1M KIO_3 stock solution to 500 mL total. Label a classroom set of small-scale pipets with a different color to distinguish them from the more concentrated KIO_3 solution that you used in Small-Scale Experiment 38.

Remind students that they do not have to find exactly 5000 mg of juice as given in the procedure, but they do have to know how much juice they massed. For example, if a student's nickel is 5080 mg, then he or she will mass 5080 mg of juice and use 5080 mg as the mass of juice in the calculation.

*Equipment for Now It's Your Turn.

REACTIONS OF BIOMOLECULES

Small-Scale Experiment for text Sections 24.2, 24.3, and 24.4

Estimated Class Time: One 50-minute period.
Estimated Teacher Preparation Time: 20 minutes.

OVERVIEW

Students explore the chemical reactions typical of the various classifications of foods: fats, carbohydrates, and proteins.

MATERIALS

Small-scale pipets of the following solutions:

potassium iodide (KI)

sodium hypochlorite (NaClO)

starch

small samples of various foods, including: dry cereal, milk, powdered milk, pasta, sugar, potato chips, crackers, peanut butter, margarine, corn oil, yeast, gelatin, and flour.

copper(II) sulfate (CuSO₄)

sodium hydroxide (NaOH)

water

Sudan III

*Benedict's solution

*galactose

*hydrochloric acid (HCl)

EQUIPMENT (per 24 students)

6 sheets of white typing paper, 150 toothpicks, *24 glass slides.

COMMON EQUIPMENT

12 pairs of scissors, *6 hot plates.

TEACHING SUGGESTIONS

A day or two before the lab, hand out zipper-locking bags and assign students to bring in various foods. This makes the lab more interesting. Just in case, you may want to take a few bags home to your own kitchen and supply the lab with what you need. Once in the lab, students can use toothpicks or small pieces of soda straw to sample messy foods like peanut butter and margarine. To sample liquid foods, dip a clean soda straw into the liquid, hold your finger over the end to capture a few drops, and release the drops onto the reaction surface.

*Equipment for Now It's Your Turn.

 HALF-LIVES AND REACTION RATES

Small-Scale Experiment for text Section 25.2

Estimated Class Time: One 50-minute period.
Estimated Teacher Preparation Time: 20 minutes.

OVERVIEW

Students study the rate of a first-order chemical reaction and plot their data to obtain the half-life and order of the reaction. Students relate what they learn to the process of nuclear decay.

MATERIALS

Small-scale pipets of the following solutions:

hydrochloric acid (HCl)

phenolphthalein

potassium hydroxide (KOH)

water

Solids: Magnesium ribbon, *calcium carbonate.

EQUIPMENT (per 24 students)

Twenty-four 1-ounce plastic cups.

COMMON EQUIPMENT

12 watches or clocks.

TEACHING SUGGESTIONS

Emphasize that although this is a chemical reaction, the same principle of half-life applies to nuclear decay. Nuclear decay simply occurs by first-order kinetics, as do many chemical reactions.

Each student needs a 2-cm or 3-cm piece of Mg ribbon. Students should be sure to stop the reaction on time by washing the magnesium thoroughly. Be sure the wash water (and the remaining acid) goes into the cup to be titrated. Also, be sure students dissolve the tarnish from the magnesium and dry it before they begin the experiment. Stirring by moving the magnesium to dislodge the bubbles is critical. Keep the magnesium submerged to a constant depth. If the reaction is too fast, try diluting the $1.0M$ HCl to $0.8M$ (80 mL HCl + 20 mL water).

PRENTICE HALL
Chemistry

Small-Scale Chemistry Laboratory Manual

Edward L. Waterman
Stephen Thompson

PEARSON

Prentice
Hall

Needham, Massachusetts
Upper Saddle River, New Jersey

Acknowledgments

Many people contributed ideas and resource during the development and writing of this small-scale laboratory manual. Mrs. Jackie Resseguie prepared solutions, organized equipment, and provided other logistical support during the early stages of the experimental design. Peter Markow created the original formulation of the Thompson-Markow universal indicator and designed the first prototype of the small-scale balance, which has since been modified and refined over the past decade by chemistry students at Rocky Mountain High School. These same students provided uncounted suggestions about the manuscript and numerous modifications of the experiments as they worked through them over the years. Bill Cook and Karen Dixon were enthusiastic cheerleaders at the appropriate moments. John Knight and Nicki Miller provided thoughts and insights as they worked through the experiments with their own students. The US West Foundation and the Hach Scientific Foundation provided resources to make the most of the time spent preparing the manuscript. Finally, a special thanks goes to Mrs. Kathryn C. Hach for her unparalleled love for and commitment to laboratory chemistry and the students who study it.

ISBN 0-13-190360-8

5 6 7 8 9 10   09 08 07 06

CONTENTS

TO THE STUDENT

Can you imagine learning how to play a musical instrument, paint a picture, or play a game by reading about it in a book? Books can give you valuable information when you are learning music, art, and sports, but to master any of these, you have to practice and think about what you are doing as you are doing it.

The same is true of chemistry. The only way to really learn chemistry is to do chemistry. Chemistry is not a body of knowledge that exists in some textbook. Like music, art, and sports, it is something you do. To learn chemistry, you have to do experiments; you have to practice interacting with matter; you have to learn how to ask questions about matter, how to interpret the answers, and how to use this information to solve problems. Textbooks can be as valuable to chemistry students as they are to music students. But to learn the art of chemistry, you have to participate in it.

This book is about practicing, or doing, chemistry. The idea is to put chemistry into your hands so you can explore chemistry for yourself. This book is designed to help you interact with matter, to interpret what you see, to solve problems, and to become inventive and creative. The experiments are designed to help you to ask questions, to help you find ways to answer your questions, and to help you contribute your original ideas and discoveries to chemistry.

Practice chemistry yourself. Your participation will take patience. You will have to observe, concentrate, think about what you are doing, learn the rules, and apply the rules in original ways. If you do, you will discover that doing chemistry can be a lot of fun!

SMALL-SCALE LABORATORY SAFETY

The chemistry laboratory is a unique place where you will have the opportunity to investigate a variety of different chemical and physical phenomena. The experiments and procedures in this book have been carefully designed and written to minimize risk and provide for your personal safety. However, safety is also your responsibility. At all times, your behavior is expected to be consistent with a safe laboratory. Here are some rules that are essential in promoting safety in the laboratory. You are responsible for knowing them and following them at all times.

1. Wear safety goggles at all times when working in the laboratory or near someone else who is working in the laboratory. Safety goggles are designed to protect your eyes from injury due to chemicals and other foreign substances. To minimize the possibility of transmitting eye and skin disease, it's best to purchase and care for your own safety goggles. Do not loan them to another person. While working in the lab, do not rub your eyes because chemicals are easily transferred from your hands to your eyes.

2. Recognize that all laboratory procedures involve some degree of risk. Take steps to reduce the risk for yourself and for your neighbors. Read and listen to all directions carefully. When in doubt, ask your teacher.

3. Use full small-scale pipets only for the carefully controlled delivery of liquids, one drop at a time. Protect yourself and your neighbors by always using small-scale pipets correctly.

4. Minimize danger, waste, extra work, and cleanup by always using minimum amounts of chemicals to perform experiments.

5. Conduct only the assigned experiments, and do them only when a teacher is present and has given you permission to work.

6. Dispose of chemicals in a way that protects you, your neighbors, and your environment. Always follow your teacher's cleanup and disposal directions.

7. Know the location of the fire extinguisher, emergency shower, eye wash station, fire blanket, and emergency exits. Know how and when to use each.

8. Never taste any chemical used in the laboratory, including food products that are the subject of an investigation. Treat all items as though they are contaminated with unknown chemicals that that may be toxic. Keep all food and drink that is not the subject of an experiment out of the laboratory. Do not eat, drink, or chew gum in the laboratory. Wash your hands thoroughly with soap and water before leaving the laboratory.

9. Report any accident, no matter how minor, to your teacher.

10. Recognize that the danger of an electrical shock is greater in the presence of water. Keep electrical appliances away from sinks and faucets. Take care not to spill water or other liquids in the vicinity of an electrical appliance. If you do, stand back, notify your teacher, and warn other students in the area.

11. Do not handle heated glass or broken glass. In case of breakage, notify your teacher and your neighbors. Sweep up broken glass with a brush and pan provided by your teacher. Do not use chipped or cracked glassware.

12. Protect your clothing and hair from chemicals and sources of heat. Tie back long hair and roll up loose sleeves when working in the laboratory. Avoid wearing bulky or loose-fitting clothing. Remove dangling jewelry.

13. Wear closed-toed shoes in the laboratory at all times.

14. Help facilitate a quick exit from the classroom by keeping classroom furniture away from escape routes and walkways. Keep your work area orderly and free of personal belongings like coats and backpacks.

15. Safety begins and continues with a clean laboratory. Report chemical spills immediately to your teacher. Clean up spills according to your teacher's directions. Warn other students about the identity and location of spilled chemicals. Clean up thoroughly every time you finish your laboratory work.

16. Take appropriate precautions whenever any of the following safety symbols appear in an experiment.

 Eye Safety
Wear safety goggles.

 Clothing Protection
Wear a lab coat or apron when using corrosive chemicals or chemicals that can stain clothing.

 Skin Protection
Wear plastic gloves when using chemicals that can irritate or stain your skin.

 Broken Glass
Do not use chipped or cracked glassware. Do not heat the bottom of a test tube.

 Open Flame
Tie back hair and loose clothing. Never reach across a lit burner.

 Flammable Substance
Do not have a flame near flammable materials.

 Corrosive Substance
Wear safety goggles, an apron, and gloves when working with corrosive chemicals.

 Poison
Don't chew gum, drink, or eat in the laboratory. Never taste a chemical in the laboratory.

 Fume
Avoid inhaling substances that can irritate your respiratory system.

 Thermal Burn
Do not touch hot glassware or equipment.

 Electrical Equipment
Keep electrical equipment away from water or other liquids.

 Sharp Object
To avoid a puncture wound, use scissors or other sharp objects only as intended.

 Disposal
Dispose of chemicals only as directed.

 Hand Washing
Wash your hand thoroughly with soap and water.

Stapler

Alcohol thermometer

Scissors

Liquid soap dispenser

Hole punch

Pipet rack

1 × 12

1 × 8

Well plates

Glass slide

Small-scale solid container/dispenser

Reagent bottle

Reagent-filling container

Plastic toothpick

Cotton swab

Small-scale spatula

Small-scale pipet

Small-scale weights

Cups

SMALL-SCALE EQUIPMENT

Alcohol Thermometer: glass; alcohol type; used to measure temperature.

Cotton Swab: cotton and plastic; used to clean well plates, reaction surfaces.

Cups: plastic, 1-ounce and 3 1/2-ounces; used for titrations, balance pans, chromatography.

Glass Slide: only glass equipment in small-scale; may be heated; used for evaporations.

Hot Plate: low-temperature capability, used for evaporations.

Liquid Soap Dispenser: plastic; used to wash hands after every laboratory.

Hole Punch, 1/4-inch: metal; used to punch holes in straws for construction of apparatus.

Pipet Rack: plastic; used to arrange and hold pipets for easy access.

Reagent Bottle: plastic; used to store solutions.

Reagent-Filling Container: plastic; used to fill pipets.

Safety Goggles: plastic; must be worn at all times while working in the laboratory.

Scissors: metal; used to cut paper and plastic for construction of instruments.

Small-Scale Balance: student-built; used for quantitative chemistry.

Small-scale reaction surface

Small-scale balance

Zipper-locking bag

Small-scale spectroscope

Safety goggles

Small-scale conductivity/electrolysis device

Hot plate

Plastic spatula

Small-Scale Conductivity/Electrolysis Device: teacher- or student-built; used to measure conductivity and to electrolyze solutions.

Small-Scale Pipet: plastic; used to store and deliver liquids.

Small-Scale Reaction Surface: plastic; used to mix chemicals qualitatively.

Small-Scale Solid Container/Dispenser: plastic; used to store and dispense solids.

Small-Scale Spatula: student-built; used to sample solids.

Small-Scale Spectroscope: student-built; used for analysis of light.

Small-Scale Weights: student-built; used with balance to measure mass.

Spatula: plastic; used to retrieve hot glass slides from hot plate.

Stapler: metal and plastic; used in making weights, chromatography, dispensing steel samples.

Toothpick: plastic; used to stir liquids in well plates.

Well Plates: plastic; common sizes are 1×12 and 1×8; used for quantitative work.

Zipper-Locking Plastic Bag: plastic; used to store weights and transfer dry-food samples.

SAFE AND EFFICIENT TECHNIQUES FOR USING SMALL-SCALE EQUIPMENT

This section will introduce you to some of the most commonly used pieces of small-scale equipment and give you tips on how to use them safely, efficiently, and without contamination. As you work your way through the experiments, you will want to refer to this information regularly. You are responsible for knowing these techniques and using them correctly!

Keep in mind that in the interest of safety, time, effort, and the environment, it's best to use only the amount of chemicals that you need. Small amounts of chemicals will do the same thing that larger amounts will do. The only difference is that small amounts are much safer, easier to clean up, and better for the environment.

The Small-Scale Pipet

The workhorse of the small-scale laboratory is the small-scale plastic pipet. Small-scale pipets serve two simultaneous functions: they store *and* dispense aqueous solutions of chemicals. Several pipets fit into the plastic pipet racks to make a convenient, readily available set of chemical solutions.

Preparing and Filling a Small-Scale Pipet

Most of the pipets you use in this course will be prepared for you. Your teacher might occasionally ask you to make and label your own. To do this, grasp a pipet firmly between your thumbs and forefingers at the center of the stem, as shown in Figure I. Gently stretch the plastic stem so that it deforms to a smaller diameter. Cut the stem squarely with sharp scissors, leaving about 1 centimeter of the smaller stem as a tip.

Cut out a paper label and tape it to the pipet bulb so you can read it when the stem points up. Be sure to wrap the tape all the way around the bulb so that the tape overlaps itself and serves as a water-tight seal for the label.

To fill the pipet, wear your safety goggles and fill a reagent-filling container half full with reagent from a reagent bottle. Be sure to read the label! Point the tip of a pipet into an overturned plastic cup to prevent scattering stray droplets of liquid, and squeeze the bulb (Figure II). Now immerse the tip into the reagent-filling container and release the bulb. The pipet will fill with solution. To avoid contamination, do not return any unused solution to the reagent bottle. Replace the caps on both the reagent bottle and the reagent-filling container.

Small-scale pipets are easy to use, and the drop size they deliver makes handling them safe and efficient. They deliver drops having a volume of only about 20 microliters (20 millionths of a liter, or about 20 millionths of a quart). These small quantities of chemicals are also easier to clean up and present only a minimal environmental waste problem.

a. Grasp

b. Pull

c. Cut

d. Label

Figure I *Making and labeling a small-scale pipet*

a. Squeeze

b. Fill

Figure II *Filling a small-scale pipet*

The Small-Scale Reaction Surface

Rather than using conventional glassware like glass test tubes and beakers, you will carry out many of your experiments on a small-scale plastic reaction surface. Depending on what your teacher decides to use, this reaction surface might be a plastic file protector, an overhead projection transparency, or even a piece of plastic wrap. Your "reaction vessel" will be the drop of an aqueous solution that forms a hemispherical bead on the plastic surface. This bead is similar to the beads of water that form on a freshly waxed car. Because of surface tension, water naturally forms beads on plastic surfaces or on car wax. Water molecules have a relatively strong attraction for each other and no particular attraction for substances like plastic. A bead of water stays together because of this strong attraction. For this reason, the bead is an ideal reaction vessel that you can use to carry out thousands of chemical reactions on a small scale. Because of its curved shape, the bead also serves as a magnifier. It enlarges the image of substances contained in the bead, making them easier to see.

The small-scale plastic surface encourages the use of smaller, safer, and more environmentally sound amounts of chemicals. An additional advantage of the small-scale reaction surface is that it allows for the placement of the directions and any special organization for an experiment in plain view, directly under the work surface. The small-scale reaction surface also allows for drops to appear on both white and black backgrounds.

Dispensing Drops From a Pipet Onto a Reaction Surface

Full small-scale pipets are to be used only for the storage and careful delivery of liquids. Delivering one drop at a time is the safest and most efficient use of the pipet. One-drop delivery is also the best way to avoid contamination. To deliver a drop, hold the pipet vertically over the small-scale reaction surface, as in Figure III, so its tip is about 1 to 2 centimeters above the surface. The first drops sometimes contains an air bubble; if this is a problem, you may want to expel them into the sink or a waste cup before you begin. Never touch the tip of the pipet to the small-scale reaction surface. "Touching" drops onto the small-scale reaction surface causes contamination and makes it difficult to reproduce drops of the same size. Remember: Always *drop* the drops, never touch the drops onto the small-scale reaction surface.

a. Hold vertically   **b.** Squeeze gently   **c.** Allow drop to fall   **d.** Perfect

Figure III *Delivering a drop*

Stirring Without Contamination

You can stir a hemispherical droplet on a small-scale reaction surface by air stirring, or gently blowing air from an empty pipet onto the droplet, as in Figure IV. Aim the tip of an empty pipet at the droplet while holding it 2 to 3 centimeters away. Gently squeeze the bulb repeatedly. Moving air from the empty bulb will stir the contents of the droplet. Be sure not to touch the tip of the stirring pipet to the droplet because this will result in contamination, or the droplet might be absorbed into the stirring pipet. Both outcomes are undesirable.

a. Aim tip of empty pipet 2 to 3 cm away   **b.** Squeeze bulb gently; moving air stirs drop

Figure IV *Stirring a drop by blowing air from a small-scale pipet*

To correct errors on small parts of the small-scale reaction surface, simply absorb small amounts of any undesired material onto a cotton swab or onto the edge of a rolled paper towel, as shown in Figure V.

a. With a cotton swab   **b.** With the edge of a rolled paper towel

Figure V *Correcting a mistake*

Cleaning the Small-Scale Reaction Surface

You can clean the small-scale reaction surface more quickly and easily than conventional glassware. To clean the entire small-scale reaction surface, absorb the liquids onto a paper towel and dispose the towel in a solid waste bin. Then wipe the surface with a damp paper towel. Finally, dry the surface with another paper towel. Take care that the chemical solutions touch only the paper towel and not your hands.

Disposal of paper towels is preferable to rinsing the chemicals down the drain because the paper towels eventually end up in landfills as solid waste. By contrast, liquid waste dumped down the drain ends up in sewage-treatment plants and can be introduced into rivers or lakes. Solid waste, while a mounting international problem, is much easier to control and to dispose of than liquid waste. Keeping solid waste to a minimum and disposing of it properly helps reduce environmental problems.

Plastic wrap as a small-scale reaction surface has the advantage that it does not need to be cleaned. When you are finished with it, simply fold it up carefully so that it contains all the chemicals you used, and dispose of it in the solid-waste bin. The disadvantage of plastic wrap is that its one-time use and disposal requires that a lot of plastic be thrown away, a less than ideal or efficient use of resources! It is always better to clean, reuse, and recycle materials whenever you can.

Plastic Cups and Well Plates

Sometimes it will be more convenient to work on scales larger than just a few drops. You will use plastic cups and well plates for larger quantities. The balance pan, made from a plastic cup, is also a convenient large-reaction vessel. Water and water solutions bead up on plastic cups just as they do on small-scale reaction surfaces. You can stir the contents of a cup by gently swirling it. Most plastic cups have white insides, which serve as ideal built-in backgrounds for viewing chemical reactions. To clean a cup, rinse it with water, shake the water out, and dry it with a paper towel. To clean a well plate, flood it with water, and scrub the wells with a cotton swab. Shake the water out and dry the wells with a clean cotton swab. When you clean plastic cups and well plates, take care not to get the chemicals on your hands.

Dispensing Solids

To dispense solids into a cup or onto a small-scale reaction surface, simply remove the tape covering the hole in the top of the plastic vial and gently shake out the quantity you need. Alternatively, you can make a small-scale spatula by cutting a soda straw at an angle, as shown in Figure VI. Use the straw to sample a portion of solid directly from the container. Your teacher will have lots of bits and pieces of recycled straws on hand for this purpose. Once a straw has been used with chemicals, do not use it again. Dispose of it according to your teacher's directions.

a. Cut at an angle

b. Two small-scale spatulas

Figure VI *Making a small-scale spatula from a soda straw*

The Safe Use of Glass Slides and Hot Plates

The glass microscope slide is one of the few pieces of glassware you will use in small-scale experiments. Before you use a glass slide, check to see that it is free of cracks and chips. Replace any broken slide with a new one. If you break a glass slide, notify your teacher. Sweep up the glass with a brush and pan. Never handle broken glass with your fingers!

From time to time, it will be necessary to heat liquid droplets. The best way to heat droplets is to dispense them onto a glass slide and heat the slide on a hot plate. Because small-scale quantities require very little heat, usually the lowest setting on the hot plate is sufficient. Even so, keep in mind that the hot plate is hot, and so is the glass slide. A hot glass slide can burn you, and it will break if you drop it! Remove the hot slide, using a plastic spatula. Even though the glass slide does not look hot, do not touch it until you have allowed it to cool on the lab bench. Do not place a hot slide on a plastic small-scale reaction surface; the thin plastic small-scale reaction surface will melt!

Keep in mind that hot plates are electrical appliances. To avoid electrical shock, keep them away from sinks, water faucets, and other sources of water.

Measuring Mass on a Small-Scale Balance

Early in this course you will construct your own small-scale balance. You will have the option of using it in a variety of experiments throughout the course to measure mass. Before you begin any massing, check to see that the balance beam swings freely, without friction and interference. Use your small-scale balance to measure mass in the following ways:

1. To measure the mass of a solid object:

   a. Place the solid object in the pan.

   b. Adjust the beam and/or the counterweight so the beam rests in the horizontal position as indicated by the pointer. To check for accuracy, tap the beam gently so it oscillates back and forth without friction or interference and comes to rest in the horizontal position.

   c. Replace the object with known weights until the beam again returns to the horizontal position, oscillating freely and without interference.

2. To measure the mass of a specified amount of a liquid:

   a. Place a known mass equal in size to the mass of the liquid you wish to measure in the pan.

   b. Adjust the beam and/or the counterweight so the beam rests in the horizontal position as indicated by the pointer. To check for accuracy, tap the beam gently so it oscillates back and forth without friction or interference and comes to rest in the horizontal position.

   c. Remove the known weight and use a small-scale pipet to deliver, drop by drop, enough liquid to return the beam to the horizontal position, oscillating freely and without interference.

3. To calibrate a small-scale pipet:

   a. Place a 1000-mg mass in the pan.

   b. Adjust the beam and/or the counterweight so the beam rests in the horizontal position as indicated by the pointer. To check for accuracy, tap the beam gently so it oscillates back and forth without friction or interference and comes to rest in the horizontal position.

c. Remove the 1000-mg weight, and count from a small-scale pipet the number of drops needed to return the beam to the horizontal position. Divide 1000 by the number of drops to obtain the volume of a drop in microliters.

4. To measure the volume of a liquid delivered by a pipet:

  a. Place a small-scale pipet full of the liquid you wish to deliver in the pan.

  b. Adjust the beam and/or the counterweight so the beam rests in the horizontal position as indicated by the pointer. To check for accuracy, tap the beam gently so it oscillates back and forth without friction or interference and comes to rest in the horizontal position.

  c. Deliver the required amount of liquid from the small-scale pipet to another container. Place the small-scale pipet back into the pan, and add enough known masses to return the beam to the horizontal position. The sum of the added masses is equal to the mass of the liquid you delivered to the container.

Measuring Mass on an Electronic Balance

As an alternative to the small-scale balance, your teacher may make an electronic balance available to you. Before proceeding with any weighing activity, push the tare control on the balance and wait for the digital display to stabilize at zero. Take care not to lean on the balance table or cause air currents to circulate about the balance. Place a clean, dry cup on the balance, push the tare control, and wait for the digital display to stabilize at zero.

1. To measure the mass of a solid object:

  a. Place the solid object in the cup and wait for the digital display to stabilize before you read the mass.

2. To measure the mass of a specified amount of liquid:

  a. Remove the cup from the balance and carefully deliver liquid to the cup from a full small-scale pipet. A full pipet is approximately 4 g. Half a pipet is approximately 2 g.

  b. Replace the cup on the balance pan and wait until the digital display stabilizes to read the mass. Keep in mind that for all the experiments, you need not use the exact quantities of liquids specified. However, you do need to know what quantities you use.

3. To calibrate a small-scale pipet:

  a. Remove the cup from the balance and, holding a full small-scale pipet vertically, carefully deliver exactly 50 drops to the cup.

  b. Replace the cup on the balance pan and wait for the digital display to stabilize before you read the mass. Divide the mass in milligrams by 50 to obtain the mass of a single drop in mg.

4. To measure the volume of a liquid delivered by a pipet:

  a. Place a full small-scale pipet of the liquid you wish to deliver in the pan and wait for the digital display to stabilize before you read the mass.

  b. Deliver the required amount of liquid from the pipet to another container. Place the pipet back into the cup and wait for the digital display to stabilize before you read the mass.

Name _____ Date _____ Class _____

SAFETY CONTRACT

I have read in the *Small-Scale Chemistry Laboratory Manual* the pages that describe laboratory safety, laboratory hazards, and safe laboratory techniques. I have asked questions about any section that is unclear to me.

I agree to behave in a way that always promotes a safe laboratory environment for me and my classmates. I agree to use chemicals and to clean them up in a way that protects me, my classmates, and my environment.

I agree to wear safety goggles at all times during chemistry laboratory experiments and whenever my teacher thinks it is appropriate.

_____
Signature

_____
Date

MAKING OBSERVATIONS OF MATTER

Small-Scale Experiment for text Section 1.3

OBJECTIVES

- **Distinguish** between the macroscopic and the microscopic worlds of matter.
- **Observe** changes in matter and interpret the observations.

INTRODUCTION

Here's an experiment you can do at home. You'll need a page of a newspaper, a handful of pencils, some color crayons, and a hand lens. Place all the objects on a table, mix them up, and you're ready to go! Your first task is to identify each object as a piece of paper, a pencil, or a crayon. "Wait a minute," you say. "That's easy!" Yes, it is easy because you can *see* the objects and identify each according to characteristics such as size or shape.

Now make a few scribbles onto the newspaper with a crayon and then with a pencil. Examine your work with a hand lens. What do you see? Perhaps you noticed that with an unaided eye the lines appear to be smooth. But under the hand lens, you can see that the lines are not smooth. You might have also noticed the fibers in the paper which aren't noticeable without a hand lens.

Objects such as crayons and paper, which are large enough to see with the unaided eye, belong to the *macroscopic* world. Within every object that you can see are objects that are too small to see with the unaided eye. These objects belong to the *microscopic* world. Depending on their size, they can be seen with a hand lens, a light microscope, or an electron microscope. You will learn about electron microscopes when you study the structure of atoms in Chapter 4. You will also learn that there are particles within atoms that are *submicroscopic*, meaning that they cannot be seen with any microscope.

In chemistry, you will make observations of the macroscopic world and learn to explain your observations by describing what is happening at the microscopic and submicroscopic levels within matter. Making observations is a necessary step in any scientific method. The observations can help to answer existing questions or can lead to new questions. It is important to record your observations so that you can refer to them as you analyze the results of an experiment.

When a chemist describes an experiment, he or she includes a purpose, a description of the procedure, the results of the experiment, an analysis of the results, and any conclusions. For many experiments in this small-scale laboratory manual, a purpose and a procedure will be provided. You will need to record your observations, analyze the results, and draw some conclusions. In later experiments, you will have a chance to design your own procedures.

PURPOSE

In this experiment, you will make observations and you will propose explanations for your observations. You will attempt to explain your observations of the macroscopic world in terms of changes that are occurring at the microscopic level. You will tear a newspaper and examine the torn edges under a hand lens. You will compare the behavior of water and mineral oil on a plastic surface. You will observe the shape of rock salt crystals and test the ability of rock salt to conduct an electric current when dry and when wet. Finally, you will produce iodine and compare its behavior in water and in mineral oil.

This early in the year, your explanations for what you observe cannot be as complete as they would be later in the year. You may have more questions than answers. What is important is beginning to think like a chemist.

SAFETY

- Wear safety goggles, an apron, and gloves.

- Use full small-scale pipets only for the controlled delivery of liquids.

MATERIALS

rock salt (sodium chloride)
Small-scale pipets containing the following:
water   potassium iodide (KI)
mineral oil   sodium hypochlorite (NaClO)

EQUIPMENT

hand lens   conductivity testing device
rounded river rock   small-scale reaction surface

EXPERIMENTAL PROCEDURE

1. Obtain a page of newspaper and tear it in half from top to bottom. Now take one half and tear it in half so the second tear is perpendicular (at a right angle) to the first tear. Examine the torn edges with a hand lens and note the differences in the two tears.

2. Observe a large piece of rock salt with a hand lens. Then use a rounded rock to gently break the large piece into a few smaller pieces. Note and record what you observe.

3. Test the dry rock salt for its ability to conduct an electric current. Add a drop of water to the salt crystals and test the mixture for its ability to conduct an electric current. Record your results.

4. Place one drop of water and one drop of mineral oil about 5 centimeters apart on a small-scale reaction surface. Observe and note any differences in the behavior of the water and oil. Examine the drops with a hand lens. Test each liquid for its ability to conduct an electric current.

5. On a small-scale reaction surface, add one drop of potassium iodide solution to one drop of sodium hypochlorite. Note and record the color of the mixture.

6. Place two drops of mineral oil on a small-scale reaction surface and add one drop of water to the mineral oil. Then add one drop of potassium iodide solution and one drop of sodium hypochlorite to the mixture. Allow the mixture to stand for a few minutes while you observe and record what happens.

EXPERIMENTAL DATA

Record your results in Table 1.1 or in a copy of the table in your notebook.

Table 1.1

Procedure	Observations
1. torn paper	The paper tears straight in one direction and ragged in the other. Fibers of paper along the torn edges can be seen through a hand lens.
2. shape of salt crystals	The rock salt breaks into cubes.
3. ability of rock salt to conduct a current	Dry rock salt does not conduct an electric current. The wet salt conducts a current.
4. oil and water on plastic	The water beads up on the plastic. The mineral oil forms a flat puddle. Neither liquid conducts an electric current.
5. potassium iodide and sodium hypochlorite	A yellow-brown mixture forms.
6. mineral oil, water, potassium iodide, and sodium hypochlorite	The water does not mix with the mineral oil. Upon standing, a pink ring forms in the mineral oil around the yellow-brown mixture.

CLEANING UP

Avoid contamination by cleaning up in a way that protects you and your environment. Carefully clean the small-scale reaction surface by absorbing the contents onto a paper towel, rinse the small-scale reaction surface with a damp paper towel, and dry it. Dispose of the paper towels in the waste bin.

QUESTIONS FOR ANALYSES

Use what you learned in this experiment to answer the following questions.

1. Are the torn edges of a newspaper different depending on the direction of the tear? Describe any difference. What did the hand lens show about the fibers in a newspaper? A hypothesis is a proposed explanation for an observation. Make a hypothesis that might explain the differences in the tears.

    Yes. From top to bottom, a newspaper page tears in a straight line, but the edge is ragged when

    the paper is torn from side to side. A hand lens reveals that the fibers are generally lined up in

    one direction. The alignment of the fibers governs the way the paper tears. The paper tears more

    evenly along the direction of the fibers.

2. Describe the general shape of the crystals you obtained when you broke the rock salt into smaller pieces. Draw a picture of one of the crystals. What might determine the shape of a solid crystal? (**Hint:** Think about the particles within the crystal that you cannot observe.)

    The salt crystals are generally cubic in shape. Accept any reasonable answer. Some students may

    hypothesize that the arrangement of particles in the crystal determines the shape of the crystal.

3. Contrast the ability of dry rock salt and a rock salt-and-water mixture to conduct an electric current. Hypothesize about what might happen to rock salt when it dissolves in water, which allows the mixture to conduct an electric current.

    The dry salt cannot conduct an electric current; the rock salt-and-water mixture can. Accept any

    reasonable hypothesis. Some students may hypothesize that the particles of salt can move more

    freely when the salt is dissolved in water and that this ability of particles to move is somehow

    connected to the ability to conduct an electric current.

4. To offer an explanation for the behavior of mineral oil and water in Step 4, you need to know that particles in matter can be attracted to one another and that the level of attraction can vary with the particles. (You will study these attractions in Chapters 7 and 8.) For now, based on their behavior, which particles have a greater attraction for one another—the particles in water or the particles in mineral oil? Explain your choice.

Accept any reasonable explanation. Some students may conclude that the more compact shape of

the beaded drops of water indicate that there is a greater attraction between particles in water.

_____

_____

_____

5. What is the color of iodine in water? What color is iodine in mineral oil? Use your observations from Steps 5 and 6 of the Procedure to explain your answers.

Yellow-brown. Pink. When only water was present, the color produced was yellow-brown. When

both water and mineral oil were present, a second color appeared.

_____

_____

_____

NOW IT'S YOUR TURN

Consider the observations and explanations you made in this experiment. Make a list of questions that you might have about matter and changes in matter based on your observations and the explanations you proposed for your observations. You don't have to provide the answers to your questions.

Answers will vary. Why are the fibers in paper aligned in one direction? What is the nature of the

the attractive forces in water? Besides salt, do other solids break into regular geometric shapes?

How will other liquids behave on a plastic reaction surface? Which materials conduct an electric

current and which do not? Why is iodine a different color in mineral oil than it is in water?

A STUDY OF CHEMICAL CHANGES

Small-Scale Experiment for text Section 2.4

OBJECTIVES

- **Observe** and **record** chemical changes involving compounds found in consumer products.
- **Design** and **carry out** experiments to identify compounds in consumer products.
- **Demonstrate** the use of the names and formulas of chemical compounds.

INTRODUCTION

Chemistry is a science that investigates physical and chemical changes in matter. The chemical changes are also called chemical reactions. Often you can observe some visible changes when a chemical reaction occurs. These include a change in color, a production of a gas, a formation of a precipitate in a liquid, or the release of energy. These visible changes are clues to what is happening to atoms within matter at the atomic level.

Chemists explain the changes they observe at the macroscopic level by the changes that occur at the microscopic level. In fact, explaining changes that are visible by changes that are not visible is fundamental to an understanding of chemistry.

PURPOSE

In this experiment, you will study some reactions of compounds found in common consumer products. You will observe and record some visible clues to these chemical reactions. Then you will use chemical reactions to identify the presence of specific substances in mixtures.

SAFETY ⬡ 🧍 ☠ ⬚ ⬚

- Wear safety goggles, an apron, and gloves when working with corrosive chemicals.
- Use full small-scale pipets only for the controlled delivery of liquids.
- Don't chew gum, drink, or eat in the laboratory. Never taste a chemical in the laboratory.
- Avoid inhaling substances that can irritate your respiratory system.

MATERIALS

Small-scale pipets of the following solutions:
sodium hydrogen carbonate ($NaHCO_3$)
hydrochloric acid (HCl)
FD&C blue No. 1 (blue dye)
sodium hypochlorite (NaClO)
potassium iodide (KI)
starch
lead(II) nitrate ($Pb(NO_3)_2$)
calcium chloride ($CaCl_2$)
sodium hydrogen sulfate ($NaHSO_4$)
sodium carbonate (Na_2CO_3)
phenolphthalein (phen)
sodium hydroxide (NaOH)
silver nitrate ($AgNO_3$)
ammonia (NH_3)
copper(II) sulfate ($CuSO_4$)

EQUIPMENT

small-scale reaction surface
empty pipet for stirring

Name _____ Date _____ Class _____

EXPERIMENTAL PAGE

Use small-scale pipets to put two drops of each chemical on the **X**'s in the indicated spaces below. For background contrast, view the drops on both the black and white backgrounds provided by the **X**'s. Stir each mixture by blowing air through an empty pipet. For parts c, d, and l, there are additional instructions within the grid. Record what you observe in Table 2.1.

a. $NaHCO_3$ + HCl

b. HCl + blue dye

c. blue dye + NaClO   Now add one drop of HCl.

d. NaClO + KI   Now add one drop of starch.

e. KI + $Pb(NO_3)_2$

f. $Pb(NO_3)_2$ + $CaCl_2$

g. $CaCl_2$ + $NaHSO_4$ Be patient! Some chemical reactions are slow!

h. NaHSO$_4$ + Na_2CO_3

i. Na_2CO_3 + phen

j. phen + NaOH

k. NaOH + $AgNO_3$

l. $AgNO_3$ + NH_3 Absorb this mixture onto a scrap of paper, expose it to sunlight, and tape it to your data table.

m. NH_3 + $CuSO_4$

n. $CuSO_4$ + $NaHCO_3$

Place this side of the Experimental Page facedown. Use the other side under your small-scale reaction surface.

EXPERIMENTAL DATA

Record your results in Table 2.1 or in a copy of the table in your notebook.

Table 2.1   Experimental Mixings

a.	bubbles	$NaHCO_3$ + HCl
b.	green	HCl + blue dye
c.	yellow then colorless	blue dye + NaClO and then HCl
d.	yellow then black	NaClO + KI and then starch
e.	bright yellow ppt	KI + $Pb(NO_3)_2$
f.	white milky ppt	$Pb(NO_3)_2$ + $CaCl_2$
g.	slow white ppt	$CaCl_2$ + $NaHSO_4$

h.	bubbles	$NaHSO_4$ + Na_2CO_3
i.	bright pink	Na_2CO_3 + phen
j.	bright pink	phen + NaOH
k.	brown ppt	NaOH + $AgNO_3$
l.	wht ppt brown paper*	$AgNO_3$ + NH_3
m.	light blue ppt	NH_3 + $CuSO_4$
n.	light blue ppt	$CuSO_4$ + $NaHCO_3$

*This fleeting, faint precipitate might be seen only by the most observant students. The paper turns brown after several hours or upon exposure to intense sunlight.

CLEANING UP

Avoid contamination by cleaning up in a way that protects you and your environment. Carefully clean the small-scale reaction surface by absorbing the contents onto a paper towel, wipe it with a damp paper towel, and dry it. Dispose of the paper towels in the waste bin. Wash your hands thoroughly with soap and water.

QUESTIONS FOR ANALYSES

Use what you learned in this experiment to answer the following questions.

1. Baking soda is sodium hydrogen carbonate, $NaHCO_3$. When HCl is added to $NaHCO_3$, carbon dioxide bubbles form. Carbon dioxide contains two atoms of oxygen for every atom of hydrogen. Write the chemical formula for carbon dioxide. In what consumer product is the gas commonly found?

   CO_2. Carbonated drinks.

2. In which of the other mixings did bubbles form?

   $NaHSO_4 + Na_2CO_3$.

3. What do you think the gas is that results from the mixing in Question 2?

   Carbon dioxide.

4. Cells in your stomach produce hydrochloric acid, HCl, to help digest food. What color does blue food dye turn when HCl is added?

   Green.

5. Sodium hypochlorite, NaClO, is an ingredient in many household bleaches and cleansers. What happened to the color of blue dye when both HCl and NaClO were added?

   It becomes colorless.

6. Potassium iodide, KI, is the source of iodine in iodized salt. What color is the KI + NaClO mixture? What color does starch change to in the presence of KI and NaClO?

   Yellow-brown. Black.

7. A precipitate is a solid that forms and settles out when some solutions are mixed. Which reaction produced a very bright-yellow precipitate?

   e. $KI + Pb(NO_3)_2$.

8. Which other mixings produced precipitates? Describe their colors and appearance with words like *milky, cloudy,* and *grainy.*

   f. white; g. white; k. brown; l. brown paper; m. light blue; n. light blue.

9. Which mixture produced a precipitate that was very slow to form?

   g. $CaCl_2 + NaHSO_4$.

10. Which solutions produced a "muddy" brown precipitate?

    k. $AgNO_3 + NaOH$.

11. Observe the scrap of paper you used to absorb the $AgNO_3 + NH_3$ mixture. What evidence do you see that indicates that silver compounds are light-sensitive?

    Light caused the damp swab to turn brown over time.

12. Review your results and list at least three different kinds of changes that indicate that a chemical reaction is occurring.

Bubbles, precipitates, and color changes.

13. Describe any other notable observations you made.

The descriptions students write here, especially adjectives, will be varied and original.

NOW IT'S YOUR TURN!

1. What two compounds turned phenolphthalein pink in the original experiment? Experiment to find out if any other mixture produces the same result.

Na_2CO_3 and NaOH. Mixing each of the other 12 chemicals with phenolphtalein will reveal

that NH_3 and $NaHCO_3$ turn pink as well.

2. What happens when you add ammonia, NH_3, to copper(II) sulfate, $CuSO_4$? Does the result depend on the amount of ammonia you add? Try adding several drops of NH_3 to just one drop of $CuSO_4$. Then try adding several additional drops of $CuSO_4$. Record your observations.

A small amount of NH_3 produces a light-blue precipitate. Excess NH_3 turns the solution

clear royal blue. Excess $CuSO_4$ brings back the light-blue precipitate.

3. Sodium hydrogen carbonate, $NaHCO_3$, produces gas bubbles when hydrochloric acid, HCl, is added.

a. Suppose a label of a household product such as baking soda says it contains sodium hydrogen carbonate (also called bicarbonate of soda). How would you test a sample to indicate the presence of sodium hydrogen carbonate, $NaHCO_3$?

Add a drop of HCl to a small amount of baking soda or other sample. Expect bubbles

if the sample contains $NaHCO_3$.

b. Try your procedure with some household products whose labels say they contain $NaHCO_3$. Record your results.

$NaHCO_3$ produces bubbles with HCl.

c. Find out if any of the other chemicals you used in this experiment produce bubbles with hydrochloric acid. Based on your results, describe any limitations this experiment might have.

A positive CO_2 test does not distinguish between $NaHCO_3$ and Na_2CO_3.

4. Many foods contain starches. A starch turns black in the presence of potassium iodide, KI, and sodium hypochlorite, NaClO. Try adding KI and NaClO to various foods to confirm the presence or absence of starch. Describe what you do, record what you observe, and explain what you think the results mean.

Add one drop of KI and one drop of NaClO to foods such as cereal, bread, crackers,

and potato chips. A black color indicates the presence of a starch.

5. Potassium iodide, KI, turns black when sodium hypochlorite, NaClO, and a starch are added. The label on a package of iodized table salt says that it contains potassium iodide, KI. Explain what you could do to confirm this statement. Try your procedure and record your results. Does your procedure work with noniodized salt? Explain.

Add one drop of starch to the edge of a conical pile of table salt so only a portion of the pile

is wet. Then add one drop of NaClO to the wet portion. As the pile absorbs the extra liquid,

a black line forms and moves with the liquid (solvent) into the dry portion. (This is tricky,

but with some experimentation, the results are obvious and gratifying!)

6. Many household products, such as dishwasher liquid, contain sodium hypochlorite, NaClO. Design an experiment to confirm the presence or absence of NaClO in dishwasher liquid and other household chemicals. Add one drop of starch and one drop of KI to a household product that lists NaClO as an ingredient. A black color confirms the presence of NaClO. (**Note:** Do not use full strength household bleach. Your teacher will dilute household bleach with water.)

Dilute 50 mL of house bleach with 200 mL of water.

Hypochlorite ion oxidizes iodide ion to iodine:
$2H^+ + OCl^- + 2I^- \rightarrow I_2 + Cl^- + H_2O$. Starch turns black in the presence of iodine: $I_2 + starch \rightarrow$ blue-black starch-iodine complex.

DESIGN AND CONSTRUCTION OF A SMALL-SCALE BALANCE

Small-Scale Experiment for text Section 3.2

OBJECTIVES

- **Design** and **build** a balance that is capable of accurately weighing 10 grams and is sensitive to 5 milligrams.
- **Explain** the relationship between the structure and function of each part of a balance.
- **Troubleshoot** the balance, and make modifications and innovations to make it work better.

INTRODUCTION

A *balance* is an instrument used to measure mass. Because it is often the most accurate instrument in the laboratory, you commonly use the balance to calibrate other instruments, such as burets and pipets, that are used to measure volume. The balance operates much like a seesaw because it consists of a *beam* that pivots on a central *fulcrum*, as shown in Figure 3.1. A *balance pan* hangs from one end of the beam, and a *counterweight* is attached to the other end. You use a *substitution balance* to determine mass by comparing the weight of an unknown object to the weights of known objects. You place a substance of unknown weight in the pan and adjust the mechanism so the beam balances. You then remove the unknown substance and substitute known weights until the beam balances again. The weight of the unknown substance is equal to the amount of known weights you used to restore the beam to the balanced position.

Sensitivity refers to the smallest weight a balance can measure accurately. Whenever you add weight to the pan, the balance beam moves. You express the sensitivity of the balance as the amount of change in the position of the beam when a known quantity of weight is added. Sensitivity can be measured by the *distance* the beam moves or the *angle* through which the beam moves per unit weight. The smaller the weights you want to measure accurately, the more sensitive your balance must be. If the balance is too sensitive, it will move with even the slightest air currents and will be difficult to use.

The *capacity* of a balance is the maximum amount of weight that can be accurately determined by the balance. Very sensitive balances generally have small capacities. With larger-capacity balances, you sacrifice sensitivity. You want a balance to be just sensitive enough to do the job in a convenient way. You design a balance to make the best compromise among sensitivity, capacity, and ease of use.

The principal moving part of the balance is the *beam*. The beam's mass, length, and flexibility affect the sensitivity of the balance. The longer, lighter, and more rigid the beam, the more sensitive the balance will be. However, the longer the beam, the heavier it is. In designing your beam, find a compromise between the extremes of length and mass, and yet design it to remain rigid under maximum loads. Very sensitive balances have the advantage of measuring the masses of very small objects accurately. Unfortunately, they cannot weigh heavy objects because the long light beam required for high sensitivity is usually too flexible to carry large loads. Balances designed to weigh larger objects must use rigid beams, which are usually very heavy. Thus, sensitivity is sacrificed for capacity and vice versa. In short, the same balance cannot be used to weigh both a truck and a feather. Designers of balances must make compromises and design balances that meet specific objectives. You want your balance to be sensitive to 5 milligrams and have a capacity of about 10 grams.

Figure 3.1 *Construction of a small-scale balance*

The most critical part of the balance is the *fulcrum*, the part on which the beam pivots. For maximum sensitivity, the fulcrum should be nearly friction-free. You should locate it above and at right angles to the beam, and as close to the beam's center of mass as possible. The beam will swing freely back and forth only if the center of mass of the beam is *below* the fulcrum. The beam will not be stable if the center of gravity is above the fulcrum.

A highly visible *pointer* readily determines the horizontal position of the beam. The balance is most sensitive when the beam is exactly horizontal. The pointer should be attached rigidly and at right angles to the beam and the fulcrum. When the beam is horizontal, the pointer will be vertical.

The *zero point* is the point indicated by the pointer when the beam is horizontal. In order to know the horizontal position reliably, the zero point must not move from one weighing to another.

The *balance posts* and *crossmember* make up the superstructure that gives support and stability to the balance and does not interfere with its operation. The balance posts must be anchored and rigid because if they move, the zero point moves. Build the posts perpendicular to the base, then center the zero point in a fixed position between the posts. With a sharp pencil, make holes in the straw posts to provide nearly frictionless surfaces to support the fulcrum. The taller the posts and the longer the pointer, the easier it is to see a small movement in the beam. However, very tall posts are sometimes not rigid enough to support the weight of the instrument.

The *pan pivot* suspends the pan from the beam. Like the fulcrum, it must be sturdy, nearly frictionless, and at right angles to the beam. The pan pivot must not move back and forth along the beam.

The *balance pan* holds the known weights and the objects you want to weigh. The balance pan should be sturdy and lightweight to keep the beam's center of mass close to the fulcrum.

The *beam stops* hit the pointer and allow the beam to move only through a small arc. By preventing excessive motion of the balance beam, they protect the vital moving parts of the balance and shorten the time the beam takes to come to the horizontal position. The sensitivity of a good balance is such that even the slightest touch will cause the balance beam, without beam stops, to rotate and the pan to swing wildly. When trying to make an accurate weighing, this situation is inconvenient at best and disastrous at worst.

The *counterweight* offsets the weight in the pan. A friction-tight but easily moved counterweight serves as a convenient adjustment device for leveling the beam. Make it light to keep the total weight of the beam assembly low.

Summary of principal parts of a balance and their functions:

- The *beam* is the principal moving part. The beam also affects sensitivity. For maximum sensitivity, it should be lightweight, rigid, and long.

- The *fulcrum* is the critical pivot point for the beam. The position and friction of the fulcrum affect accuracy and sensitivity. The fulcrum should be frictionless at the posts, friction-tight at the pointer, close to the beam's center of mass and just above it, and at right angles to the beam and the posts.

- The *counterweight* moves to offset the weight in the pan. The counterweight is light and friction-tight but easily moved.

- The *pointer* points to the zero point when the beam is horizontal. The pointer should be long, visible, and at right angles to the beam.

- The *zero point* shows when the beam is horizontal. The zero point is positioned so the pointer points to it when the beam is horizontal.

- The *posts* support the weight of the balance. They should be sturdy, friction-tight, and out of the way of moving parts.

- The *crossmember* keeps the balance rigid and square. The crossmember is friction-tight and at right angles to the posts.

- The *pan pivot* is the critical point upon which the pan rests. The pan pivot is frictionless at the beam, at right angles to the beam, and foolproof so the pan does not fall off.

- The *beam stops* keep the beam from swinging wildly. The beam stops are sturdy and out of the way of moving parts.

PURPOSE

In this experiment, you will design and construct a balance out of common objects such as soda straws, pins, tape, wood blocks, wire, and plastic cups. For optimal use in small-scale chemistry, your balance should be sensitive to 5 mg and have a capacity of 10 grams. Your balance should be sturdy and foolproof so it can make many accurate weighings in very short times with little trouble. You should build your balance with careful consideration of features that make it function accurately and reliably. The preceding paragraphs provided information about the working parts of a balance. Reread them and refer to these criteria as you design and build your balance.

SAFETY ✂

- Behave in a way that is consistent with a safe laboratory.
- To avoid a puncture wound, use scissors or other sharp objects only as intended.

EQUIPMENT

6 long soda straws	wire
scissors	1/4-inch hole punch
sharp pencil	pre-drilled wood block
extra long pin (1-1/4 inch)	4 square centimeters of graph paper
2 paper clips	1-ounce plastic cup
adhesive label	cellophane tape
thread	standard 5-mg weights

Name _____ Date _____ Class _____

EXPERIMENTAL PROCEDURE

Use the following template to assemble the proper pieces for constructing your small-scale balance. Use the template to cut the soda straws to the appropriate lengths. Use a 1/4-inch hole punch to make holes where indicated. Use a sharp pencil to make holes in the posts for the fulcrum. Assemble the parts as shown in the template and in Figure 3.1.

counterweight

crossmember

fulcrum

straw-beam

pan pivot

straw-pointer

12.0 cm wire or thread

straw-post

straw-post

1-oz plastic cup

beam stop

beam stop

grid paper

EXPERIMENTAL DATA

As you assemble your balance according to the template on the Experimental Page, check it and make adjustments and/or modifications until the answer to each of the following questions is "yes."

_____ **1.** Is the fulcrum perpendicular to both the beam and the pointer?

_____ **2.** Is it just *above* and *touching* the beam?

_____ **3.** Does the fulcrum rotate freely from the holes in the post?

_____ **4.** Are the holes round and large enough to allow a pin head to pass through?

_____ **5.** Is the fulcrum friction-tight at the pointer?

_____ **6.** Is the pin straight?

_____ **7.** Are the posts friction-tight at the base?

_____ **8.** Is the crossmember friction-tight?

_____ **9.** Are the posts and crossmember rigid and out of the way of the moving parts?

_____ **10.** Do the beam stops keep the beam from swinging excessively?

_____ **11.** Are the beam stops out of the way of all other moving parts?

_____ **12.** Does the pan stay on consistently?

_____ **13.** Is the pan easily loaded with weight?

_____ **14.** Does the pan pivot at right angles to the beam?

_____ **15.** Does the beam not bend under weight?

_____ **16.** Is the end of the pointer easy to see?

_____ **17.** Does the pointer point at the zero point when the beam is horizontal?

_____ **18.** Is the zero point positioned to indicate when the beam is horizontal?

_____ **19.** Is the pointer at right angles to the beam?

_____ **20.** Is the counterweight easily moved but friction-tight to stay in place?

_____ **21.** Can you easily fix anything that goes wrong with your balance?

_____ **22.** Does the pointer move when a 15-mg weight is placed on the pan?

_____ A 10-mg weight?

_____ A 5-mg weight?

_____ The *sensitivity* of the balance is the minimum weight on the pan that will cause the pointer to move. Each of the three weights causes the beam to move how many graph-paper units?

CLEANING UP

Please clean up at the end of the period. Recycle all the materials you do not use. Dispose of unusable scraps in the waste bin. Label your balance with your name, and store it as directed by your teacher.

You may want to store balances on shelves or in cabinets.

QUESTIONS FOR ANALYSES

Use what you learned in this experiment to answer the following questions.

1. How does a substitution balance work? Does it measure mass or weight? Explain. On a separate sheet of paper, make a rough sketch of your balance and label all the parts.

A substitution balance is used to measure mass by comparing weights of

known objects with those of unknown objects. An object of unknown mass

is placed in the pan. The beam is balanced. The object is removed and

substituted with known masses until the beam is again balanced. Because

the gravitational force of each object is the same, it is cancelled out, giving

a good approximation of mass.

2. What is sensitivity? What is capacity?

The smallest weight the balance can accurately measure. The maximum

amount of weight that can be determined accurately by the balance.

3. What critical part of a balance most affects its sensitivity? Give three important criteria for this critical part.

The fulcrum. Frictionless at the posts, friction-tight at the pointer, and

perpendicular to the beam and the posts.

4. Name another part of a balance that also affects its sensitivity.

The beam.

5. At what position is the beam most sensitive?

Horizontal.

6. What is the function of the pointer? Of the zero point?

Both indicate when the beam is horizontal.

7. Why is it important for the balance posts and crossmember to be well-anchored and rigid?

They keep the angles square and the zero point fixed.

8. What aspects of your balance are most important?

A frictionless fulcrum and a free-swinging beam.

9. What other criterion besides sensitivity must be considered when creating a balance beam?

Capacity.

10. Explain how each of the following materials would affect the *sensitivity* and *capacity* of your balance if each material was used for the beam. Give the advantages and disadvantages of each: **a.** a solid steel rod, **b.** a hollow aluminum tube, and **c.** a wood dowel.

a. decreased sensitivity, increased capacity; b. decreased sensitivity,

increased capacity; c. decreased sensitivity, increased capacity.

11. The sensitivity of a balance increases with increasing length and decreasing mass of the beam. Why is the ideal case of having an infinitely long beam of zero mass not possible?

The longer the beam, the heavier it must be.

12. How many graph-paper units did the pointer move upon addition of a 10-mg weight? Explain how you might make your balance even more sensitive.

Typically about one. Make the beam lighter or longer.

13. Why is it important to have the holes in which the fulcrum rest at exactly the same height? If they are not at the same height, how might you be able to fix them without remaking one or both the posts?

To keep the fulcrum perpendicular to the posts. Trim the bottom of the longer post.

14. If the fulcrum pin was placed at a 45-degree angle to the beam, how would this affect the function and sensitivity of your balance?

The beam assembly would hit other parts of the balance. Sensitivity would decrease

because the angle through which it moves would be less per unit mass.

NOW IT'S YOUR TURN

1. Why must the fulcrum be placed *above the beam*? What will happen to a balance beam set in motion if the fulcrum is below it? (To answer these questions, see what happens when you place the fulcrum below the beam. Go ahead; you can always move it back!)

Gravity will restore the beam to the horizontal position only if the fulcrum

is above the beam.

2. Design a longer beam for your balance. Use a 1/4-inch wood dowel, an aluminum tube, and an extra-long soda straw, or try to put together one or more soda straws. What are some of the advantages and disadvantages of your longer beam?

3. Design a better way to hold your balance up. Redesign the posts into a more rigid superstructure. Try building a triangular or a rectangular superstructure.

4. A taller balance will be more sensitive because the movement of a long pointer will be easier to detect for a small weight. Try modifying your balance so that it is very tall.

5. Try redesigning the beam-fulcrum assembly. You might consider using permanent magnets to suspend the beam-fulcrum.

DESIGN AND CONSTRUCTION OF A SET OF STANDARDIZED MASSES

Small-Scale Experiment for text Section 3.2

OBJECTIVES

- **Distinguish** between mass and weight.
- **Construct** a set of weights to use with a small-scale balance.
- **Weigh** objects accurately using your weights.

INTRODUCTION

Now that you've built a balance, you can use it to measure mass. To do so, you must first make a set of known weights to use with your balance for comparison with unknown weights. But before you make the weights, let's clarify a few things about how mass is different from weight.

Mass is the quantity of matter in an object. *Weight*, on the other hand, is the gravitational force of attraction exerted between the mass of an object and its surroundings, principally Earth. The weight of an object on Earth will differ slightly depending on its geographical location. Because the gravitational field is weaker at the equator than at the poles, the same object will weigh less in Mexico City than in Anchorage, Alaska. The gravitational pull also decreases with higher elevation. An object will weigh slightly less in Denver, "the mile-high city," than in New York, which is at sea level.

In chemistry, you are always interested in the determination of mass because you do not want the results to depend on where you are. You can readily determine mass by comparing the weight of an unknown object to the weights of known objects through the use of a *balance*, a device used to compare weights. Since gravity will affect both known and unknown objects to exactly the same extent, the effect of gravity will cancel, and a measure of mass will result.

It is important to note that the distinction between mass and weight in chemistry is not commonly observed. For example, determining the mass of an object is called *weighing*. Known masses that are used to compare unknown masses are called *weights*. Hereafter, we will use the terms *mass* and *weight* synonymously, but strictly speaking, we are referring to *mass*.

To weigh things accurately, your small-scale balance is used with a set of weights. The set of weights must be calibrated, that is, compared to accurately known weights. Calibration is usually done with a balance more sensitive and accurate than your small-scale balance. Once calibrated, this known set of weights will become your set of standardized weights.

The number and sizes of standardized weights in a set should be such that any combination of weight can be added within the sensitivity and capacity of the balance. Your balance has a sensitivity of 5 mg and a capacity of about 10 g (10,000 mg). Thus, you need to build a set of weights that can combine to provide any number of milligrams between 5 mg and 10,000 mg in intervals of 5 mg.

Name _____ Date _____ Class _____

PURPOSE

In this experiment, you will take advantage of small objects that can be uniformly reproduced to make a set of standardized weights. Common objects such as staples, soda straws, graph paper, and wire all have reproducible weights for equal-sized pieces. The plastic "disks" punched from super-jumbo soda straws all weigh exactly 5 mg. Standard staples all weigh 33 mg, and graph paper, if cut precisely, can produce very uniform small weights. Large objects are not as uniformly produced, but they can be standardized by weighing them and labeling them with their milligram values.

SAFETY ✂

- To avoid a puncture wound, use scissors or other sharp objects only as intended.
- Behave in a way that is consistent with a safe laboratory.

EQUIPMENT

soda straws
scissors
1/2 sheet of graph paper
stapler with standard staples
standard paper clip
adhesive labels
jumbo paper clip
penny
nickel
1/4-inch hole punch
zipper-locking plastic bag

EXPERIMENTAL PROCEDURE

Use the information below to design a set of weights, and then make them with the available materials. Where you can, write the weight value and your name on each weight. Place them in a labeled zipper-locking plastic bag for storage.

Weights with the following milligram values will enable you to weigh any object between 5 mg and 10,000 mg. Your set of weights will probably not be ideal; that is, some of the values will not be exactly the values listed below.

5 mg	10 mg	20 mg	30 mg
50 mg	100 mg	200 mg	300 mg
500 mg	1000 mg	2500 mg	5000 mg

1. One 1/4-inch plastic disk cut from a soda straw weighs 5 mg. Make enough plastic disks to weigh things between 5 and 45 mg.

2. Design and make weights from 50 to 500 mg, using the following information:
   1 square inch of graph paper (cut very carefully) weighs 50 mg.
   1 standard staple weighs 33 mg.

   Keep in mind that the staples tend to be more precise than the graph paper, and the weights need to be within only a few (2 to 3) milligrams of the ideal values.

3. Make the following larger weights, and then use your small-scale balance and your smaller weights to determine their masses.

    1 standard paper clip with an adhesive label attached.
    1 jumbo paper clip with an adhesive label attached.
    1 penny with an adhesive label attached.
    1 nickel with an adhesive label attached.

To use your balance to determine the mass of a larger weight, follow these steps:

a. Place the larger weight in the pan, and slide the beam and/or the counterweight back and forth so the pointer indicates the beam is horizontal.

b. Remove the larger weight from the pan, and replace it with smaller weights until the pointer again indicates the beam is horizontal.

c. The weight of the larger weight is the sum of the small weights in the pan.

d. Write this milligram value on the label of the larger weight.

4. If your lab has a precision or an analytical balance, use it to check the weights of your larger weights, following the directions of your teacher. Also, in the next experiment, you will find out how good your weights really are!

EXPERIMENTAL DATA

1. Draw a picture of each standardized weight you make, tell what it is made from, and label it with its milligram value.

 1/4-inch disk cut from straw—5 mg

 50 mg—1 square inch graph paper

 5083 mg
nickel with adhesive label

 525 mg
standard paper clip with adhesive label

standard staples

 100 mg

 300 mg

 1610 mg
jumbo paper clip with adhesive label

 200 mg

 500 mg

 2550 mg
penny with adhesive label

CLEANING UP

Please recycle all the materials you do not use. Dispose of unusable scraps in the waste bin. Store your labeled weights as directed by your teacher.

QUESTIONS FOR ANALYSES

Use what you learned in this experiment to answer the following questions.

1. Distinguish between the terms *mass* and *weight*. Why do we often use them interchangeably?

A mass is a quantity of matter. Weight is the force of gravity acting on that

mass. You usually encounter various weights in the same gravitational

field on Earth.

2. What is the mass of an object in outer space, where there is no gravitational field? What is its weight?

The same as anywhere. Zero.

3. Will the mass of an object be the same on Earth as it is on the moon? Explain.

Yes. An object, assuming no gains or losses, will always have the same

quantity of matter.

4. Is the weight of an object the same on Earth as it is on the moon? Explain.

No. The moon's gravitational field is different from Earth's gravitational field.

5. Would your balance work equally well on the moon as it does on Earth? Explain. Would the result of each weighing be the same? Explain.

Yes. The moon's gravity would act on both the known and unknown

weights. Yes. The moon's gravity would be canceled out in the same way Earth's gravity is

canceled out.

6. Would your balance work equally well in the absence of a gravitational field, for example, in outer space? Explain.

No. The balance needs gravity to restore the beam to the horizontal position.

7. Explain what we mean by the *sensitivity* and *capacity* of a balance.

Sensitivity is the smallest mass that a balance will weigh accurately. Capacity is

the largest mass that a balance will weigh accurately.

8. Your balance is sensitive to 5 mg, and its capacity is about 10 g, or 10,000 mg. Are the weights you made sufficient to measure any unknown weight up to 10,000 mg to a sensitivity of 5 mg?

Yes, if their sum is at least 10,000 mg and any combination will sum to any

number between 5 and 10,000 that is divisible by 5.

9. The mass of a carbon atom is about 2.0×10^{-23} g. Discuss the major problems associated with determining the mass of a carbon atom by using a balance of the design you have constructed.

Such a small mass would require a beam of unusual sensitivity. It would

have to be extremely light and very long, so light that almost no mass

could be used for its construction and so long that a lot of mass must be

used. The length and mass requirements are mutually exclusive.

10. If you weigh an object in Panama and again in Canada on the same balance, will you get the same value for its weight? Explain.

Yes. Even though the gravitational fields vary slightly from equator to pole,

they both cancel.

11. Which of the following would be useful in studying the small differences in gravitational field in various locations: a balance or a spring scale that measures weight? Explain.

A spring scale measures weight, the force of Earth's gravitational field.

NOW IT'S YOUR TURN!

1. Can you devise another way to make small-scale weights? If your laboratory has a precision or an analytical balance, you may want to use it to investigate the weights of various common objects to see if you can devise a better set of standardized weights.

2. If your lab does have a very sensitive balance, you can make larger weights from a standardized spool of brass or steel wire. Since wire is very uniform, its length is proportional to its weight. All you need to know is how much a certain length of wire weighs, and you can make any size weight you want by measuring the appropriate length. Notice that you are basing mass on the fundamental quantity of length. By using a very sensitive and accurate analytical balance, you can determine what the mass of one meter of any wire is. From this, you can calculate what length of wire must be cut to make a weight of any desired quantity. Typical results might look something like this:

One meter (100 cm) of wire weighs 936.8 mg, so:

to make a wire of this *weight* (mg)	cut a wire to this *length* (cm)
500.0	53.4
300.0	32.0
200.0	21.3
100.0	10.7
50.0	5.34
30.0	3.20
20.0	2.13
10.0	1.07
5.0	0.534

Each spool of wire is slightly different in weight, so each must be calibrated and a table of weights made accordingly. Also, the smaller weights (100 mg and smaller) are often difficult to store and handle, so it is less convenient to make these smaller weights from wire.

Beginning with the largest weight measure, cut the indicated length of wire by stretching it along a meter stick, smoothing out any bends and kinks as you go. Keep in mind that wire is ductile; it will become longer if stretched too hard. The trick is to smooth out the bends and kinks while handling the wire gently.

To store the larger wire weights, you can wrap the wire in a tight coil around a nail and poke one end into a straw on the beam stop. You should mark each one to distinguish it from other weights.

MASSING ACTIVITIES FOR A SMALL-SCALE BALANCE

Small-Scale Experiment for text Sections 3.1, 3.2, and 3.3

OBJECTIVES

- **Determine** accurate weights of various objects by using a small-scale balance.
- **Calibrate** a pipet by weighing drops of water.

INTRODUCTION

How accurate are your weights? How well does your balance work? Will it help you get the right answers? What is a "right answer," anyway? Now that you've spent so much time building your balance and weights, what kinds of problems can you solve with them?

PURPOSE

In this experiment, you will explore a few of these questions. You will begin by tuning your balance and set of weights by using them to weigh objects of known mass. You will compare your results to the known values to evaluate how good your balance is. Then you will make any necessary adjustments and explore ways you can use your balance to investigate matter, answer questions, and solve problems.

The first thing you will do is weigh a penny and compare it to its known weight. If your result is not close, you will make the necessary adjustments to your balance and/or weights and try again until you can consistently weigh known objects to a high degree of accuracy. Then you can rely on your balance and use it to find unknown masses.

SAFETY

- Behave in a way that is consistent with a safe laboratory.

EQUIPMENT

various objects to weigh, such as pennies, nickels, and dimes
adhesive labels
small-scale balance
small-scale pipet filled with water

EXPERIMENTAL PROCEDURE

Part A. Weighing Pennies

1. Place a small adhesive label on a penny and weigh the penny as follows. Record your results in Table 5.1.

   a. Place the penny in the balance pan, and move the beam and the counterweight until the pointer indicates the beam is horizontal.

   b. Remove the penny and substitute weights until the pointer is again zeroed. If you go too far, do not be afraid to remove a larger weight and replace it with a smaller one.

   c. When you think the beam is horizontal, tap the beam gently and allow it to make a few oscillations before coming to rest. This avoids a false rest point due to friction at the fulcrum.

   d. The weight of the penny in milligrams is the sum of the weights in the pan. Calculate the *error* and *percent error* of the penny weighed on your small-scale balance compared to the same penny weighed on an electronic balance, as follows. (Assume that the electronic weight is the actual or theoretical weight.)

   $$\text{error} = |\text{small-scale weight} - \text{electronic weight}|$$

   $$\%\ \text{error} = \frac{|\text{small-scale weight} - \text{electronic weight}|}{\text{electronic weight}} \times 100$$

2. Weigh a second penny (with a label) and calculate its percent error. Record your results in Table 5.1. If the error in the case of either penny is greater than about 10 mg, and the percent error is greater than about 0.5%, work with your balance and your weights to determine the cause. Obtain another penny, and repeat Part A until you can weigh a penny to within a 0.5% error. Label this penny with your name and its weight in milligrams, and keep it as a standard weight. (**Hint:** The most common problem is friction at the fulcrum. Adjust your balance so the beam assembly moves freely. You can also ask your teacher to weigh your larger weights for you to determine if they are accurate.)

Part B. Weighing Experiments

3. Weigh a nickel and calculate the error and percent error of your measurement. Record your results in Table 5.1. Label your nickel as you labeled your penny, and keep it as a standard weight.

4. Weigh a dime and calculate the error and percent error of your measurement. Record your results in Table 5.1.

5. Design an experiment to find the weight in milligrams of 1 drop of water. Record your results in Table 5.2. Count the number of drops it takes to equal a certain weight. (Any weight will do!) Divide that weight by the number of drops to get the weight of a drop. Repeat the experiment with various sizes of weights to see how consistent you can be. Try 100-, 300-, 500-, and 1000-mg weights.

6. Design an experiment to determine if the size of drops varies with the angle at which they are delivered. Record your results in Table 5.3. Use a 1000-mg weight. Try vertical (90°), horizontal (0°), and halfway between (45°).

Name _____ Date _____ Class _____

EXPERIMENTAL DATA

Record your results in Tables 5.1, 5.2, and 5.3 or in copies of the tables in your notebook.

Table 5.1 Weighing Coinage

Object	Small-Scale Weight (mg)	Electronic Weight (mg)	Error (mg)	Percent Error
penny #1	2560	2550	10	0.39%
penny #2	3110	3125	15	0.48%
nickel	5025	5015	10	0.20%
dime	2220	2212	8	0.36%

Table 5.2 Weighing a Drop of Water

Weight (mg)	Number of Drops	Weight of Drops (mg)
100	4	25
300	15	20
500	24	21
1000	48	21

Table 5.3 Checking Drop Angle

Drop Angle	Number of Drops	Weight of Drop (mg)
vertical (90°)	48	21
horizontal (0°)	36	28
halfway (45°)	40	25

CLEANING UP

Please recycle all the materials you do not use. Store your balance and weights according to your teacher's directions.

QUESTIONS FOR ANALYSES

Use what you learned in this experiment to answer the following questions.

1. Discuss some major sources of error if a weighing has a percent error of greater than about 0.5%.

   Friction at the fulcrum. Inaccurate counting of weights. Inaccurate larger weights.

   _____

   _____

2. If your weighings exceed about 0.5% error, what changes might you make to get better results?

   Adjust the fulcrum so that it is friction free. Check the accuracy of the

   weights on an analytical balance.

3. How many milligrams does one drop of water weigh?

   Approximately 20 to 25, depending on the pipet.

4. How many grams does one drop of water weigh? (1000 mg = 1 g.)

   $$x \text{ g} = 1 \text{ drop} \times \frac{\text{wt. of drops (mg)}}{\text{no. of drops}} \times \frac{1 \text{ g}}{1000 \text{ mg}} = 0.020 \text{ to } 0.025 \text{ g}$$

5. If you use a larger weight to determine the size of a drop, will you get a more accurate or less accurate result than with a smaller weight? Explain.

   More accurate. A larger weight requires more drops, so the error is smaller.

6. What angle for holding the pipet is best? Explain. Why is it important to expel the air bubble before you begin the experiment?

   The best angle is vertical (90°) because it's easiest to control. It's important

   to expel the air bubble because the drop containing the air bubble contains

   less water than the others.

7. What is the volume in cm³ of one drop? The density of water is 1.00 g/cm³. This means that 1 g of water occupies a volume of 1 cm³. Thus, if we measure weight, we can calculate volume as a function of weight. That is, if we weigh a certain amount of water, we will know its volume.

   $$x \text{ cm}^3 = 1 \text{ drop} \times \frac{\text{no. of grams}}{1 \text{ drop}} \times \frac{1 \text{ cm}^3}{1 \text{ g}} = 0.020 \text{ to } 0.025 \text{ cm}^3$$

   Calculate the volume of a single drop in mL. (1 mL = 1 cm³) What is the volume of a drop in microliters, μL? (1000 μL = 1 mL)

   0.020 mL. 20 μL.

8. What is the density of water in units of mg per cm^3? (1 gram = 1000 mg) Express the density in units of mg per mL.

1000 mg/cm^3. 1 mg/mL.

NOW IT'S YOUR TURN!

1. The United States government changed the composition of the American penny, which had remained essentially the same for nearly 120 years. Older pennies are made of an alloy consisting of 95% copper and 5% zinc. The newer penny's copper coating comprises only 2.4% of its total weight. This copper-coated zinc slug looks just like its copper ancestor, but it is easily distinguished by its different weight. Because the density of zinc is less than that of copper, the newer pennies are lighter than the older ones.

   Obtain a set of ten pennies dated 1978–1987 from your teacher. Use your balance to determine in which year the penny's composition changed. (**Hint:** If you're clever, you don't have to find the exact milligram weight of each penny.) Describe your problem-solving strategy in the space below. Record in your lab notebook the date and any weight data you have for each penny.

   Please do not break up the set. Return the entire set to your teacher when you finish.

   Place any of the pennies in the balance pan, and slide the beam so that the

   pointer is at zero. Without adjusting the balance systematically, replace

   each penny with another one, noting which are about the same weight and

   which are heavier or lighter than the first penny.

   _____

   _____

   _____

   a. In the year the penny's composition was changed, some of the pennies were made of copper and some of zinc. In what year was the change made? How do you know? On what property do you base your answer?

   1982. Pre-1982 pennies are heavier than post-1982 pennies. Copper is more

   dense than zinc.

   b. Calculate the average weight of a copper penny and the average weight of a zinc penny. (density Zn = 7.14 g/cm^3; density Cu = 8.92 g/cm^3) How are these densities consistent with the relative weights of the two kinds of pennies?

   Copper is more dense than zinc, so copper pennies will weigh more than

   zinc pennies.

c. Using the average weights of the zinc and copper pennies and the percentage of copper and zinc in each kind of penny, calculate the actual worth of each kind of penny in terms of zinc and copper prices. You'll need to get the current cost per pound of copper and of zinc from your teacher. A copper penny is 95% copper and 5% zinc:

$$\text{weight (mg)} \times \frac{95 \text{ mg Cu}}{100 \text{ mg penny}} \times \frac{1 \text{ g Cu}}{1000 \text{ mg Cu}} \times \frac{1 \text{ pound Cu}}{454 \text{ g Cu}} \times \frac{\text{cost(\$) Cu}}{\text{pound of Cu}} = \$ \text{ Cu}$$

$$\text{weight (mg)} \times \frac{5 \text{ mg Zn}}{100 \text{ mg penny}} \times \frac{1 \text{ g Zn}}{1000 \text{ mg Zn}} \times \frac{1 \text{ pound Zn}}{454 \text{ g Zn}} \times \frac{\text{cost (\$) Zn}}{\text{pound of Zn}} = \$ \text{ Zn}$$

A zinc penny is 2.4% copper and 97.6% zinc:

$$\text{weight (mg)} \times \frac{2.4 \text{ mg Cu}}{100 \text{ mg penny}} \times \frac{1 \text{ g Cu}}{1000 \text{ mg Cu}} \times \frac{1 \text{ pound Cu}}{454 \text{ g Cu}} \times \frac{\text{cost (\$) Cu}}{\text{pound of Cu}} = \$ \text{ Cu}$$

$$\text{weight (mg)} \times \frac{97.6 \text{ mg Zn}}{100 \text{ mg penny}} \times \frac{1 \text{ g Zn}}{1000 \text{ mg Zn}} \times \frac{1 \text{ pound Zn}}{454 \text{ g Zn}} \times \frac{\text{cost (\$) Zn}}{\text{pound of Zn}} = \$ \text{ Zn}$$

d. Any coin that is composed of metals worth less than the face value of the coin is called a subsidiary coin. Which of the two kinds of pennies is a subsidiary coin?

Any penny whose total Cu and Zn value is less than $0.01 is a subsidiary coin.

_____

_____

2. Devise a way to weigh a Sunday edition of a major newspaper by using your balance. Weigh the Sunday edition.

Tear out one page, weigh it, and multiply by the total number of pages.

_____

_____

_____

6   ISOTOPES AND ATOMIC MASS

Small-Scale Experiment for text Section 4.3

OBJECTIVES

- **Determine** the average weights of each isotope of the fictitious element vegium.
- **Determine** the relative abundance of isotopes of vegium.
- **Calculate** from experimental data the atomic mass of vegium.

INTRODUCTION

Isotopes are atoms of the same atomic number having different masses due to different numbers of neutrons. The atomic mass of an element is the weighted average of the masses of the isotopes of that element. The weighted average takes into account both the mass and relative abundance of each isotope as it occurs in nature. The relative abundances and masses of small atomic particles are measured in the laboratory by an instrument called a mass spectrometer. The mass spectrometer separates particles by mass and measures the mass and relative abundance of each. From these data, a weighted average is calculated to determine the atomic mass of the element.

PURPOSE

In this experiment, you will perform the necessary calculations to determine the atomic mass of the fictitious element vegium. The three different isotopes of vegium are beanium, peaium and cornium. As in real elements, these isotopes are collections of particles having different masses. Your job will be to obtain a sample of vegium and determine the relative abundance of each isotope and the mass of each type of particle. From this data, you will calculate the weighted average mass, or atomic mass, of vegium. Unlike real isotopes, the individual isotopic particles of vegium differ slightly in mass, so you will determine the average mass of each type of isotopic particle. Then you can calculate the weighted average mass, or atomic mass, of vegium.

SAFETY

- Behave in a way that is consistent with a safe laboratory environment.

EQUIPMENT

a sample of vegium in a plastic cup
balance

EXPERIMENTAL PROCEDURE

Carry out the following steps, and record your results in Table 6.1.

1. Weigh all the beans, all the peas, and all the corn.

2. Count all the beans, all the peas, and all the corn.

3. Divide the mass of each isotope (beans, peas, and corn) by the number of each isotope to get the average mass of each isotope.

4. Divide the number of each isotope, the total number of particles, and multiply by 100 to get the percent abundance of each isotope.

5. Divide the percent abundance from Step 4 by 100 to get the relative abundance of each isotope.

6. Multiply the relative abundance from Step 5 by the average mass of each isotope to get the relative weight of each isotope.

7. Add the relative weights to get the average mass of all particles in vegium, the atomic mass. Note: When you weigh the various isotopes of vegium, you may encounter some problems. For example, the sample of beans might be too large to weigh on your small-scale balance. You might solve this problem by making more weights or by using a larger counterweight on your small-scale balance. This approach increases the capacity of your small-scale balance. Keep in mind that it also results in a heavier beam, which reduces the sensitivity of your small-scale balance. Alternatively, you might weigh a portion of your vegetables, for example, half, and then multiply your result by 2 (or a fifth and multiply by 5). The beans are of various sizes, so if you weigh just one bean and multiply by the number of beans to get the total weight of beans, a significant error might result. Weigh a large enough sample so you get a good estimation of the average weight of a bean.

EXPERIMENTAL DATA

Record your results in Table 6.1 or in a copy of the table in your notebook.

Table 6.1   Atomic Mass of Vegium

	Beans	Peas	Corn	Total
1. Mass of each isotope (mg)	6766	7451	10,151	24,368
2. Number of each isotope	22	115	104	241
3. Average mass of each (mg)	307.5	64.8	97.6	101.1
4. Percent of each	9.1	47.7	43.2	100
5. Relative abundance	0.091	0.447	0.432	1.0
6. Relative weight (mg)	27.9	31.1	42.0	101

CLEANING UP

Place the entire sample of vegium back in the plastic cup. Make sure that none of the particles are in the sink or on the floor.

QUESTIONS FOR ANALYSES

Use what you learned in this experiment to answer the following questions.

1. Which of your data in Table 6.1 must be measured and which can be calculated?

   The data for the individual vegetables in Steps 1 and 2 are measured; the

   rest are calculated.

2. In all except Step 3 in Table 6.1, the numbers in the "Total" column can be obtained by adding the numbers across each row. Step 3 is an exception because it does not take into account the fact that there are different numbers of each kind of particle. Rather than add across, calculate this number in the same way you calculated the other numbers in row 3.

   Divide the total weight of all the particles by the total number of particles.

3. What is the difference between percent and relative abundance?

   Relative abundance is percent divided by 100.

4. What is the result when you total the individual percentages? The individual relative abundances?

   100. 1.

5. The percentage of each vegetable tells you how many of each kind of vegetable there are in every 100 particles. What does relative abundance tell you?

The decimal fraction of each kind of vegetable out of one total.

6. Compare the total values for Steps 3 and 6 on Table 6.1.

They are equal.

7. Why can't atomic masses be calculated the way the total for row 3 is calculated?

A mass spectrometer yields only information about the masses of atomic

particles and their relative abundances. It does not count each individual

particle, nor does it measure their total mass as you did.

8. Explain any differences between the atomic mass of your vegium sample and that of your neighbor. Explain why the difference would be smaller if larger samples were used.

The samples are probably similar but not exactly the same. Differences are

largely due to errors in sampling. Not all the samples are the same. The larger

the sample, the smaller the expected error due to sampling procedures.

NOW IT'S YOUR TURN!

1. Do the experiments to determine the atomic weight of a second sample of vegium. How does it compare to the first? Why?

It's similar but not exactly the same because of sampling errors.

2. Select three beans from your sample—the largest, the smallest, and one bean that appears to be average in size. Determine the mass of each of the three. Compute the average mass of the largest and smallest, and compare this average to the mass of the "average" bean and to the average mass of beans you determined in Step 2 on Table 6.1. Which average mass do you think is most reliable? Why?

The one in Table 6.1 because it relies on a larger sample. Small errors in

individual beans cancel out in larger samples.

7 DESIGN AND CONSTRUCTION OF A QUANTITATIVE SPECTROSCOPE

Small-Scale Experiment for text Section 5.2

OBJECTIVES

- **Design** and **construct** a quantitative spectroscope.
- **Build** a device to calibrate the spectroscope.

INTRODUCTION

Chemistry is used to solve problems by identifying materials. Criminologists solve crimes by identifying minute quantities of blood, soil, paint, and other materials that link the criminal with the crime. Radio astronomers identify molecules in outer space. Chemists routinely detect and identify pollutants in our air, water, and soil. Most often these identifications are made by using some form of spectroscopic analysis, or spectroscopy. Spectroscopy is a term that describes a wide range of chemical analyses that probe the interaction of light with matter. Many spectroscopic instruments have been developed to measure different features of light as it interacts with matter.

Perhaps the most obvious feature of visible light is color. When white light from a lamp or the sun travels through a drop of water, it is dispersed into its component colors. This familiar rainbow of colors is known as the visible spectrum. You can produce the same effect by passing light through a prism or diffraction grating. By investigating the visible spectra of various light sources, you can learn about how light interacts with matter.

PURPOSE

In this experiment, you will design and build a spectroscope, a device with which you can observe the spectra of various light sources. The body of the spectroscope will be a rectangular box, about 2-cm thick, made from dark-colored poster board. The spectroscope will have a narrow slit at one end to allow light to enter it. A diffraction grating at the other end will disperse white light into a spectrum by bending it at different angles. You should make the box relatively "light-tight" except for the slit and the diffraction grating. Finally, you will build a device to calibrate the spectroscope by taking advantage of a principle called total internal reflection. You will use a plastic rod to "pipe" light into the spectroscope box. A grid scratched on the rod will scatter light and appear to glow inside the box.

SAFETY 🧤 🔥 ✂

- Behave in a way that is consistent with a safe laboratory.
- Do not look directly at sunlight with your eyes or with the spectroscope. Look at the bright sky away from the sun or at the sun's reflection off snow or a sidewalk.
- Keep all electrical light sources away from water, water faucets, and sinks.
- To avoid a puncture wound, use scissors or other sharp objects only as intended.

EQUIPMENT

diffraction grating
teacher-built spectroscope
ruler and 2-cm guide strip
poster board
scissors

3 rubber bands
tape
plastic light rod
nail
adhesive labels

EXPERIMENTAL PROCEDURE

Part A. The Structure and Function of a Spectroscope

1. Hold a slide-mounted diffraction grating up to your eye and look at a light source. Be careful not to touch the plastic surface of the grating with your fingers. Record what you see.

2. Look at the plastic surface of the grating. Again, don't touch the plastic! Record what you see.

3. Look through the teacher-built spectroscope (without a diffraction grating) at a light source. Record what you see.

4. Place the slide-mounted diffraction grating over the square hole in the teacher-built spectroscope. Hold the grating and spectroscope up to your eye and look through it at a light source. Record what you see.

5. Look through the spectroscope with both your left and right eyes. Record similarities and differences.

Part B. Building Your Own Spectroscope

6. Use a guide strip to draw a 2-cm-wide border around a piece of poster board. Draw a 2-cm-wide center strip, as shown in Figure 7.1.

Figure 7.1 *The body of the spectroscope showing folds and cuts*

7. Cut out the diagonal corners entirely as shown. Cut out the four slits 0.5 cm wide and 1 cm from each indicated edge.

8. Use the straight edge of a ruler and fold the poster board along all the dotted lines to form a rectangular box. The slits should line up when the poster board is folded. If they don't, simply cut the poster board so they do. Use rubber bands to hold the folded spectroscope together.

9. Tape a small rectangle of diffraction grating over one slit. Then tape two small pieces of poster board over the other slit to make it 2 mm wide. Take care not to touch the diffraction grating.

10. Place the plastic light rod over the template in Figure 7.2. Using the template as a guide, use a nail to carefully trace a grid onto the light rod. First trace the horizontal scratch and then the evenly spaced parallel scratches onto the light rod.

Figure 7.2 *Template for tracing grid onto light rod*

11. Slide the light rod into the end of the spectroscope opposite the diffraction grating (Figure 7.3), and look through it at a white light source. What do you see?

Figure 7.3 *Positioning of the light rod in the spectroscope*

12. When you're sure everything is square and lines up correctly, tape the box together so it's "light tight."

EXPERIMENTAL DATA

Part A. Record your data as you examine the spectroscope.

1. What do you see when you hold a slide-mounted diffraction grating up to your eye?

A rainbow of colors.

2. What do you see on the plastic surface of the grating?

Many tiny parallel lines.

3. What do you see when you look through the teacher-built spectroscope at a light source?

White light coming through the slit.

4. What colors do you see and in what order are they when you add the slide-mounted diffraction grating?

Red, orange, yellow, green, blue, and violet (or reverse order with other eye).

5. Do the colors appear in the same order when you look to the left of the slit as opposed to the right of the slit?

No, they are in opposite order.

Part B. Building Your Own Spectroscope

6. Draw a picture of your completed spectroscope.

folded poster
board

slit

light rod

diffraction
grating

7. What do you see when you look through the completed spectroscope?

A rainbow with a lighted grid superimposed on it.

CLEANING UP

Label your spectroscope with your name. Clean up all scraps of paper. Please recycle all usable materials.

QUESTIONS FOR ANALYSES

Use what you learned in this experiment to answer the following questions.

1. What is a spectroscope?

A device that disperses white light into a spectrum.

2. What is a spectrum?

A broad range of colors of light.

3. What is white light? How do you know?

A mixture of all colors. The spectroscope disperses a white light source

into a rainbow.

4. Which part of the spectroscope separates light into its component colors?

The diffraction grating.

5. What are the colors of the visible spectrum?

Red, orange, yellow, green, blue, and violet.

6. How does the light rod work?

Light travels through it from the outside to the inside of the box. The grid

scratched on the rod scatters light so it appears to glow.

NOW IT'S YOUR TURN!

1. Try using various boxes to build spectroscopes. Try a shoe box, a cracker box, a safety-glasses box, a toothpaste box, a pizza box, a cereal box, or any other box available to you. Design each spectroscope so that you can use the same diffraction grating interchangeably.

2. Investigate new ways to calibrate the spectroscope, using various light rods.

3. Investigate the effect of changing the size and shape of the slit on your spectroscope.

8 VISIBLE SPECTRA AND THE NATURE OF LIGHT AND COLOR

Small-Scale Experiment for text Section 5.3

OBJECTIVES

- **Calibrate** a quantitative spectroscope.
- **Compare** visible spectra of common light sources, using a quantitative spectroscope.
- **Plot** graphic representations of various visible spectra.
- **Measure** the wavelength of any colored line in the visible spectrum and **identify** the range of wavelengths that comprise each color.

INTRODUCTION

The diffraction grating in a spectroscope breaks white light into a series of colors called the *visible spectrum*. The visible spectrum is the entire range of colors your eyes can see. A quick look through the spectroscope you built in Small-Scale Experiment 7 will show you that visible white light is a mixture of all colors of the rainbow.

When you look at fluorescent light, three very prominent lines or narrow bands of bright color are superimposed on this continuous rainbow. One line is *violet*; one is *green*; and one is *yellow*. These three lines are caused by the light emission of glowing gaseous mercury atoms in the fluorescent tube. The lines all have characteristic specific positions in the visible spectrum, or *wavelengths*, measured in nanometers (nm):

    violet = 436 nm   green = 546 nm   yellow = 580 nm

PURPOSE

In this experiment, you will use the characteristic wavelength of the prominent spectral lines of mercury to calibrate your spectroscope. The spectroscope contains a plastic light rod that you will use to mark the positions of mercury emission lines. Scratches on the rod appear to glow inside the box. You can use the lighted ruler to mark any place on the visible spectrum. You will move the light rod so that the longest lighted scratch on the ruler is centered over the prominent violet line of the spectrum. You will then note the positions of the other lines on the ruler. These positions are related to the corresponding wavelengths of the prominent lines. Once you have identified the positions of two of the three lines for which you know the wavelength in nanometers, you can calculate the number of nanometers each graduation on the grid represents. The entire process is called *calibration*.

You can then measure any wavelength of visible light in nanometers, represented by the scratches. All you have to do is note the place on the spectrum you wish to know and compare it to the grid you have scratched out on the light rod.

SAFETY 🥽 🧤

- Behave in a way that is consistent with a safe laboratory.
- Do not look directly at sunlight with the spectroscope. Look at a bright sky away from the sun or at the sun's reflection off snow or a sidewalk.
- Keep all electrical light sources away from water, water faucets, and sinks.

EQUIPMENT

spectroscope
fluorescent and incandescent light sources
graph paper

EXPERIMENTAL PROCEDURE

Part A. Calibrating the Spectroscope

1. View the visible spectrum (rainbow) of fluorescent light through your spectroscope. Identify the three prominent colored lines or narrow bands of brightly colored light superimposed on the rainbow (violet, green, and yellow). Make a rough sketch of the rainbow with its three most prominent bands in your Experimental Data.

2. Move the plastic light rod so that the longest parallel scratch is exactly superimposed over the center of the prominent violet line in the spectrum. Fix the position of the rod with tape if necessary. The spectroscope is now calibrated.

3. Find the center of the green line relative to the violet line by counting the number of spaces between scratches that separate them. (If this is not a whole number of spaces, estimate the fraction of space.) Repeat for the center of the more diffuse yellow line.

4. Draw in the positions of the green and yellow lines on Figure 8.1 of the Experimental Data section.

Part B. The Visible Spectrum of Fluorescent Light

5. Look through your spectroscope at fluorescent light again.

   a. Note and record the position in spaces from the violet line that marks the *outer edge of the red* region of the spectrum (where red meets black).

   b. Note and record the position of the spectrum where *red meets orange*. This is not very distinct. There is a gradual change from red to orange. Make your own judgement!

   c. Note and record the other places on the spectrum where one color appears to fade into another. Use your judgement!

   d. Use your data to plot a visible spectrum of *fluorescent light* in the Experimental Data section. Find the point on the calibration grid that corresponds to each position of the mark. Read the wavelength that corresponds to that point.

6. Use your spectroscope and the same calibration grid to plot the visible spectrum of *incandescent light* (light from an overhead projector reflected off a white wall or screen, for example).

EXPERIMENTAL DATA

Part A. Calibrating a Spectroscope

1. Make a rough sketch of the rainbow produced from fluorescent light, clearly showing the three prominent colored lines or bands of light (violet, green, and yellow).

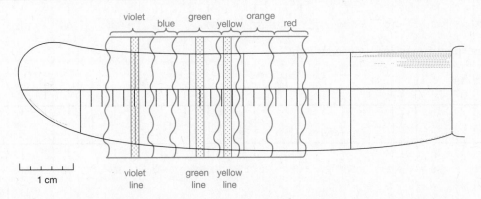

2. Superimpose the light rod on your drawing, showing the approximate positions of the scratches.

3. How many spaces from the violet line is the green line? The yellow line?

   Approximately 6.0 and 8.5 spaces, respectively (assuming the scratches

   are 2 mm apart and the spectroscope was built as in the last lab).

4. The grid shown in Figure 8.1 below is a representation of the grid on the light rod. The violet line is superimposed on the longest scratch.

   a. Draw in the positions of the green and yellow lines with their wavelengths.

   b. Find how many nanometers each small graduation represents by dividing the difference in wavelengths of the green and violet lines (538 − 436 = 102 nm) by the number of spaces between them. Mark the grid in nanometers.

   102/6.0 = 17 nm per graduation.

Figure 8.1 *Representation of the grid on the light rod*

Part B. The Visible Spectrum of Fluorescent Light

5. Plot the spectrum of fluorescent light.

6. Plot the spectrum of incandescent light.

CLEANING UP

Put all the equipment back in its proper place.

QUESTIONS FOR ANALYSES

Use what you learned in this experiment to answer the following questions.

1. Explain why the scratched grid on the rod appears to glow.

   Light entering the rod from outside the box reflects off the inside of the

   plastic until it hits an imperfection (a scratch) and is scattered.

2. What part of the spectroscope separates white light into its component colors?

   The diffraction grating.

3. For each of the spectra you plotted, name the colors in the order they appear, and state the wavelengths that border each color.

   Fluorescent light: violet, 419–453 nm; blue, 453–470 nm; green, 470–572 nm;

   yellow, 572–589 nm; orange, 589–606 nm; red, 606–691 nm. Incandescent

   light: violet, 436–453 nm; blue, 453–470 nm; green, 470–572 nm; yellow,

   572–589 nm; orange, 589–606 nm; red, 606–708 nm.

4. Compare the plots of the visible spectra of fluorescent and incandescent light. Point out the similarities and differences of each. Which source of light has more red in it? Which has more blue?

   Fluorescent has more violet and less red than incandescent.

5. Which color forms the widest band in each spectrum?

   Green.

6. Why does the incandescent light have the three prominent colored lines in it?

Incandescent light bulbs contain no mercury vapor, as do the fluorescent

lights.

7. Why does each different spectroscope need to be calibrated?

The size of the box and spaces between scratches will affect the results.

NOW IT'S YOUR TURN!

1. Use your spectroscope and a calibration grid like Figure 8.1 to plot the visible spectra of two other light sources: candlelight and sunlight. Don't look directly at the sunlight! Look away from the sun at a bright sky or at sunlight reflected off snow or a sidewalk. How are sunlight and candlelight the same? How are they different?

Both spectra have all colors of the visible spectrum, red, orange, yellow, green, blue,

indigo, and violet. Sunlight has more of the blue and violet bands than candlelight.

2. A *reflectance spectrum* is the spectrum of light that is reflected off an opaque object from a source of white light. Use your spectroscope and the same calibration grid to plot the *visible reflection* of various colors of construction paper. What interesting observations do you make?

3. An *absorption spectrum* is the spectrum of light that is transmitted through a translucent material like a colored solution or plastic film. Measure the absorption spectra of several colored plastic films. What can you conclude about the colors your eye perceives and the actual colors of light passing through the films?

4. Measure the absorption spectra of various colored solutions. Place the fluorescent light box behind the solutions. What can you conclude about the colors your eye perceives and the actual colors of light passing through the colored solutions?

5. An *atomic emission spectrum* is the spectrum that is emitted from glowing gaseous atoms. Examine the atomic emission spectra of several gas discharge tubes. Make a rough sketch of each in your notebook. What is distinctive about all these atomic emission spectra?

6. Propose how you can make the spectroscope better. Reinvent it. Build another model and test its performance based on various construction parameters.

7. The wavelength of light is the distance between two adjacent peaks of a light wave. The wavelength of visible light is most commonly measured in nanometers (nm). One nanometer is 10^{-9} meters. The frequency of light is the number of waves passing a given point in 1 second. Its units are s^{-1}. The velocity of light in a vacuum is about 3×10^8 meters/second. The wavelength, frequency, and speed of light are related in terms of the following equation:

$$\text{frequency} = \text{velocity/wavelength}$$
$$v = c/\lambda$$

Choose any visible spectrum you plotted and use the above equation to convert all the measured wavelengths into frequencies.

8. Mix equal quantities of red, blue, and yellow food coloring in all possible binary combinations (any one with any other one.) What do you conclude?

Red + blue = violet; red + yellow = orange; yellow + blue = green. All

colors of the visible spectrum can be generated by mixing the three

primary colors together.

9　A PERIODIC TABLE LOGIC PROBLEM

Small-Scale Experiment for text Section 6.3

OBJECTIVES

- **Analyze** properties and relationships of 26 elements.
- **Identify** each element's place in the periodic table based on these properties and relationships.

INTRODUCTION

When elements are arranged in the periodic table in order of increasing atomic number, there is a periodic repetition of their physical and chemical properties. The way properties change from left to right across a period and from top to bottom within a group are called periodic trends. Here is a summary of some periodic trends.

Atomic size can be expressed by a measurement called the atomic radius. *Atomic radius* is one half the distance between the nuclei of two atoms of the same element when the atoms are joined. The atomic radius generally increases from top to bottom within a group. The atomic radius generally decreases from left to right across a period.

Ionization energy is the energy required to remove an electron from an atom. This energy is measured when the atom is in the gaseous state. The first ionization energy is the energy required to remove the first electron from an atom. The second ionization energy is the energy required to remove an electron from a cation with a 1+ charge. The third ionization energy is the energy required to remove an electron from a cation with a 2+ charge. The second ionization energy for an element is always larger than the first ionization energy. The third ionization energy is always larger than the second ionization energy. In general, first ionization energy decreases from top to bottom within a group and increases from left to right across a period.

Electronegativity is the ability of an atom of an element to attract electrons when the atom is in a compound. In general, electronegativity values decrease from top to bottom within a group and increase from left to right across a period. Because noble gases do not tend to form compounds, electronegativity values for noble elements are usually omitted from data tables.

Metals tend to have low first ionization energies and low electronegativity values. Nonmetals tend to have high first ionization energies and high electronegativity values.

Name _____ Date _____ Class _____

PURPOSE

In this experiment, you will use a series of clues to arrange a set of unknown elements in a periodic table. The elements are the elements with atomic numbers 1–20 and 31–36. A letter of the alphabet is used to represent each unknown element. The letter designation is not related to an element's chemical symbol. Each clue refers to a property of an element or a relationship an element has to other elements in the periodic table. Along with logic and knowledge of properties, you will use periodic trends to solve the puzzle. When you are done, each element will be in its unique place on the table. Good luck!

SAFETY

- Behave in a way that is consistent with a safe classroom.

EQUIPMENT

sharp pencil

EXPERIMENTAL PROCEDURE

Use the following periodic trend clues to place the elements in their proper places in the short form of the periodic table provided.

A Has one of the highest electronegativities on the table

B Has one electron in a $3p$ orbital

C Has five electrons in the fourth energy level

D Forms the smallest 2+ ion

E Tends to gain one electron

F Electronic configuration is $1s^2 2s^2 2p^6 3s^2 3p^3$

G Is the most electronegative element

H An ion of this element with a 2+ charge has 18 electrons.

I Its second ionization energy is large compared to its first ionization energy.

J Its highest occupied energy level is full.

K This nonmetal is likely to form an ion with a 3− charge.

L Has the highest first ionization energy in the table

M Has the smallest atomic radius in the third period

N Is the smallest atom in its group

O The first element with an electron in the second energy level

P The only nonmetal in a group with highly reactive metals

Q Has eight fewer protons than its "groupmate" H

R The most likely element of the ones included to lose an electron

© Pearson Education, Inc., publishing as Pearson Prentice Hall. All rights reserved.

S A metalloid in period 4

T Its ionic radius is larger than its atomic radius.

U The ion with a 2− charge that it forms has 18 electrons.

V Atomic number is 34

W Metalloid that forms an ion with a 3+ charge

X Has characteristics of both a metal and a nonmetal

Y Has a lower first ionization energy than S

Z Has a first ionization energy that is higher than T but lower than M

EXPERIMENTAL DATA

Using the clues given in the Experimental Procedure, place the letter of each element in its place on the following short form of the periodic table.

1A	2A		3A	4A	5A	6A	7A	8A	
P 1								L 2	1
O 3	D 4		W 5	N 6	K 7	A 8	G 9	J 10	2
I 11	Q 12		B 13	X 14	F 15	U 16	E 17	M 18	3
R 19	H 20		Y 31	S 32	C 33	V 34	T 35	Z 36	4

QUESTIONS FOR ANALYSES

Use what you learned in this experiment to answer the following questions.

1. Which elemental clues contain sufficient information to place the element, using no other information?

   B (aluminum), C (arsenic), D (beryllium), F (phosphorus), G (fluorine), H (calcium), L (helium),

   M (argon), O (lithium), P (hydrogen), R (potassium), U (sulfur), V (selenium), and W (boron).

2. Excluding elements identified in your answer to Question 1, for which clues could you identify a group based solely on an individual clue?

   E, I, J, K.

3. Which elements were you able to place based on electronegativity?

   Elements G (chlorine) and A (oxygen).

4. Which of the following properties increase from top to bottom within a group? Which increase from left to right across a period?

   a. first ionization energy

   b. electronegativity

   c. atomic radius

   C increases from top to bottom within a group. A, b, and c increase from left to right

   across a period.

NOW IT'S YOUR TURN!

1. Design your own periodic table logic problem based on the 26 elements with atomic numbers 1–20 and 31–36. Name each element after your friends, sports teams, favorite movies, musical groups, colors, or anything you like. Assign a symbol to each element and place it on the table. Devise and write one clue for each element that will lead to its placement. For example, "Turquoise, Tu, is the second lightest noble gas." Have a classmate solve your puzzle and advise you about any problems he or she might encounter in solving it. Revise the logic problem according to your classmate's suggestions.

2. Search the Internet to find and solve other periodic logic problems or post your own!

10 ELECTRON CONFIGURATIONS OF ATOMS AND IONS

Small-Scale Experiment for text Sections 7.1 and 7.2

OBJECTIVES

- **Observe** colors of various chemical solutions.
- **Write** electron configurations for various metals, nonmetals, cations, and anions.
- **Relate** the presence of color in an ionic solution as a characteristic of electron configurations.

INTRODUCTION

Metals tend to have relatively low ionization energies. Thus, they generally lose electrons readily. Loss of electrons by a metal atom produces a positively charged ion called a cation. The electrical charge of a metal cation depends on the number of electrons the metal loses. When they form cations, the representative metals usually lose their valence electrons. *Valence electrons* are the electrons in the highest occupied energy level of an atom. For representative elements, the electrons in the highest occupied orbitals are in *s* and *p* sublevels. A representative element's group number on the periodic table tells you its number of valence electrons. For example, sodium in Group 1A has one valence electron. Magnesium in Group 2A has two, and aluminum (Group 3A) has three valence electrons. Thus, upon producing a cation, sodium loses one electron, magnesium loses two electrons, and aluminum loses three electrons. The formulas showing the charges of the respective cations are Na^+, Mg^{2+}, and Al^{3+}. Upon losing all its valence electrons, a representative metal cation generally has the stable outer electron configuration of a noble gas.

Nonmetals have relatively high ionization energies, so they tend not to lose electrons. Instead they gain electrons to produce negative anions. They generally gain just enough electrons to attain the stable electron configuration of a noble gas, or eight outer orbital *s* and *p* electrons. As with a metal, a nonmetal's group number indicates the number of electrons that nonmetal is likely to gain. For example, nitrogen (Group 5A) has five valence electrons and will gain three more electrons to produce the nitride ion, N^{3-}. Nitride contains a total of eight outer orbital electrons, the same as a stable noble gas. Similarly, oxygen (Group 6A) will gain two electrons to produce the oxide ion, O^{2-}, and fluorine (Group 7A) will gain one electron to produce fluoride, F^-. To write the electron configuration of any cation or anion of a representative element, write the electron configuration of the neutral atom and add or subtract the required number of electrons.

Transition metals also lose electrons to produce cations. Unlike most representative metals, the number of electrons that can be lost by transition metals can vary. Iron, for example, can form the iron(II) ion, Fe^{2+}, or the iron(III) ion, Fe^{3+}, by losing two or three electrons, respectively. In general, transition metals lose their outer *s* orbital electrons before they lose their outer *d* orbital electrons. This explains why many transition metals produce cations that carry a 2+ charge. Transition-metal ions can have higher charges by losing one or more electrons from their *d* orbitals. Transition-metal ions having partially filled *d* orbital electron configurations usually have a color. Metal cations that have no *d* electrons or completely full *d* orbitals are usually not colored.

Name _____ Date _____ Class _____

PURPOSE

In this experiment, you will observe a variety of chemical solutions containing common cations and anions. You will write electron configurations for many of the ions contained in the solutions. You will observe the colored solutions and draw conclusions about the electron configurations of the metal ions in the colored solutions.

SAFETY

- Wear safety goggles.
- Use small-scale pipets only for the controlled delivery of liquids.
- Don't chew gum, drink, or eat in the laboratory. Never taste a chemical in the laboratory.

MATERIALS

Small-scale pipets of the following solutions:

sodium chloride (NaCl)	copper(II) sulfate ($CuSO_4$)
magnesium sulfate ($MgSO_4$)	silver nitrate ($AgNO_3$)
aluminum chloride ($AlCl_3$)	sodium hydroxide (NaOH)
iron(III) chloride ($FeCl_3$)	sodium carbonate (Na_2CO_3)
calcium chloride ($CaCl_2$)	sodium phosphate (Na_3PO_4)
nickel(II) sulfate ($NiSO_4$)	

EQUIPMENT

small-scale reaction surface

EXPERIMENTAL PAGE

1. Place one drop of each of the indicated solutions in the space provided. Record the color of each solution.

NaCl	$MgSO_4$	$AlCl_3$
colorless no ppt	colorless white ppt	colorless white ppt
$FeCl_3$	$CaCl_2$	$NiSO_4$
yellow rust ppt	colorless white ppt	green green ppt
$CuSO_4$	$ZnCl_2$	$AgNO_3$
blue blue ppt	colorless white ppt	colorless brown ppt

2. A precipitate is a solid that separates upon mixing solutions. Predict which of the metal cations in this experiment will form colored precipitates upon the addition of NaOH. Add one drop of NaOH to find out. Record your results.

CLEANING UP

Avoid contamination by cleaning up in a way that protects you and your environment. Carefully clean the small-scale reaction surface by absorbing the contents onto a paper towel, rinse the small-scale reaction surface with a damp paper towel, and dry it. Dispose of the paper towels in the waste bin.

QUESTIONS FOR ANALYSES

Use what you learned in this experiment to answer the following questions.

1. Write the electron configurations of Na, Mg, and Al.

Na $1s^2 2s^2 2p^6 3s^1$.

Mg $1s^2 2s^2 2p^6 3s^2$.

Al $1s^2 2s^2 2p^6 3s^2 3p^1$.

2. Metal ions form when metal atoms lose valence electrons—the number of electrons lost equals the ion's charge. Write the electron configurations of Na^+, Mg^{2+} and Al^{3+}. What do they all have in common?

All have the same configuration: $1s^2 2s^2 2p^6$.

3. Write the electron configurations of Cl and Cl^-.

Cl $1s^2 2s^2 2p^6 3s^2 3p^5$.

Cl^- $1s^2 2s^2 2p^6 3s^2 3p^6$.

4. Transition-metal ions with partially filled d orbitals usually have a color. Based on your observations, which solutions contain transition-metal ions with partially filled d orbitals?

$CuSO_4$, $FeCl_3$, and $NiSO_4$.

5. Transition metals usually lose s orbital electrons first and then d electrons when they produce ions. Write electron configurations for Fe and Fe^{3+} and Ni and Ni^{2+}.

Ni $1s^2 2s^2 2p^6 3s^2 3p^6 3d^8 4s^2$.

Ni^{2+} $1s^2 2s^2 2p^6 3s^2 3p^6 3d^8$.

Fe $1s^2 2s^2 2p^6 3s^2 3p^6 3d^6 4s^2$.

Fe^{3+} $1s^2 2s^2 2p^6 3s^2 3p^6 3d^5$.

6. Copper and silver both have exceptional electron configurations because they both have full d orbitals at the expense of an s orbital. Write the electron configurations of Cu and Ag.

Cu $1s^2 2s^2 2p^6 3s^2 3p^6 3d^{10} 4s^1$.

Ag $1s^2 2s^2 2p^6 3s^2 3p^6 3d^{10} 4s^2 4p^6 4d^{10} 5s^1$.

7. Write the electron configurations of Cu^{2+} and Ag^+. Is each electron configuration consistent with the color your observed for each cation? Explain.

$Cu^{2+}\ 1s^2 2s^2 2p^6 3s^2 3p^6 3d^9$.

$Ag^+\ 1s^2 2s^2 2p^6 3s^2 3p^6 3d^{10} 4s^2 4p^6 4d^{10}$.

Yes. Copper(II) ion is colored and has a partially filled *d* orbital. Silver ion is colorless

and has a full *d* orbital.

8. The solution Zn^{2+} ions is not colored. What does this suggest about its electron configuration? Write the electron configuration of Zn^{2+}.

The electron configuration contains a completely full *d* orbital.

$Zn^{2+}\ 1s^2 2s^2 2p^6 3s^2 3p^6 3d^{10}$.

9. Predict which of the following transition-metal ions has a color: Cr^{3+}, Cd^{2+}, Hg^{2+}, V^{2+}. Explain your answers.

Cr^{3+} and V^{2+} are colored because their electron configurations have partially filled *d* orbitals.

Hg^{2+} and Cd^{2+} are colorless because their configurations contain completely full *d* orbitals.

10. Do the colored precipitates all contain transition-metal ions with partially filled *d* orbitals?

Yes, except the precipitate produced by silver nitrate.

NOW IT'S YOUR TURN!

1. Predict which of the metal cations in this experiment will form colored precipitates upon the addition of Na_2CO_3. Design an experiment to find out.

Add one drop of Na_2CO_3 to one drop of each of the metal salts in this experiment.

The iron, copper, and nickel salts produce colored precipitates.

2. Design and carry out an experiment to find out which metal ions form precipitates with sodium phosphate. What color are the precipitates?

Add one drop of Na_3PO_4 to one drop of each of the metal salts in this experiment.

The iron, copper, and nickel salts produce colored precipitates.

11 PAPER CHROMATOGRAPHY

Small-Scale Experiment for text Section 8.3

OBJECTIVES

- **Separate** mixtures of compounds, using the technique of paper chromatography.
- **Identify** compounds contained in some common ink dyes.
- **Compare** formulations of inks in various brands of pens.

INTRODUCTION

Chromatography is a technique for separating mixtures of compounds. It is a powerful and versatile method used widely in chemistry and in the biological sciences. Chromatography can also be used to identify unknown substances. All of the several types of chromatography employ two different immiscible phases in contact with each other. One of the phases is moving, *the mobile phase*, and the other is not, *the stationary phase*. In paper chromatography, for example, a solvent moves from one end of a piece of paper to the other end, as the paper absorbs it. The solvent is the mobile phase because it is moving, and the paper is the stationary phase. (In reality, there are water molecules attached to the paper that serve as the stationary phase.)

A mixture of chemicals can be separated using paper chromatography. A small amount of mixture to be separated is placed near the edge of an absorbent paper. That edge of the paper is wetted with solvent. The solvent travels up the paper by capillary action, carrying the mixture with it. Separation occurs because different chemicals in the mixture travel different distances. The physical interaction of each compound in the mixture with the solvent (the mobile phase) and with the water molecules attached to the paper (the stationary phase) determines the distance it travels. Substances that dissolve more readily in the solvent will move farther than substances that have a higher affinity for the water attached to the paper. When the solvent has moved the entire length of the paper, the paper is removed from the solvent and dried. Once developed, the paper, called a *chromatogram*, will contain different chemicals located at different positions on the paper.

The various chemicals visible on the chromatogram can often be identified by their positions and/or their colors. If the mixture contains colored compounds, each different compound will appear on the chromatogram as a colored spot or a streak in a particular place. The color and location of each compound can be used as a basis for identification. The color and location of unknown compounds separated under specific chromatographic conditions can be matched with the color and location of known compounds subjected to the same conditions.

PURPOSE

In this experiment you will use the technique of paper chromatography to separate the colored dyes in a variety of felt-tipped pens. You will then compare the chromatograms of the pens to those of known dyes to identify the dyes used in the pens.

SAFETY

- Wear your safety goggles.
- Assume that all the colored food and candy in this lab is contaminated with toxic chemicals. Do not eat or even taste anything in the laboratory.
- To avoid a puncture wound, use scissors or other sharp objects only as intended.

MATERIALS

scissors	stapler
chromatography paper	2 clear plastic cups
template cards	solvent
pencil	set of FD&C dyes
2 sets of colored felt-tipped pens	typing paper

EXPERIMENTAL PROCEDURE

1. Cut and mark two identical pieces of chromatography paper as follows. Use the cardboard template as a guide. Use *only black pencil* to write on the paper.

2. Obtain a set of marking pens and draw a small dot of ink from a red pen on the first pencil dot on one piece of chromatography paper. Continue placing colored dots on the pencil dots in the *same order as the visible spectrum*: red, orange, yellow, green, light blue, dark blue, and violet. Place other colors such as black, brown, and pink at the end. Record in your notebook the number, color, and brand of the pen.

3. Mark the second piece of chromatography paper with a second set of felt-tipped pens (a different brand). Place the colors *in the same order* as on your first chromatogram. Record this data in your notebook.

4. Staple the two papers into cylinders, dot side out, being careful not to allow the edges to touch each other (Figure 11.1).

Figure 11.1

edges do
not touch

staples

pencil line

colored dots

plastic cup

solvent

Figure 11.2

5. Wet the bottom of two plastic cups with solvent and place a paper cylinder in each, colored sides down. Initially, the colored dots should be above the solvent, as shown in Figure 11.2.

6. Spot the following FD&C dyes onto a third chromatography paper: red #3, red #40, yellow #5, yellow #6, green #3, blue #1, and blue #2. These dyes will help you to identify the dyes in the marking pens. Use a tiny triangle of *typing paper* to spot these dyes onto the chromatography paper. Cut the triangle and wet one tip in a dye solution. Touch the wet tip lightly to a pencil spot. Use a new triangle for each different dye.

7. While you wait for the solvent to move up the paper (about 10–15 minutes), begin answering the Questions for Analyses.

8. Remove the paper cylinders when the solvent reaches 1/2−1 cm from the top of the chromatography paper. Mark the highest point the solvent reached with a pencil and allow the paper to dry upright on a paper towel. When the paper is dry, remove the staples. Keep all of the chromatograms obtained from this experiment and attach them to your laboratory notebook or report.

EXPERIMENTAL DATA

Tape or staple your dry chromatograms here or in your lab notebook for easy reference.

CLEANING UP

Avoid contamination by cleaning up in a way that protects you and your environment. Leave your chromatograms to dry in a place designated by your teacher. Once dry, attach each to your laboratory notebook or report. Dispose of extra solvents down the drain, and rinse and dry the plastic cups. Clean up the area thoroughly, and be sure to recycle usable pieces of paper. Wash your hands thoroughly with soap and water.

QUESTIONS FOR ANALYSES

Use what you learned in this experiment to answer the following questions.

1. What happens to the ink spots as the chromatogram develops? Why?

   Carried by the solvent, they travel up the paper.

2. If one dye moves faster than another, which one dissolves more readily in the moving solvent? Which one dissolves more readily in the water that is attached to the stationary paper?

   The fast ones dissolve more readily in the moving solvent; the slow ones,

   in the stationary phase.

3. Which ink dyes (specify original color) are probably made up of only one compound? How can you tell?

Any that have only one color and one spot or streak.

_____

4. How can you tell which ink dyes are made up of two compounds?

They have two colors and/or two spots or streaks.

_____

5. Which ink dyes are made up of more than two compounds?

Any that have more than two colors and/or two spots or streaks.

_____

6. How can you tell if both brands of pens use the same combination of dyes to make black? Brown? How can you tell?

They are the same only if they have the same pattern of colors and streaks.

_____

7. Compare your two chromatograms of the pens by placing one directly above the other. Which colors of ink use the same compound(s) for both brands?

Any that have the same patterns of colors and spots.

_____

8. Compare your two chromatograms by placing them side by side. By noting the color and position of each spot, tell which pens (color and brand) contain the same (a) light blue dye; (b) red dye; (c) yellow dye.

Answers will vary.

_____

9. You can identify the ink dyes by their *positions* and *colors* on the chromatogram. Compare the positions and colors of the known FD&C dyes with the positions and colors of the unknown dyes in the pens. Identify as many dyes as you can like this: "The orange brand X pen contains red #40 and yellow #5."

Answers will vary.

_____

_____

10. Which ink dyes (color and brand) can you *not* identify?

Answers will vary.

_____

NOW IT'S YOUR TURN!

1. Design and carry out some experiments to answer one or more of the following questions:

a. What are the identities of the dyes in other brands of pens? How do they compare to the ones you already tested?

Make a chromatogram of the brand and compare to the FD&C standards.

b. What is the effect of the kind of paper you used on your results?

Coffee filters, unsized (large-pulp) tablet paper, and some paper towels

work well.

c. What is the effect of the solvent you used?

Try water, rubbing alcohol, and mixtures of these.

_____

2. Use paper chromatography to identify dyes in various consumer food products such as soft drinks, powdered drinks, instant breakfast drinks, gelatin, candy, and food coloring. You may have to invent ways to extract the dyes from the products.

For example, place a drop of water on a colored candy and use a triangle of

_____

typing paper to extract the dye.

_____

3. In chromatography, the symbol R_f is used to denote the position of a component on a chromatogram relative to the distance the solvent moved. This R_f value is a quantitative reflection of the physical interaction of each component with the mobile phase (the solvent) and stationary phase (the water molecules on the paper).

$$R_f = \frac{\text{distance component moved}}{\text{distance solvent moved}}$$

Measure the distance from the origin to the center of each spot and the distance from the origin to the solvent front. Calculate the R_f values for each spot. The best way to estimate the center of a noncircular spot is to draw the best ellipse around the spot and estimate its center.

4. Water is a very polar solvent that has a particularly strong tendency to form hydrogen bonds. Isopropyl alcohol (rubbing alcohol) is less polar than water and hydrogen bonds less strongly. Because of their differences in polarity and hydrogen bonding, these solvents will interact differently in the chromatographic separation of mixtures.

Generally, if the solvent (mobile phase) is more polar than the stationary phase, the more polar compounds will tend to dissolve more readily and spend more time in the solvent. As a result, they will move farther than the less polar ones. The more polar compounds will appear near the top of the chromatogram, and the less polar compounds will appear near the bottom.

If the solvent (mobile phase) is less polar than the stationary phase, the more polar compounds will spend more time in the stationary phase. As a result, they will move more slowly and appear near the bottom of the chromatogram.

What will happen if you run two chromatograms of pen dyes, one in a very polar solvent such as 0.1% aqueous NaCl, and one in a less polar solvent like 70% rubbing alcohol? Try it to see for yourself! Particularly, note any differences in the two chromatograms. Explain the differences.

12 CHEMICAL NAMES AND FORMULAS

Small-Scale Experiment for text Section 9.2

OBJECTIVES

- **Write** the chemical names and formulas of common chemical compounds.
- **Describe** the colors and textures of common ionic compounds.
- **Synthesize** chemical compounds, and write their names and formulas.

INTRODUCTION

Chemical substances are described not only by unique names but also by chemical formulas. A chemical name will describe a unique chemical formula, and a chemical formula will have a unique chemical name. We use this language to communicate about chemistry.

All ions, of which some substances are made, have unique chemical names. The names and formulas of common monatomic and polyatomic anions and cations are listed below.

Name	Formula	Name	Formula
fluoride	F^-	oxide	O^{2-}
chloride	Cl^-	sulfide	S^{2-}
bromide	Br^-	sulfate	$SO_4{}^{2-}$
iodide	I^-	carbonate	$CO_3{}^{2-}$
ethanoate	CH_3COO^-	hydrogen phosphate	$HPO_4{}^{2-}$
nitrate	$NO_3{}^-$	phosphate	$PO_4{}^{3-}$
nitrite	$NO_2{}^-$		
hydroxide	OH^-		
hydrogen carbonate	$HCO_3{}^-$		
dihydrogen phosphate	$H_2PO_4{}^-$		
sodium	Na^+	magnesium	Mg^{2+}
potassium	K^+	calcium	Ca^{2+}
copper(I)	Cu^+	copper(II)	Cu^{2+}
ammonium	$NH_4{}^+$	iron(II)	Fe^{2+}
		iron(III)	Fe^{3+}
		lead(II)	Pb^{2+}
		lead(IV)	Pb^{4+}
		tin(II)	Sn^{2+}
		tin(IV)	Sn^{4+}

Most transition metals and the representative elements tin and lead form two or more cations. To distinguish different cations of the same element, a Roman numeral is used in the name to indicate the numerical value of the charge.

Cations and anions combine in a ratio that makes all ionic compounds electrically neutral. Formulas for ionic compounds are written so that the positive charge contributed by the cations exactly balances the negative charge contributed by the anions. For example, the formula for the ionic compound formed from Na^+ cations and O^{2-} anions is Na_2O. The formula for the cation is always written first. The subscript, 2, refers to two Na^+ ions that exactly balance the 2^- charge on one O^{2-} ion. To name an ionic compound, state the name of the cation and the name of the anion. Don't forget to use a Roman numeral to specify the numerical value of the positive charge of those atoms that form more than one cation. Some examples of formulas and names of ionic compounds are listed below.

Na_2O	sodium oxide	$CaSO_4$	calcium sulfate
KF	potassium fluoride	NH_4Br	ammonium bromide
FeS	iron(II) sulfide	$Cu_3(PO_4)_2$	copper(II) phosphate
$FeCl_3$	iron(III) chloride	$Pb(OH)_2$	lead(II) hydroxide

PURPOSE

In this experiment, you will observe and describe the colors and textures of various ionic compounds. Either the names or formulas of these compounds will be given. If the name is given, you will write its formula, and if the formula is given, you will write its name.

SAFETY 🗑 ☠

- Wear your safety goggles.
- Use full small-scale pipets only for the controlled delivery of liquids.
- Don't chew gum, drink, or eat in the laboratory. Never taste a chemical in the laboratory.

EQUIPMENT

empty pipet for stirring
small-scale reaction surface with dried solid ionic compounds

EXPERIMENTAL PAGE

1. Observe the solid compounds below. Write the color and any other descriptive information. If the name is given, write the formula. If the formula is given, write the name. Record your results in Table 12.1.

potassium iodide	sodium chloride	magnesium sulfate	copper(II) sulfate

$NaHCO_3$	$AgNO_3$	$NaNO_2$	KF

sodium carbonate	lead(II) nitrate	sodium ethanoate	ammonium chloride

sodium phosphate	calcium hydroxide	tin(IV) chloride	potassium bromide

$CaCl_2$	$FeCl_3$	Na_2HPO_4	NaH_2PO_4

Place this side of the Experimental Page facedown. Use the other side under your small-scale reaction surface.

EXPERIMENTAL DATA

Record your results in Table 12.1 or in a copy of the table in your notebook.

Table 12.1   Names and Formulas of Ionic Solids

potassium iodide	sodium chloride	magnesium sulfate	copper(II) sulfate
white	white	white	blue
KI	NaCl	$MgSO_4$	$CuSO_4$

$NaHCO_3$	$AgNO_3$	$NaNO_2$	KF
white	brown	light yellow	white
sodium hydrogen carbonate	silver nitrate	sodium nitrite	potassium fluoride

sodium carbonate	lead(II) nitrate	sodium acetate	ammonium chloride
white	white	white	white
Na_2CO_3	$Pb(NO_3)_2$	CH_3COONa	NH_4Cl

sodium phosphate	calcium hydroxide	tin(IV) chloride	potassium bromide
white	white	white	white
Na_3PO_4	$Ca(OH)_2$	$SnCl_4$	KBr

$CaCl_2$	$FeCl_3$	Na_2HPO_4	NaH_2PO_4
white	yellow	white	blue
calcium chloride	iron(III) chloride	sodium hydrogen phosphate	sodium dihydrogen phosphate

CLEANING UP

Avoid contamination by cleaning up in a way that protects you and your environment. When you have finished answering the questions, return to your teacher the small-scale reaction surface with its solid ionic compounds in place.

Name _____ Date _____ Class _____

QUESTIONS FOR ANALYSES

Use what you have learned in this experiment to answer the following questions.

1. Write the formulas (with charges) and names of all the cations represented in this experiment.

   K^+, potassium; Na^+, sodium; Mg^{2+}, magnesium; Cu^{2+}, copper(II); Ag^+, silver;

   Pb^{2+}, lead(II); NH_4^+, ammonium; Ca^{2+}, calcium; Sn^{4+}, tin(IV); Fe^{3+}, iron(III).

2. Write the formulas (with charges) and names of all the anions represented in this experiment.

   I^-, iodide; Cl^-, chloride; SO_4^{2-}, sulfate; NO_3^-, nitrate; NO_2^-, nitrite; PO_4^{3-},

   phosphate; OH^-, hydroxide; Br^-, bromide; HCO_3^-, hydrogen carbonate;

   HPO_4^{2-}, hydrogen phosphate; $H_2PO_4^-$, dihydrogen phosphate; F^-, fluoride;

   CH_3COO^-, acetate.

3. Write some simple rules for naming an ionic compound.

   Name the cation. Name the anion.

4. When is it appropriate to use Roman numerals in naming compounds?

   When the cation has more then one possible ionic charge.

5. What does a numerical subscript following an element in a chemical formula mean?

   It tells how many atoms of the element are in one molecule or formula unit.

6. What does a numerical subscript following a set of parentheses in a chemical formula mean?

   It tells how many of the polyatomic ions are in one formula unit.

7. Write some simple rules for writing the formula for an ionic compound.

   Write the cation first and the anion last. Use subscripts to indicate the

   number of cations and anions in a way that makes the total of the positive

   and negative charges add to zero. Use parentheses to multiply polyatomic

   ions by subscripts.

Name _____ Date _____ Class _____

NOW IT'S YOUR TURN!

1. **a.** Place one drop of each solution in the indicated spaces below. Stir by blowing air from a dry pipet.

   b. Combine the ions to write the formulas of the chemical compounds that are produced by the mixings. Name each compound.

   c. What happened with each mixing? Make a table describing your results. Write the formula and name of each compound produced by the mixings.

	$AgNO_3$ Ag^+	$Pb(NO_3)_2$ Pb^{2+}	$CuSO_4$ Cu^{2+}	$MgSO_4$ Mg^{2+}	$FeCl_3$ Fe^{3+}
$FeCl_3$ (Cl^-)	white ppt AgCl X silver chloride	white ppt $PbCl_2$ X lead(II) chloride			
KI (I^-)	light yellow AgI X silver iodide	yellow PbI_2 X lead(II) iodide			
NaOH (OH^-)	brown *AgOH X *silver hydroxide	white $Pb(OH_2)$ X lead(II) hydroxide	light blue $Cu(OH)_2$ X copper(II) hydroxide	white $Mg(OH)_2$ X magnesium hydroxide	orange $Fe(OH)_3$ X iron(III) hydroxide
Na_2CO_3 (CO_3^{2-})	tan Ag_2CO_3 X silver carbonate	white $PbCO_3$ X lead(II) carbonate	light blue $CuCO_3$ X copper(II) carbonate	white $MgCO_3$ X magnesium carbonate	orange **$Fe_2(CO_3)_3$ X iron(III) carbonate
Na_3PO_4 (PO_4^{3-})	white Ag_3PO_4 X silver phosphate	white $Pb_3(PO_4)_2$ X lead(II) phosphate	light blue $Cu_3(PO_4)_2$ X copper(II) phosphate	white $Mg_3(PO_4)_2$ X magnesium phosphate	orange $FePO_4$ X iron(III) phosphate

* This brown precipitate is really silver oxide, Ag_2O: $2Ag^+ + 2OH^- \rightarrow Ag_2O + HOH$.

** Because of the acidity of Fe^{3+}, iron(III) carbonate does not exist. This is probably an amorphous iron(III) hydroxy carbonate.

Place this side of the Experimental Page facedown. Use the other side under your small-scale reaction surface.

13 MEASURING MASS: A MEANS OF COUNTING

Small-Scale Experiment for text Section 10.1

OBJECTIVES

- **Measure** masses of common compounds, objects, and minerals.
- **Calculate** moles and atoms from experimental masses.

INTRODUCTION

You can often measure how much of something you have by counting individual objects. For example, you can count the number of pennies you have in your pocket or the number of pencils you have in your locker. You learned in Chapter 10 that in chemistry there is a name for a number of atoms, ions, or molecules. One mole of a substance is equal to 6.02×10^{23} atoms, ions, or molecules of that substance. You also learned that you can "count" the number of moles in a substance by obtaining the mass of the substance.

PURPOSE

In this experiment, you will measure the masses of samples of various common compounds such as water, salt, and sugar. You will use your results as a means of counting the atoms, ions, and molecules in your samples. You will extend your technique to common objects that you can consider to be pure substances, such as glass marbles, pieces of chalk, and polystyrene peanuts. Finally, you will measure the masses of various mineral samples and use your results to find the number of atoms in each.

SAFETY ☠

- Behave in a way that is consistent with a safe laboratory.
- Don't chew gum, drink, or eat in the laboratory. Never taste a chemical in the laboratory.

MATERIALS

sodium chloride (NaCl)   polystyrene peanuts
sucrose ($C_{12}H_{22}O_{11}$)   sulfur
glass slides   fluorite
chalk ($CaCO_3$)   hematite
other common minerals specified by your teacher

EQUIPMENT

plastic spoons   balance

EXPERIMENTAL PROCEDURE

1. Mass one level teaspoon of sodium chloride (NaCl). Record the mass in Table 13.1. Repeat for one level teaspoon of water and one of sucrose ($C_{12}H_{22}O_{11}$).

2. Obtain the mass of a glass slide, and record its mass in Table 13.2. Repeat for a piece of chalk and a polystyrene peanut.

3. Measure the mass of a piece of sulfur, and record its mass in Table 13.3. Repeat for a piece of fluorite and a piece of hematite.

EXPERIMENTAL DATA

Record your results in Tables 13.1, 13.2, and 13.3 or in copies of the tables in your notebook.

Table 13.1   Counting Particles in Common Substances

Formula	Name	Mass in mg	Molar mass	Moles in 1 teaspoon	Moles of each element	Atoms of each element
NaCl	sodium chloride	5090	58.5	0.087	0.087 Na 0.087 Cl	5.2×10^{22} Na 5.2×10^{22} Cl
H_2O	water	4300	18	0.24	0.24 O 0.48 H	1.4×10^{23} O 2.8×10^{23} H
$C_{12}H_{22}O_{11}$	sucrose	3990	342	0.012	0.14 C 0.26 H 0.13 O	8.4×10^{22} C 1.6×10^{23} H 7.8×10^{22} O

Table 13.2   Counting Particles in Common Items

Formula	Name	Mass in mg	Molar mass	Moles in 1 sample	Moles of each element	Atoms of each element
SiO_2	glass slide	5020	60*	0.084	0.084 Si 0.17 O	5.1×10^{22} Si 1.0×10^{23} O
$CaCO_3$	chalk	9680	100**	0.097	0.097 Ca 0.097 C 0.29 O	5.8×10^{22} Ca 5.8×10^{22} C 1.7×10^{23} O
$\left(\begin{array}{c} - CHCH_2 - \\ \mid \\ C_6H_5 \end{array}\right)_n$	polystyrene peanut	55	104***	5.3×10^{-4}	4.2×10^{-3} C 4.2×10^{-3} H	2.5×10^{21} C 2.5×10^{21} H

* assuming the slide is pure SiO_2

** assuming the chalk is pure $CaCO_3$

*** per unit molecule

Table 13.3   Counting Particles in Minerals

Formula	Name	Mass in mg	Molar mass	Moles	Moles of each element	Atoms of each element
S	sulfur	485	32	0.015	0.015	9.1×10^{21}
CaF_2	fluorite	890	78	0.011	0.011 Ca 0.022 F	6.9×10^{21} Ca 1.3×10^{22} F
Fe_2O_3	hematite	2545	160	0.016	0.032 Fe 0.048 O	1.9×10^{22} Fe 2.9×10^{22} O

CLEANING UP

Avoid contamination by cleaning up in a way that protects you and your environment. Return all the materials to their proper places. Sweep up and dispose of any spilled salt or sugar. Wash your hands thoroughly with soap and water.

QUESTIONS FOR ANALYSES

Use what you learned in this experiment to answer the following questions.

1. Calculate the number of moles of one level teaspoon of NaCl. Repeat for all the other compounds in Tables 13.1, 13.2, and 13.3.

$$x \text{ mol NaCl} = \text{mass in mg NaCl} = \frac{1\,\text{g}}{1000\,\text{mg}} \times \frac{1\,\text{mol}}{58.5\,\text{g}} = \text{mol NaCl}$$

2. Calculate the moles of each element in H_2O. Repeat for all the other compounds in Tables 13.1, 13.2, and 13.3.

$$x \text{ mol H} = \text{mol H}_2\text{O} \times \frac{2\,\text{mol H}}{1\,\text{mol H}_2\text{O}} = \text{mol H}$$

$$x \text{ mol O} = \text{mol H}_2\text{O} \times \frac{1\,\text{mol O}}{1\,\text{mol H}_2\text{O}} = \text{mol O}$$

3. Calculate the atoms of each element in H_2O. Repeat for all the other compounds in Tables 13.1, 13.2, and 13.3.

$$x \text{ atoms H} = \text{mol H} \times \frac{6.02 \times 10^{23}\,\text{atoms}}{1\,\text{mol H}} = \text{atoms H}$$

4. In Step 1, you measured equal volumes of three different compounds. Which of the three compounds has the greatest number of moles in one teaspoon?

   Water.

5. Which of the three compounds in Step 1 has the greatest total number of atoms?

   Water.

6. Why can we use the technique of measuring volume as a means of counting?

Once we know the mass of a unit volume, we can use volume to determine

mass and mass to determine moles.

NOW IT'S YOUR TURN!

1. Design and carry out an experiment that will determine the number of atoms of calcium, carbon, and oxygen it takes to write your name on the chalkboard with a piece of chalk. Assume chalk is 100 percent calcium carbonate ($CaCO_3$).

Determine the mass of a piece of chalk, write your name, and determine the mass again. The

difference is the mass of $CaCO_3$ needed to write your name.

2. A nickel coin is a mixture of metals called an alloy. It consists of 75 percent copper and 25 percent nickel. Design and carry out an experiment to find out how many nickel atoms are in one 5-cent piece.

Measure the mass of a nickel in grams, and do the following calculation.

$$x \text{ atoms} = \text{grams of coin} \times \frac{25 \text{ g Ni}}{100 \text{ g coin}} \times \frac{1 \text{ mol Ni}}{58.7 \text{ g}} \times \frac{6.02 \times 10^{23} \text{ atoms}}{\text{mol}}$$

3. A common mineral used in wallboard and plaster of Paris is gypsum, $CaSO_4 \cdot 2\,H_2O$. Gypsum is an example of a hydrate. A hydrate is a compound that has water molecules incorporated into its crystal structure. The chemical formula of gypsum indicates that there are two water molecules for every calcium and sulfate ion within the crystal structure of gypsum. These water molecules are called water of hydration. Design an experiment to determine the number of water molecules in a sample of gypsum.

Measure the mass of the gypsum, and do the following calculation.

$$x \text{ water molecules} = \text{grams gypsum} \times \frac{1 \text{ mol}}{172 \text{ g}} \times \frac{2 \text{ mol } H_2O}{1 \text{ mol gypsum}} \times \frac{6.02 \times 10^{23} \text{ molecules}}{1 \text{ mol}}$$

4. Determine the number of atoms in various samples of other minerals such as graphite (C); barite ($BaSO_4$); calcite ($CaCO_3$); pyrite (FeS_2); and galena (PbS_2).

Use the same method as in Question 3.

Chapter 11 • *Chemical Reactions*   **SMALL-SCALE EXPERIMENT**

14   CHEMICAL EQUATIONS

Small-Scale Experiment for text Section 11.1

For your course planning, you may not want to use this lab until Chapter 19.

OBJECTIVES

- **Classify** solutions as acids and bases.
- **Describe** chemical reactions by writing chemical equations.
- **Identify** household products as acidic, basic, or neutral, on the basis of their reactions with indicators.
- **Investigate** the behavior of other synthetic and natural indicators in the presence of acids and bases.

INTRODUCTION

All chemical reactions involve changes in substances. These changes are often visible; you can call them macroscopic changes. Macroscopic changes can help you to classify chemical reactions. For example, in Small-Scale Experiment 2, the macroscopic changes you observed included the formation of precipitates, color changes, and the production of bubbles. The chemical reactions in Small-Scale Experiment 2 may be classified based on the macroscopic changes you observed.

When chemical reactions occur, changes take place in individual atoms and molecules that cause the macroscopic changes you observe. To understand chemistry, you must make many careful macroscopic observations and learn to infer from them the submicroscopic interactions of atoms and molecules.

Chemical equations are used to represent symbolically what happens to atoms, ions, and molecules in chemical reactions. You learned in Section 11.1 that a chemical equation consists of an arrow separating the chemical formulas of the reactants (on the left) and the chemical formulas of products (on the right).

reactants → products

Acids and bases are classified on the basis of their chemical properties. (Acids and bases are discussed more fully in Chapter 19.) Acids are recognized as a group of chemical compounds that have similar macroscopic chemical properties. They were originally classified on the basis of their sour taste (the word *acid* is derived from the Latin word for "sour.") Further work showed that acids had other common properties, among them the ability to cause vegetable dyes to change colors and the ability to dissolve a wide variety of substances. Bases have a bitter taste and the ability to destroy, or *neutralize,* the properties of acids.

The fact that different acids show similar characteristic macroscopic chemical properties suggests that they are somehow related on the submicroscopic level. Similarly, bases must be related to each other.

The macroscopic changes associated with acids and bases are seen in changes in indicators. An indicator signals the occurrence of a chemical reaction by changing colors. You have already used phenolphthalein, a common synthetic acid–base indicator. Recall that it turned from colorless to bright pink in the presence of sodium hydroxide, a base. Other indicators exhibit other distinct color changes, signaling the occurrence of a chemical reaction.

PURPOSE

In this experiment, you will mix various solutions of acids and bases with an indicator and observe the macroscopic color changes that occur. You will classify solutions as acids or bases based on the color change they impart to the indicator, bromthymol blue (BTB). That is, you will classify solutions according to their macroscopic behavior. (Acids turn BTB yellow, and bases turn BTB blue.) Then you will repeat the experiment twice with two different indicators—phenolphthalein (phen), and bromphenol blue (BPB).

Finally, you will interpret your results in terms of submicroscopic properties, the behavior of atoms and molecules. You will learn how to express these unseen submicroscopic properties in a symbolic language of chemical formulas and equations. For example, one common submicroscopic property of acids is that they produce H_3O^+ ions in water. This can be explained by the following chemical equation:

$$HCl + H_2O \rightarrow H_3O^+ + Cl^-$$

The acid, HCl, transfers an H^+ ion to the water molecule to form H_3O^+.

SAFETY 🔬 🥼 ☠ 🧤 ⚗

- Wear safety goggles, an apron, and gloves when working with corrosive chemicals.
- Use full small-scale pipets only for the controlled delivery of liquids.
- Don't chew gum, drink, or eat in the laboratory. Never taste a chemical in the laboratory.
- Avoid inhaling substances that can irritate your respiratory system.

MATERIALS

Small-scale pipets of the following solutions:

sodium hydrogen carbonate (NaHCO$_3$)	ammonia (NH$_3$)
ethanoic acid (CH$_3$COOH)	phosphoric acid (H$_3$PO$_4$)
hydrochloric acid (HCl)	sodium dihydrogen phosphate (NaH$_2$PO$_4$)
sodium carbonate (Na$_2$CO$_3$)	sodium hydrogen phosphate (Na$_2$HPO$_4$)
sulfuric acid (H$_2$SO$_4$)	sodium phosphate (Na$_3$PO$_4$)
sodium ethanoate (CH$_3$COONa)	sodium hydrogen sulfite (NaHSO$_3$)
sodium hydroxide (NaOH)	bromthymol blue (BTB)
nitric acid (HNO$_3$)	phenolphthalein (phen)
sodium hydrogen sulfate (NaHSO$_4$)	bromphenol blue (BPB)

EQUIPMENT

empty pipet for stirring
small-scale reaction surface

EXPERIMENTAL PAGE

1. Mix 1 drop of BTB with one drop of each of the indicated solutions. Record the color change in Table 14.1

	1 drop BTB		1 drop BTB		1 drop BTB
1 drop		1 drop		1 drop	
a. $NaHCO_3$		**f.** CH_3COONa		**k.** H_3PO_4	
b. CH_3COOH		**g.** $NaOH$		**l.** NaH_2PO_4	
c. HCl		**h.** HNO_3		**m.** Na_2HPO_4	
d. Na_2CO_3		**i.** $NaHSO_4$		**n.** Na_3PO_4	
e. H_2SO_4		**j.** NH_3		**o.** $NaHSO_3$	

2. Repeat Step 1, using phenolphthalein (phen), in place of BTB as the indicator. Record the color change in Table 14.1.

3. Repeat Step 1, using bromphenol blue (BPB), as the indicator. Record the color change in Table 14.1.

Place this side of the Experimental Page facedown. Use the other side under your small-scale reaction surface.

Name _____ Date _____ Class _____

EXPERIMENTAL DATA

Record your results in Table 14.1 or in a copy of the table in your notebook.

Table 14.1   Macroscopic and Submicroscopic Changes

a. BTB NaHCO₃ phen BPB	blue pink blue	**f.** CH₃COONa	blue pink blue	**k.** H₃PO₄	yellow colorless yellow
b. BTB CH₃COOH phen BPB	yellow colorless yellow	**g.** NaOH	blue pink blue	**l.** NaH₂PO₄	yellow colorless yellow
c. BTB HCl phen BPB	yellow colorless yellow	**h.** HNO₃	yellow colorless yellow	**m.** Na₂HPO₄	blue pink blue
d. BTB Na₂CO₃ phen BPB	blue pink blue	**i.** NaHSO₄	yellow colorless yellow	**n.** Na₃PO₄	blue pink blue
e. BTB H₂SO₄ phen BPB	yellow colorless yellow	**j.** NH₃	blue pink blue	**o.** NaHSO₃	yellow colorless yellow

CLEANING UP

Avoid contamination by cleaning up in a way that protects you and your environment. Carefully clean the small-scale reaction surface by absorbing the contents onto a paper towel, rinse the small-scale reaction surface with a damp paper towel, and dry it. Dispose of the paper towels in the waste bin.

QUESTIONS FOR ANALYSES

Use what you learned in this experiment to answer the following questions.

1. Define an acid and a base in terms of the color each turns BTB.

    An acid turns BTB yellow. A base turns BTB blue.

2. Name each acid and base you classified in this experiment. (See Chapter 9.)

a. sodium hydrogen carbonate

b. acetic acid

c. hydrochloric acid

d. sodium carbonate

e. sulfuric acid

f. sodium acetate

g. sodium hydroxide

h. nitric acid

i. sodium hydrogen sulfate

j. ammonia

k. phosphoric acid

l. sodium dihydrogen phosphate

m. sodium hydrogen phosphate

n. sodium phosphate

o. sodium hydrogen sulfite

3. What is the common feature of the formula of each acid?

    Each contains the H⁺ ion.

Name _____ Date _____ Class _____

4. What is an indicator? What purpose does it serve in this experiment?

An indicator signals the occurrence of a chemical reaction—in this case,

reactions of acids and bases in water.

5. On a macroscopic level, your observations are that all acids turn BTB yellow. The common explanation on the submicroscopic level is that an acid produces H_3O^+ ions in water solution. Such submicroscopic interactions are described by the following chemical equations:

   b. $CH_3COOH + H_2O \rightarrow H_3O^+ + CH_3COO^-$

   c. $HCl + H_2O \rightarrow H_3O^+ + Cl^-$

   i. $HSO_4^- + H_2O \rightarrow H_3O^+ + SO_4^{2-}$

Notice that in all three examples, a hydrogen ion, H^+, moves from the acid to a water molecule. Notice also that in **i**, you can take away the Na^+ ion before you write the equation. Write hydrogen-ion-transfer chemical equations, like the examples above, that describe the reactions of the other acids with water. Remember that whenever BTB turns yellow, one product is always H_3O^+.

   e. $H_2SO_4 + H_2O \rightarrow H_3O^+ + HSO_4^-$

   h. $HNO_3 + H_2O \rightarrow H_3O^+ + NO_3^-$

   k. $H_3PO_4 + H_2O \rightarrow H_3O^+ + H_2PO_4^-$

   l. $H_2PO_4^- + H_2O \rightarrow H_3O^+ + HPO_4^{2-}$

   o. $HSO_3^- + H_2O \rightarrow H_3O^+ + SO_3^{2-}$

6. On a macroscopic level, a base turns BTB blue. The common explanation on the submicroscopic level is that a base produces OH^- ions in aqueous solution. Chemical equations to describe these interactions can be written like those below:

   a. $HCO_3^- + HOH \rightarrow H_2CO_3 + OH^-$

   j. $NH_3 + HOH \rightarrow NH_4^+ + OH^-$

Notice that in each case, a base accepts a hydrogen ion (H^+) from a water molecule and produces a hydroxide ion (OH^-). Write hydrogen-ion-transfer chemical equations like those above to describe the reactions of the other bases with water. Every time you see BTB turn blue, one product is OH^-.

   d. $CO_3^{2-} + HOH \rightarrow HCO_3^- + OH^-$

   f. $CH_3COO^- + HOH \rightarrow CH_3COOH + OH^-$

   g. $OH^- + HOH \rightarrow HOH + OH^-$

   m. $HPO_4^{2-} + HOH \rightarrow H_2PO_4^- + OH^-$

   n. $PO_4^{3-} + HOH \rightarrow HPO_4^{2-} + OH^-$

7. Define an acid and a base in terms of what ions they produce in solution.

An acid produces H_3O^+ in solution. A base produces OH^- in solution.

8. What macroscopic changes did you find when you used phen and BPB to classify solutions as acids and bases?

Phen turned pink in base but remained colorless in acids. BPB turned yellow

in acids but remained blue in bases.

NOW IT'S YOUR TURN!

1. Use BTB to classify several household products as acids or bases. Read the product labels to determine as best you can (name or formula) which acids or bases they contain. Organize your data into a concise table. While you're at it, test water from the tap.

2. BTB, BPB, and phen are only a few of many synthetic acid–base indicators. Design experiments that use other indicators to classify as acids or bases the solutions you used in this lab. Make a table of your results and explain what you did. You may use any of the following synthetic indicators or any that your teacher provides:

methyl red (MR)   alizarin yellow R (AYR)
bromcresol green (BCG)   thymol blue (TB)
phenol red (PR)   meta cresol purple (MCP)

(**Hint:** One such experiment might use methyl red (MR) to test both NaOH and HCl.) You can then report the color of the indicator in each solution, draw a conclusion about the color the indicator changes in acids and bases, and test your hypothesis by using other acids and bases. Finally, you can organize your results into a concise table. Cite advantages and disadvantages of using other indicators to classify acids and bases.

3. Many common substances also act as acid–base indicators. Design and carry out an experiment to use some or all of the following to classify solutions as acids or bases: grape juice, cabbage juice, food dyes, flower petals, vegetable juices, fabric dyes, and water-soluble pen inks. Can you think of anything else to try? Make a table of your results and explain your procedure.

Chapter 11 • *Chemical Reactions*   **SMALL-SCALE EXPERIMENT**

15 BALANCING CHEMICAL EQUATIONS

Small-Scale Experiment for text Section 11.2

For your course planning, you may not want to use this lab until Chapter 19.

OBJECTIVES

- **Probe** the occurrence of neutralization reactions by using an acid–base indicator.
- **Balance** chemical equations that describe reactions between acids and bases.
- **Test** other means to detect neutralization reactions.

INTRODUCTION

In Small-Scale Experiment 14, you saw that acids and bases can be distinguished by the color changes they induce in indicators. For example, bromthymol blue is yellow in acid solution and blue in basic solution.

On the submicroscopic level, acids produce H_3O^+ ions in solution, and bases produce OH^- ions in solution. Acids and bases also react with each other in a *neutralization reaction*. In general, an acid and a hydroxide base react to produce a salt and water. A salt is any ionic compound produced by a neutralization reaction. For example, the reaction of hydrochloric acid (HCl) with sodium hydroxide (NaOH) produces sodium chloride (NaCl) and water. The chemical equation that represents this neutralization reaction is written as follows:

$$HCl + NaOH \rightarrow NaCl + HOH$$

$$\text{acid} + \text{base} \rightarrow \text{salt} + \text{water}$$

Two more examples of neutralization reactions are:

$$H_2SO_4 + 2NaOH \rightarrow Na_2SO_4 + 2HOH$$

$$\text{acid} + \text{base} \rightarrow \text{salt} + \text{water}$$

$$H_3PO_4 + 3KOH \rightarrow K_3PO_4 + 3HOH$$

$$\text{acid} + \text{base} \rightarrow \text{salt} + \text{water}$$

Notice that each equation is balanced; the same number of each kind of atom is on both sides of the equation. Notice also that these neutralization reactions are examples of double-replacement reactions, which involve an exchange of positive ions between two compounds. In the examples above, a sodium or potassium ion is exchanged with a hydrogen ion.

PURPOSE

In this experiment, you will use bromthymol blue to examine neutralization reactions more closely and learn to balance the chemical equations that describe them. An indicator is usually necessary to detect acid–base neutralization reactions because often the reaction is invisible without an indicator. The reason is that often both the reactants and the products of neutralization reactions are colorless solutions. You can use an acid–base indicator such as BTB to detect a neutralization reaction.

Name _____ Date _____ Class _____

SAFETY 🔬 🧤 🥽 🧹 ☠️ 🔥 ♨️

- Wear safety goggles, an apron, and gloves when working with corrosive chemicals.
- Use full small-scale pipets only for the controlled delivery of liquids.
- Don't chew gum, drink, or eat in the laboratory. Never taste a chemical in the laboratory.
- Do no touch hot glassware or equipment.
- Tie back hair and loose clothing. Never reach across a lit burner.
- Avoid inhaling substances that can irritate your respiratory system.

MATERIALS

Small-scale pipets of the following solutions:
bromthymol blue (BTB)
sodium hydroxide (NaOH)
potassium hydroxide (KOH)
calcium hydroxide (Ca(OH)$_2$)
ammonia (NH$_3$)
hydrochloric acid (HCl)
nitric acid (HNO$_3$)
sulfuric acid (H$_2$SO$_4$)
ethanoic acid (CH$_3$COOH)
phosphoric acid (H$_3$PO$_4$)

EQUIPMENT

small-scale reaction surface
glass slide
empty pipet for stirring
hot plate
cotton swab

EXPERIMENTAL PAGE

1. Add one drop of BTB to each square. Then add one drop of base and finally two drops of acid. Record in Table 15.1 the initial color, the color after addition of base, and the color after addition of acid.

| Bases | Strong Acids | | | Weak Acids | |
	HCl	HNO$_3$	H$_2$SO$_4$	CH$_3$COOH	H$_3$PO$_4$
NaOH	a	b	c	d	e
KOH	f	g	h	i	j
Ca(OH)$_2$	k	l	m	n	o
NH$_3$ (NH$_4$OH)	p	q	r	s	t

2. Add one drop of NaOH to two drops of HCl. Record your observation.

3. Predict what will happen if you add a few drops of base to each yellow mixture on the small-scale reaction surface. Try it and find out! Record your observations.

4. Mix one drop of each solution below on a glass slide, and evaporate on a hot plate set to a low temperature. **Caution:** *The glass will be hot. Handle with a plastic spatula.* Record what you observe.

NaOH	NaOH	KOH	NH$_3$
+	+	+	+
HCl	HNO$_3$	H$_2$SO$_4$	CH$_3$COOH

5. Place one drop of ammonia (NH$_3$ [also NH$_4$OH]) on one end of a clean cotton swab. Carefully note its odor. **Caution:** *Both NH$_3$ and HCl can have strong odors. Avoid prolonged inhalation of fumes from these solutions.* Now place two drops of hydrochloric acid (HCl), on your small-scale reaction surface, and absorb this acid onto the cotton swab containing the ammonia. Note and record its odor.

EXPERIMENTAL DATA

1. Record your results in Table 15.1 or in a copy of the table in your notebook.

Table 15.1   Reactions of Acids and Bases

Bases	Strong Acids			Weak Acids	
	HCl	HNO$_3$	H$_2$SO$_4$	CH$_3$COOH	H$_3$PO$_4$
NaOH	Green to blue with base, then yellow with acid for all reactions.				
KOH					
Ca(OH)$_2$					
NH$_3$ (NH$_4$OH)					

2. What did you observe when you mixed an acid and a base without BTB as an indicator? Why is the indicator necessary to detect these reactions?

   No change. The reactants and products are both colorless.

3. What happened when you added a few drops of base to each yellow mixture?

   They turned blue again.

4. What did you observe when you evaporated the mixtures on a hot plate?

   White solid salts appeared.

5. What happened to the ammonia odor from the cotton swab when you added HCl?

   The odor disappeared.

CLEANING UP

Avoid contamination by cleaning up in a way that protects you, your neighbors, and your environment. Carefully clean the small-scale reaction surface by absorbing the contents onto a paper towel (not onto your hands). Rinse the small-scale reaction surface with a damp paper towel and dry it. Dispose of the paper towels in the waste bin. Clean the glass slide, rinse it thoroughly with water, and dry it with a paper towel. Wash your hands thoroughly with soap and water.

Name _____ Date _____ Class _____

QUESTIONS FOR ANALYSES

Use what you learned in this experiment to answer the following questions.

1. Why is the indicator necessary to detect acid–base reactions?

These reactions have colorless reactants and colorless products.

2. Besides indicators, what other ways are there to detect neutralization?

Evaporation and odor.

3. What is the chemical formula for ethanoic acid? What is its common name?

CH_3COOH. vinegar.

4. The complete chemical equations for reactions **a–e** on the Experimental Page are listed below. Balance each equation by placing the proper coefficient in front of each chemical formula so that each side of the equation has the same number of atoms of each element.

   a. 1 $NaOH$ + 1 $HCl \rightarrow$ 1 $NaCl$ + 1 HOH

   b. 1 $NaOH$ + 1 $HNO_3 \rightarrow$ 1 $NaNO_3$ + 1 HOH

   c. 2 $NaOH$ + 1 $H_2SO_4 \rightarrow$ 1 Na_2SO_4 + 2 HOH

   d. 1 $NaOH$ + 1 $CH_3COOH \rightarrow$ 1 CH_3COONa + 1 HOH

   e. 3 $NaOH$ + 1 $H_3PO_4 \rightarrow$ 1 Na_3PO_4 + 3 HOH

5. Write down the chemical formulas for the reactants for reactions **f–j** on the Experimental Page. Now write an arrow and the formulas of the products. Finally, balance each chemical equation you write. (**Hint:** Equations **f–j** will look just like equations **a–e**, except K replaces Na.)

   f.   1 KOH + 1 $HCl \rightarrow$ 1 KCl + 1 HOH

   g.   1 KOH + 1 $HNO_3 \rightarrow$ 1 KNO_3 + 1 HOH

   h.   2 KOH + 1 $H_2SO_4 \rightarrow$ 1 K_2SO_4 + 2 HOH

   i.   1 KOH + 1 $CH_3COOH \rightarrow$ 1 CH_3COOK + 1 HOH

   j.   3 KOH + 1 $H_3PO_4 \rightarrow$ 1 K_3PO_4 + 3 HOH

6. Balance equations **k–o**, below.

   k. 1 $Ca(OH)_2$ + 2 $HCl \rightarrow$ 1 $CaCl_2$ + 2 HOH

   l. 1 $Ca(OH)_2$ + 2 $HNO_3 \rightarrow$ 1 $Ca(NO_3)_2$ + 2 HOH

   m. 1 $Ca(OH)_2$ + 1 $H_2SO_4 \rightarrow$ 1 $CaSO_4$ + 2 HOH

   n. 1 $Ca(OH)_2$ + 2 $CH_3COOH \rightarrow$ 1 $(CH_3COO)_2Ca$ + 2 HOH

   o. 3 $Ca(OH)_2$ + 2 $H_3PO_4 \rightarrow$ 1 $Ca_3(PO_4)_2$ + 6 HOH

7. Ammonia is a base that reacts with water to produce ammonium ion and hydroxide ion:

$$NH_3 + HOH \rightarrow NH_4^+ + OH^-$$

Often the formula for aqueous ammonia is written as if it was ammonium hydroxide (NH_4OH). Balance equations **p–t** below.

p. __1__ NH_4OH + __1__ HCl → __1__ NH_4Cl + __1__ HOH

q. __1__ NH_4OH + __1__ HNO_3 → __1__ NH_4NO_3 + __1__ HOH

r. __2__ NH_4OH + __1__ H_2SO_4 → __1__ $(NH_4)_2SO_4$ + __2__ HOH

s. __1__ NH_4OH + __1__ CH_3COOH → __1__ CH_3COONH_4 + __1__ HOH

t. __3__ NH_4OH + __1__ H_3PO_4 → __1__ $(NH_4)_3PO_4$ + __3__ HOH

8. Define neutralization. Write a chemical equation to illustrate your answer.

A reaction between an acid and a base that usually produces a salt and

water. $HCl + NaOH \rightarrow HOH + NaCl$.

9. Define a salt. Write the chemical formulas for examples from this experiment.

Any ionic compound that is the result of a neutralization reaction. NaCl,

$NaNO_3$, Na_2SO_4, KCl, KNO_3, K_2SO_4, CH_3COONa, Na_3PO_4, K_3PO_4, NH_4Cl, etc.

10. What is a double-replacement reaction? How is a double-replacement reaction different from a single-replacement reaction?

A reaction in which reactants switch cations and anions. Only one reactant

swaps in a single-replacement reaction.

11. Give two ways of expressing the formula for water.

HOH and H_2O.

12. What is the name and chemical formula of the white solid that remains upon evaporation of the NaOH + HCl reaction? Write a chemical equation to explain your answer.

Sodium chloride (NaCl). $HCl + NaOH \rightarrow HOH + NaCl$.

13. What happened to the ammonia odor when you added HCl to it? Write a chemical equation to explain your answer.

The odor disappeared because ammonia is neutralized by acid.

$NH_4OH + HCl \rightarrow NH_4Cl + HOH$.

NOW IT'S YOUR TURN!

1. Design an experiment using several different indicators to detect neutralization reactions. Write down what you do, what happens, and what it means. Design a concise data table to summarize your results.

   Do the same experiment with other indicators such as phenolphthalein,

   bromphenol blue, and methyl red.

2. Design an experiment to see if you can neutralize the ammonia odor with acids other than hydrochloric acid.

   Repeat Step 5 and use other acids in place of HCl.

3. Describe a procedure you would use to neutralize the ammonia smell in household ammonia or glass cleaner. Try it in the lab! Can a similar procedure be used to neutralize the smell of vinegar, CH_3COOH? Try it in the lab! Does your procedure work to neutralize the smell of other acids such as lemon juice?

   Absorb a drop of ammonia onto a swab, and add a drop or two of acid

   (vinegar or lemon juice) until the ammonia smell is gone. A base such as NaOH

   will neutralize vinegar and lemon juice.

4. Antacids are so named because they are designed to neutralize stomach acid (HCl). Design some experiments using indicators to show that antacids really do neutralize acids. Use acids other than just HCl. Write down each experiment you do, what happens, and what it means.

   Add a drop of BTB to a drop of acid, then add a few grains of crushed

   antacid tablet. The BTB will turn from yellow to blue.

Chapter 11 • *Chemical Reactions*   **SMALL-SCALE EXPERIMENT**

16 TITRATION OF BLEACH

Small-Scale Experiment for text Section 11.3

For your course planning, you may not want to use this lab until Chapter 19.

OBJECTIVE

- **Measure** and **record** the amount of sodium hypochlorite in household bleach.

INTRODUCTION

Sodium hypochlorite, NaClO, is a common chemical that has many household applications. Sodium hypochlorite is the active ingredient in household bleach, liquid drain openers, powdered cleansers, and dishwasher liquids. The hypochlorite ion, ClO^-, is useful in these cleaners because it is a powerful oxidizing agent. Hypochlorite ion as an oxidizing agent is able to whiten, brighten, or otherwise remove the color from all sorts of materials. For example, manufacturers of paper and textiles often use some sort of bleach to whiten their products and prepare them to be dyed.

The hypochlorite ion is also useful as a disinfectant. Hypochlorous acid, HClO, is very toxic to bacteria. A very small concentration of about one part per million (1 ppm) is required to kill bacteria. The small ClO^- ion easily penetrates the cell of a bacterium. Once inside, its strong oxidizing effect destroys the bacterium protein.

Swimming pools are typically treated with hypochlorite ion to disinfect the water and keep it sanitary. One pool sanitizer is calcium hypochlorite, $Ca(ClO)_2$, which introduces hypochlorite ion directly into the water. Larger pools commonly contain chlorine gas, which reacts with water to produce hypochlorous acid:

$$Cl_2(g) + H_2O \rightarrow HClO + H^+ + Cl^-$$

Another kind of bleach is an "oxygen bleach." Examples of oxygen bleaches are hydrogen peroxide, H_2O_2, and sodium perborate, Na_3BO_4. Many laundry detergents advertise that they contain "color safe" bleach, meaning that the active ingredient is sodium perborate. Sodium perborate, an oxygen bleach, is much milder than sodium hypochlorite, the active ingredient in "chlorine bleach." In fact, sodium hypochlorite is so powerful it can fray or discolor fabric, and dissolve stitching. Even so, consumer tests have shown repeatedly that chlorine bleach (containing sodium hypochlorite) is superior to oxygen bleaches (containing hydrogen peroxide or sodium perborate) at removing stains and brightening fabrics.

The use of all products that contain sodium hypochlorite can be dangerous. Sodium hypochlorite reacts with hydrochloric acid to produce toxic chlorine gas:

$$NaClO + 2HCl \rightarrow NaCl + H_2O + Cl_2(g)$$

For this reason, one should avoid mixing household bleach or any other product containing sodium hypochlorite with other household products such as toilet-bowl cleaners that contain acid. Warning labels on bottles of household bleach are very clear about this:

Warning! Do not mix with other chemicals, such as toilet-bowl cleaners, rust removers, acid, or ammonia-containing products. To do so will release hazardous gases.

PURPOSE

In this experiment, you will use sodium thiosulfate, $Na_2S_2O_3$, to determine the amount of sodium hypochlorite, NaClO, in household bleach. Your method will be iodometric titration. That is, you will add starch, ethanoic acid (CH_3COOH), and iodide ion (KI) to a dilute solution of bleach (NaClO). This will cause a reaction producing iodine. The starch acts as an indicator, turning the mixture blue-black in color. You will then titrate the iodine with thiosulfate. In the titration, you will measure the amount of sodium thiosulfate it takes to change the mixture from blue-black to colorless at the end point. The measured amount of $Na_2S_2O_3$ is directly proportional to the amount of NaClO in the bleach.

You will begin by examining the chemistry of the titration and then apply it to the analysis of a bleach sample. Finally, you will design and carry out experiments to find out how much sodium hypochlorite there is in other consumer products.

SAFETY 🔬 ☠️

- Wear your safety goggles.
- Use full small-scale pipets only for the controlled delivery of liquids.
- Don't chew gum, drink, or eat in the laboratory. Never taste a chemical in the laboratory.

MATERIALS

Small-scale pipets of the following solutions:

sodium hypochlorite (NaClO)
potassium iodide (KI)
ethanoic acid (CH_3COOH)

starch
sodium thiosulfate ($Na_2S_2O_3$)
diluted household bleach

EQUIPMENT

small-scale reaction surface
12-well strip
plastic cup

EXPERIMENTAL PROCEDURE

Part A. Some Chemistry of NaClO

1. Place one drop of NaClO on a small-scale reaction surface and add the solutions mentioned in the following steps. Stir each mixture and record your results in Table 16.1.

a. Add one drop of KI and one drop of CH_3COOH to the drop of NaClO in Step 1. In acid solution, hypochlorite ion oxidizes iodide ion to iodine:

$$ClO^- + 2I^- + 2H^+ \rightarrow Cl^- + H_2O + I_2$$

b. Add a few more drops of KI to the mixture. Excess iodide ion reacts with iodine to form triodide ion: $I^- + I_2 \rightarrow I_3^-$

c. Now add a drop of starch. Starch reacts with triodide ion to form a starch-iodine complex: I_3^- + starch $\rightarrow$ starch-iodine complex.

d. Now add several drops of $Na_2S_2O_3$ until the reaction mixture turns colorless. Thiosulfate ion reduces triodide to iodide ion:

$$I_3^- + 2S_2O_3^{2-} \rightarrow 3I^- + S_4O_6^{2-}$$

Part B. Titration of Sodium Hypochlorite in Bleach with Sodium Thiosulfate

2. Carry out the following procedure for the titration of bleach.

   a. Calibrate a $Na_2S_2O_3$ pipet. (Count the number of drops to fill a well.)

   b. Calibrate a NaClO (bleach) pipet. (Count the number of drops to fill a well.)

   c. Using the same pipet, add the same number of drops of NaClO it took to fill a well to a clean, dry cup.

   d. Add in order: three drops starch, 25 drops KI, and 20 drops CH_3COOH.

   e. Titrate the NaClO with $Na_2S_2O_3$ to a colorless end point. (Count the number of drops of $Na_2S_2O_3$ it takes to change the mixture from black to colorless.)

   f. Repeat the experiment until your results are consistent.

Name _____ Date _____ Class _____

EXPERIMENTAL DATA

Record your results in Tables 16.1 and 16.2 or in copies of the tables in your notebook.

Table 16.1   Chemistry of NaClO

	NaClO	KI + CH₃COOH	Excess KI	Starch	Na₂S₂O₃
Color	colorless	yellow	dark yellow	black	colorless

Table 16.2   Titration of Bleach

NaClO Sample	Drops Na₂S₂O₃ to fill	Drops NaClO to fill	Drops NaClO in cup	Drops Na₂S₂O₃ to end point	NaClO conc. mol/L
1	19	21	21	48	0.13
2	19	21	21	48	0.13
3	19	21	21	48	0.13

Calculate the concentration in mol NaClO/L of sodium hypochlorite in the bleach samples you titrated. Record your results in Table 16.2. To do the calculation, you will need the following pieces of information:

a. The drops of $Na_2S_2O_3$ used to obtain a colorless end point in the titration.

b. The drops of NaClO added to the cup.

c. The drops of NaClO needed to fill a well in drops/well.

d. The drops of $Na_2S_2O_3$ needed to fill a well in drops/well.

e. The concentration of $Na_2S_2O_3$ = 0.1M.

f. The overall stoichiometry = 1 mol NaClO/2 mol $Na_2S_2O_3$.

$$\frac{x \text{ mol NaClO}}{\text{L NaClO}} = \frac{\mathbf{a}}{\mathbf{b}} \times \frac{\mathbf{c}}{\mathbf{d}} \times \mathbf{e} \times \mathbf{f}$$

To be sure you understand the calculation, substitute each quantity (number and unit) into the equation and cancel the units. For subsequent calculations, simplify the equation by combining terms that are always constant. For example, in this experiment, the number of drops of NaClO added to the cup is equal to the number of drops of NaClO it took to fill a well, so **b** = **c** and they cancel.

$$xM \text{ NaClO} = \frac{a}{1} \times \frac{1}{d} \times e \times f = \frac{aef}{d}$$

CLEANING UP

Avoid contamination by cleaning up in a way that protects you and your environment. Carefully clean the small-scale reaction surface by absorbing the contents onto a dry paper towel, wipe it with a damp paper towel, and dry it. Rinse out the cup, wipe it with a damp paper towel, and dry it. Dispose of the towels in the waste bin. Wash your hands thoroughly with soap and water.

QUESTIONS FOR ANALYSES

Use what you learned in this experiment to answer the following questions.

1. What happens when you add NaClO to KI and CH_3COOH? What is the colored product? Write the net ionic equation (see Experimental Procedure).

    The solution turns yellow. I_2. $ClO^- + 2I^- + 2H^+ \rightarrow Cl^- + H_2O + I_2$.

2. A few more drops of KI produces what change? Write the net ionic equation for the reaction of excess potassium iodide with iodine (see Experimental Page).

    The yellow color darkens. $I^- + I_2 \rightarrow I_3^-$.

3. What happens when you add starch? Write the equation for the reaction between triodide and starch.

    The solution turns black. $I_3^- + \text{starch} \rightarrow \text{starch-iodine complex}$.

4. What color is the final mixture after you add sodium thiosulfate? Write the net ionic equation for the reaction between triodide and sodium thiosulfate.

    Colorless. $I^- + 2S_2O_3^{2-} \rightarrow 3I^- + S_4O_6^{2-}$.

5. Explain how starch acts as an indicator for the presence or absence of triodide.

    It turns black when I_3^- is present.

6. Calculate the percent of NaClO in the bleach, using the number of moles of NaClO per liter that you calculated from your Experimental Data.

    $$\% \text{ NaClO} = \frac{\text{g NaClO}}{100 \text{ g soln}} = \frac{0.13 \text{ moles NaClO}}{\text{L soln}} \times \frac{74.5 \text{ g NaClO}}{\text{mol NaClO}} \times \frac{1 \text{ L soln}}{1000 \text{ g soln}} \times 100 = \mathbf{0.97\%}$$

7. Multiply the percent of NaClO in bleach from Question 6 by 5 (the bleach sample you titrated was diluted by a factor of 5), and compare your result to the percent of NaClO listed on the bleach bottle's label by calculating the percent error and suggesting possible sources of error.

$$\% \text{ error} = \frac{5 \times \text{your result} - \% \text{ on label}}{\% \text{ on label}} \times 100 = \frac{(5 \times 0.97) - 5.25}{5.25} \times 100 = 7.6\% \text{ error}$$

As bleach gets older, the NaClO loses chlorine in the form of chlorine gas.

Thus, it is reasonable that the experimentally determined percent of NaClO

would be lower than the percent on the bottle. Also, adding ethanoic acid

to the bleach accelerates the loss of chlorine.

NOW IT'S YOUR TURN!

1. Design and carry out some weight titration experiments, using your small-scale balance or other balance to determine the molar concentration of NaClO in bleach. Compare your results to your volumetric titrations.

   Weigh about 500 mg of bleach. Add three drops of starch, 25 drops of KI, and 20

   drops of ethanoic acid. Balance a pipet full of $Na_2S_2O_3$, and titrate the

   bleach to colorless. Find the weight loss of $Na_2S_2O_3$. mol/L of NaClO =

   wt. of bleach/(wt. loss of $Na_2S_2O_3$)(20).

2. The labels of many household products say they contain sodium hypochlorite. Dishwasher liquids often contain NaClO. Design and carry out some experiments to determine the molar concentration of NaClO in some household dishwasher liquids.

3. Design some experiments to show that sodium hypochlorite is not "color-safe."

   Add NaClO to food dyes, colored paper, and colors made from marker

   pens on paper.

Chapter 11 • *Chemical Reactions*   **SMALL-SCALE EXPERIMENT**

17   HALOGEN IONS IN SOLUTION

Small-Scale Experiment for text Section 11.3

OBJECTIVES

- **Observe** the chemical properties of halide ions in aqueous solution.
- **Identify** halide ions by noting the differences in their chemical properties.
- **Describe** the chemical reactions of halide ions by writing and balancing chemical and net ionic equations.

INTRODUCTION

Halogens is the name given to the family of elements that comprise Group 17 (7A) on the periodic table. The individual elements are fluorine, chlorine, bromine, iodine, and astatine. All but astatine are relatively common elements. Because they are chemically reactive, the halogens never occur as single, free atoms in nature. In elemental form, halogens occur as the diatomic molecules F_2, Cl_2, Br_2, and I_2. The halogens form a large number of compounds and have many uses.

   The reactivity of the halogens and their similar properties are due to their very similar electron configurations. All halogens have seven valence (outer orbital) electrons, and each halogen readily gains one electron to form an anion with a single negative charge:

$$X + e^- \rightarrow X^- \qquad \text{where } X = \text{F, Cl, Br, I}$$

   These halogen anions are called halide ions. Their individual names are derived from their element names: F^- = fluoride, Cl^- = chloride, Br^- = bromide, and I^- = iodide.

PURPOSE

In this experiment, you will observe some of the chemical reactions of the halide ions. You will learn to write chemical equations to describe their reactions and to use these chemical reactions to distinguish one halide ion from another.

SAFETY 🧤🧴☠️🧪🫧

- Wear safety goggles, an apron, and gloves when working with corrosive chemicals.
- Use full small-scale pipets only for the controlled delivery of liquids.
- Don't chew gum, drink, or eat in the laboratory. Never taste a chemical in the laboratory.
- Avoid inhaling substances that can irritate your respiratory system.

MATERIALS

Small-scale pipets of the following solutions:

calcium chloride (CaCl$_2$)

lead(II) nitrate (Pb(NO$_3$)$_2$)

silver nitrate (AgNO$_3$)

sodium hypochlorite (NaClO)

ammonia (NH$_3$)

potassium fluoride (KF)

potassium chloride (KCl)

potassium bromide (KBr)

potassium iodide (KI)

starch

sodium thiosulfate (Na$_2$S$_2$O$_3$)

hydrochloric acid (HCl)

hydrogen peroxide (H$_2$O$_2$)

FD&C blue #1 (blue dye)

bromothymol blue (BTB)

copper(II) sulfate (CuSO$_4$)

iron(III) chloride (FeCl$_3$)

EQUIPMENT

small-scale reaction surface

empty pipet for stirring

clear plastic cup

EXPERIMENTAL PAGE

Part A. Chemistry of the Halide Ions

1. Add one drop of each of the indicated solutions on the **X**. Stir each mixture by blowing air with an empty small-scale pipet. Record your results in Table 17.1.

	KF (F⁻)	KCl (Cl⁻)	KBr (Br⁻)	KI (I⁻)	
a. CaCl₂ (Ca²⁺)	X	X	X	X	
b. Pb(NO₃)₂ (Pb²⁺)	X	X	X	X	
c. AgNO₃ (Ag⁺)	X	X	X	X	Now add 5–10 drops NH₃ to each and stir. Look for a change.
d. AgNO₃ (Ag⁺)	X	X	X	X	Now add 5–10 drops Na₂S₂O₃ to each and stir. Look for a change.
e. NaClO (ClO⁻)					Now add one drop of starch and one drop of HCl to each and stir. Look for a change.

Part B. Chemistry of Chlorine Gas, Cl₂(g)

2. Place one drop of each solution in the indicated space. Add one drop of NaClO to the HCl and cover the entire array with a cup. Observe the drops for any change over time, about 10 minutes. After you record your results in Table 17.2, turn this page over and continue the experiment.

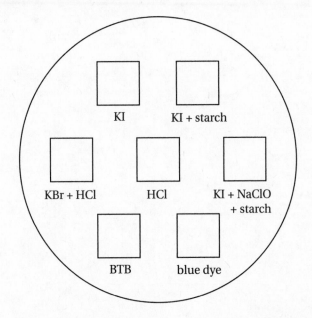

Place this side of the Experimental Page facedown. Use the other side under your small-scale reaction surface.

Part C. Chemistry of the Iodide Ion

3. Mix one drop of each of the following solutions on the X's. Record your results in Table 17.3.

	NaClO	CuSO$_4$	FeCl$_3$	H$_2$O$_2$	
KI	X	X	X	X	Now add one drop of starch to each mixture, then one drop of HCl.

Place this side of the Experimental Page facedown. Use the other side under your small-scale reaction surface.

Name _____ Date _____ Class _____

EXPERIMENTAL DATA

Record your results in Tables 17.1, 17.2, and 17.3 or in copies of the tables in your notebook.

Table 17.1 Chemistry of the Halide Ions

	KF (F⁻)	KCl (Cl⁻)	KBr (Br⁻)	KI (I⁻)	
a. $CaCl_2$ (Ca^{2+})	light white ppt	NVR	NVR	NVR	
b. $Pb(NO_3)_2$ (Pb^{2+})	NVR	white ppt	white ppt	bright yellow ppt	
c. $AgNO_3$ (Ag^+)	NVR	white ppt	white ppt	lime green ppt	ppts dissolve or lighten with NH_3
d. $AgNO_3$ (Ag^+)	NVR	white ppt	white ppt	lime green ppt	ppts dissolve or lighten with $Na_2S_2O_3$
e. $NaClO$ (ClO^-)	NVR	NVR	NVR, brown	yellow soln, black with starch	

Table 17.2 Chemistry of Chlorine Gas, $Cl_2(g)$

	KI colorless	KBr + HCl colorless	BTB green	KI + starch colorless	blue dye blue	Starch + KI + NaClO black
HCl + NaClO	yellow	brown	yellow	black	gray	no change

Table 17.3 Chemistry of Iodide Ion

	NaClO	CuSO₄	FeCl₃	H₂O₂
KI	yellow soln black with starch	yellow ppt black with starch	orange soln black with starch	NVR black with starch + HCl

CLEANING UP

Avoid contamination by cleaning up in a way that protects you and your environment. Carefully clean the small-scale reaction surface by absorbing the contents onto a paper towel. Rinse the small-scale reaction surface with a damp paper towel and dry it. Clean the plastic cup by wiping it with a dry paper towel. Dispose of the paper towels in the waste bin. Wash your hands thoroughly with soap and water.

QUESTIONS FOR ANALYSES

Use what you have learned in this experiment to answer the following questions.

1. What similarities did you observe in the reactions of halogens in Part A?

   All of the ions but F^- formed precipitates with the Ag^+ and Pb^{2+} ions.

2. Describe how the four halide ions—F^-, Cl^-, Br^-, and I^-—can be distinguished from one another. (That is, what chemical solutions undergo reactions that are unique to each ion?)

   Only F^- precipitates with Ca^{2+}. I^- is bright yellow with Pb^{2+}. AgCl and AgBr

   dissolve in NH_3 and $Na_2S_2O_3$, but only Br^- turns brown with NaClO and HCl.

3. Lead(II) ion reacts with iodide ion to produce a lead(II) iodide precipitate:

   $$Pb^{2+} + 2I^- \rightarrow PbI_2(s)$$

   Write similar net ionic equations to describe the other precipitation reactions you observed.

   $Pb^{2+} + 2Br^- \rightarrow PbBr_2(s)$. $Pb^{2+} + 2Cl^- \rightarrow PbCl_2(s)$.

   $Ca^{2+} + 2F^- \rightarrow CaF_2(s)$. $Ag^+ + Cl^- \rightarrow AgCl(s)$.

   $Ag^+ + Br^- \rightarrow AgBr(s)$. $Ag^+ + I^- \rightarrow AgI(s)$.

4. Would you get different results if you used aqueous solutions of sodium halides rather than potassium halides? Explain.

   No. The chemistry is due to the halide ions. Na^+ would be a spectator ion

   like K^+.

5. Silver forms a *complex* ion with ammonia:

   $$AgX(s) + 2NH_3 \rightarrow Ag(NH_3)_2^+ + X^-$$

   In the equation above, X represents a halide ion. Write equations for the reactions of ammonia for the silver halides that dissolve in ammonia by replacing X with each halide ion that dissolves.

   $AgCl(s) + 2NH_3 \rightarrow Ag(NH_3)_2^+ + Cl^-$.

   $AgBr(s) + 2NH_3 \rightarrow Ag(NH_3)_2^+ + Br^-$.

   $AgI(s) + 2NH_3 \rightarrow Ag(NH_3)_2^+ + I^-$.

6. Silver halide precipitates also dissolve in excess thiosulfate, $S_2O_3{}^{2-}$, to form the complex ion $Ag(S_2O_3)_2{}^{3-}$.

$$AgX(s) + 2S_2O_3{}^{2-} \rightarrow Ag(S_2O_3)_2{}^{3-} + X^-$$

Write equations for each reaction you observed with thiosulfate.

$AgCl(s) + 2S_2O_3{}^{2-} \rightarrow Ag(S_2O_3)_2{}^{3-} + Cl^-$.   **$AgI(s) + 2S_2O_3{}^{2-} \rightarrow Ag(S_2O_3)_2{}^{3-} + I^-$.**

$AgBr(s) + 2S_2O_3{}^{2-} \rightarrow Ag(S_2O_3)_2{}^{3-} + Br^-$.

7. The reaction of iodide ion (I^-) with NaClO can be described by the following equation:

$$ClO^- + 2H^+ + 2I^- \rightarrow Cl^- + I_2 + HOH$$

Write an equation for the reaction of bromide ion with NaClO.

$ClO^- + 2H^+ + 2Br^- \rightarrow Cl^- + Br_2 + HOH$.

8. Which chemical product in the sample equation in Question 7 is responsible for the formation of the black color with starch?

I_2.

9. Describe in your own words what must have happened under the cup to cause reactions in the solutions without mixing them with any other solution.

A gas that formed in the center diffused to the other drops and reacted

with them.

10. Sodium hypochlorite (NaClO) reacts with hydrochloric acid to yield chlorine gas, sodium chloride, and water. Write the chemical equation.

$NaClO + 2HCl \rightarrow Cl_2(g) + NaCl + H_2O$.

11. Given the word equation, write a balanced chemical equation to describe each reaction between chlorine gas and the indicated reagent. In each case, explain the change in the reagent.

a. Chlorine gas reacts with water to produce hydrochloric acid and hypochlorous acid (HClO).

$Cl_2 + H_2O \rightarrow HCl + HClO$. BTB turns yellow, indicating the presence of

acid.

b. Chlorine reacts with iodide ion to form iodine and chloride ion.

$Cl_2 + 2I^- \rightarrow I_2 + 2Cl^-$. I_2 turns black with starch. As I_2 forms, its

characteristic yellow color appears in aqueous solution.

c. Chlorine reacts similarly with bromide ion.

$Cl_2 + 2Br^- \rightarrow Br_2 + 2Cl^-$. The characteristic brown color of Br_2 appears.

12. What color do all the reaction mixtures in Part C have in common? What chemical species is indicated by this color?

Black. I_2.

13. Write and balance chemical equations for all the reactions you observed in Part C. Here are some hints.

$Cl_2 + I^- \rightarrow Cl^- + ?$ $Cl_2 + 2I^- \rightarrow 2Cl^- + I_2$

$Cu^{2+} + I^- \rightarrow CuI(s) + ?$ $2Cu^{2+} + 4I^- \rightarrow 2CuI(s) + I_2$

$Fe^{3+} + I^- \rightarrow Fe^{2+} + ?$ $2Fe^{3+} + 2I^- \rightarrow 2Fe^{2+} + I_2$

$H_2O_2 + I^- + H^+ \rightarrow H_2O + ?$ $H_2O_2 + 2I^- + 2H^+ \rightarrow 2H_2O + I_2$

NOW IT'S YOUR TURN!

1. Study the chemistry of bromine (Br_2) by setting up KI, KI + starch and BTB indicators like those in Part B. Instead of using NaClO and HCl in the center, use one drop each of the following: KBr, KIO_3, and HCl. The reaction is

$$6Br^- + IO_3^- + 6H^+ \rightarrow 3Br_2 + I^- + 3H_2O$$

Report the results of each mixing. Complete and balance the following chemical equations. (**Hint:** They are like the reactions of Cl_2.)

$Br_2 + I^- \rightarrow$ $Br_2 + H_2O \rightarrow$

$Br_2 + 2I^- \rightarrow 2Br^- + I_2$ $Br_2 + H_2O \rightarrow HBr + HOBr$

	KI colorless	KI + starch colorless	BTB green
HCl + KBr + KIO_3	yellow	black	yellow

2. Both I_2 and Br_2 are nonpolar molecules. This means that they are more soluble in nonpolar solvents such as baby oil than they are in polar solvents such as water. On the other hand, I^- and Br^- are water-soluble ions. Use aqueous solutions of I^- and Br^- to generate some I_2 and Br_2, and watch them dissolve in a nonpolar solvent such as baby oil. On a glass slide, mix one drop of each of the following:

	KI + HCl	KBr + HCl
NaClO + baby oil	+	+

Observe over time. Write chemical equations for each reaction. What color does each halogen appear to be in the baby oil?

$Cl^- + ClO^- + 2H^+ \rightarrow Cl_2 + H_2O$ $Cl_2 + 2Br^- \rightarrow Br_2 + 2Cl^-$

$Cl_2 + 2I^- \rightarrow I_2 + 2Cl^-$ (brown)

(violet)

18 TITRATION: DETERMINING HOW MUCH ACID IS IN A SOLUTION

Small-Scale Experiment for text Section 12.2

For your course planning, you may not want to use this lab until Chapter 19.

OBJECTIVES

- **Demonstrate** an understanding of the meaning of each of the following terms: qualitative, quantitative, calibration, titration, equivalence point, end point.
- **Calibrate** pipets by measuring volumes of drops.
- **Measure** the molar concentration of acid solutions by using the technique of titration.

INTRODUCTION

If you read the label on a typical chemical consumer product, you can often find both qualitative and quantitative information. Qualitative information answers the question, "What?" Quantitative information answers the question, "How much?" For example, a typical bottle of toilet-bowl cleaner tells you that it contains 9.5% (how much) hydrochloric acid, HCl (what). Hydrochloric acid is the "active ingredient," the ingredient that performs the specific function for which the product is designed. Hydrochloric acid helps dissolve mineral deposits that build up on the inside of the toilet bowl.

A *titration* is a way to measure the number of moles of a substance dissolved in a liter of solution. The resulting quantity is called the molarity of the substance and is expressed in units of moles per liter (mol/L), or simply *M*. An acid–base titration typically uses a known amount of base to measure an unknown amount of acid in a solution. In a typical titration, you slowly add a base with a known concentration, such as NaOH, to a measured volume of unknown acid solution, such as HCl. The neutralization reaction occurs:

$$\text{acid} + \text{base} \rightarrow \text{salt} + \text{water}$$

$$\text{HCl} + \text{NaOH} \rightarrow \text{NaCl} + \text{HOH}$$

When all the acid is just neutralized by the base, the *equivalence point* has been reached. (The number of moles of base is equivalent to the number of moles of acid at the equivalence point.) You use the volume of base needed to reach the equivalence point to calculate how many moles of acid were neutralized by that volume of base. Because the reactants and products are colorless, it is often necessary to use an indicator to determine the equivalence point of the reaction. Phenolphthalein is an indicator that is colorless in acid solution but bright pink in basic solution. If phenolphthalein is present in the titration mixture, it will remain colorless until one drop of base neutralizes the last of the acid and makes the solution very slightly basic. At this point, called the *end point*, a dramatic color change from colorless to pink occurs.

Notice that the end point and the equivalence point are not necessarily the same. In the case of phenolphthalein, the end point occurs when the solution turns just slightly basic, not when the solution is exactly neutral, the equivalence point. Accurate titrations require the use of an indicator that will give an end point that is very close to the equivalence point.

Name _____ Date _____ Class _____

PURPOSE

In this experiment, you will use the quantitative technique of titration to determine the concentrations in moles per liter, M, of various acid samples using exactly 0.50M sodium hydroxide, NaOH. In a typical experiment, you will deliver a specific number of drops of an acid to a reaction vessel and add an indicator such as phenolphthalein. You will then count the number of drops of NaOH that is needed to turn the indicator pink. To find the volume of a drop, you will calibrate pipets by counting the number of drops each pipet delivers to fill the same size volume. You will carry out several experiments to determine what is the best way to calibrate (measure the drop size of) a pipet so that it always delivers the same size drops. Calibration is a way to correct for the different-sized drops delivered by different pipets.

SAFETY 🥼 👙 ☠ 🧤 ☣

- Wear safety goggles, an apron, and gloves when working with corrosive chemicals.
- Use full small-scale pipets only for the controlled delivery of liquids.
- Don't chew gum, drink, or eat in the laboratory. Never taste a chemical in the laboratory.
- Avoid inhaling substances that can irritate your respiratory system.

MATERIALS

Small-scale pipets of the following solutions:
hydrochloric acid (HCl)
sodium hydroxide (NaOH)
phenolphthalein (phen)
nitric acid (HNO₃)
ethanoic acid (CH₃COOH)
sulfuric acid (H₂SO₄)

EQUIPMENT

well plate
plastic cup
cotton swab

EXPERIMENTAL PROCEDURE

Part A. Calibrating a Small-Scale Pipet: Measuring the Relative Sizes of Drops

1. Perform a series of experiments that will answer the following questions. Work individually, as it is important that you become skilled in calibrations. Record your results in Table 18.1.

   a. How many drops of water from a small-scale pipet are needed to fill a well? Can you repeat this result?

   b. What is the best way to tell exactly when the well is full?

   c. Is it important to expel the air bubble before you begin?

    d. Try delivering drops with the pipet vertical, horizontal, and at a 45° angle. At which angle do you obtain the most number of drops? The least? Which angle delivers the smallest drops?

    e. What will happen if you do not always hold the pipet at the same angle?

    f. Do different pipets give different results at the same angle? Why is it important to calibrate each different pipet you use?

2. Calibrate an HCl pipet and a NaOH pipet. Count the number of drops of each needed to fill a well for each substance. Repeat until your results are reproducible. Record your results in Table 18.2.

Part B. The Titration

3. Carry out a titration of HCl as follows:

    a. Holding the pipet vertically, count 20 drops of HCl into a plastic cup. Take care not to touch the ends of the pipet to the cup or to the solution in the cup. Let D_a equal this number of drops.

    b. Add one drop of phenolphthalein to the HCl in the cup.

    c. Add NaOH slowly, counting the number of drops of NaOH needed to obtain a stable pink end point. As you titrate, swirl the cup gently. Let D_b equal this number of drops.

    d. Repeat Steps **a–c** in a clean, dry cup until your results are consistent.

4. Titrate HNO_3 and CH_3COOH, each with NaOH in the same way. Here are some tips for accuracy and to avoid contamination. Use a clean cup. Take care not to let the ends of the pipets touch the cup or the solution in the cup. Hold the pipets vertically. As you titrate, swirl gently and count the number of drops of NaOH it takes to get a stable pink color. Clean and dry the cup before each titration. When the pipets are empty, take care to refill them with the proper solutions. Read the labels twice!

EXPERIMENTAL DATA

Record the results of your calibrations and titrations in Tables 18.1, 18.2, and 18.3 or in copies of the tables in your notebook.

Table 18.1   Calibration of Small-Scale Pipet

| | Drops to fill | | |
	Trial 1	Trial 2	Trial 3
Vertical	21	21	21
Horizontal	15	16	17
45° angle	18	16	19

Summarize a method that will always accurately *calibrate* or determine the number of drops delivered by any pipet to fill a well.

Hold the pipet vertically, expel the air bubble, and deliver drops slowly with

the tip about 1 cm above the well.

Table 18.2   Calibration of HCl and NaOH Pipets

| | Drops to fill | | |
	Trial 1	Trial 2	Trial 3
HCl	23	22	23
NaOH	19	18	19

Table 18.3　Titrations of Acids

Acid		Drops to fill C_a	Drops NAOH to fill C_b	Drops NaOH to pink D_b	M of acid M_a
Acid	HCl	23	19	33	1.0
	HCl	23	19	33	1.0
	HNO$_3$	17	19	45	1.0
	HNO$_3$	17	19	45	1.0
	CH$_3$COOH	21	19	29	0.8
	CH$_3$COOH	21	19	29	0.8

Calculate the molar concentration, M_a, of HCl and of the other two acids by substituting the following pieces of data into the expression below.

M_b = molar concentration of NaOH (M_b = 0.50M in this experiment)

D_a = drops of acid used (20 drops in this experiment)

D_b = drops of NaOH to pink end point

C_a = drops of acid needed to fill a well

C_b = drops of NaOH needed to fill a well

$$M_a = \frac{M_b \times D_b}{D_a} \times \frac{C_a}{C_b}$$

This equation really calculates normality. Because the stoichiometry is 1:1 in this case, it also calculates molarity.

$$M_{HCl} = \frac{0.50M \times 33 \text{ drops}}{20 \text{ drops}} \times \frac{23 \text{ drops}}{19 \text{ drops}} = 1.0M$$

$$M_{HNO_3} = \frac{0.50M \times 45 \text{ drops}}{20 \text{ drops}} \times \frac{17 \text{ drops}}{19 \text{ drops}} = 1.0M$$

$$M_{CH_3COOH} = \frac{0.50M \times 29 \text{ drops}}{20 \text{ drops}} \times \frac{21 \text{ drops}}{19 \text{ drops}} = 0.80M$$

CLEANING UP

Avoid contamination by cleaning up in a way that protects you and your environment. Carefully clean the plastic cup and well plate by disposing of the liquid contents in the sink and rinsing them thoroughly with water. Dry both pieces of equipment with a paper towel. Wash your hands thoroughly with soap and water.

QUESTIONS FOR ANALYSES

Use what you learned in this experiment to answer the following questions.

1. What is an acid–base titration? Is titration a qualitative or quantitative method? Explain.

   A method to measure how much acid is in a solution. Quantitative because

   it answers the question, "How much?"

2. What does it mean to calibrate a pipet? Is calibration a qualitative or quantitative method? Explain.

   To measure the size of a drop (in this case in terms of "wells"). Quantitative

   because it tells "how much."

3. Why is it important to calibrate each pipet when measuring the volumes of solutions?

   Each pipet delivers different-sized drops.

4. Why is it important to repeat a calibration or a titration until the results are consistent?

   The greater the repeatability of the answer the less doubt there is that it

   is reasonable.

5. Summarize the steps it takes to calibrate a small-scale pipet.

   Hold the pipet vertically, expel the air bubble, and deliver drops slowly with

   the tip about 1 cm above a well.

6. Why do your calculations of acid concentrations include the number of drops of NaOH and HCl needed to fill a well?

   Because the drop sizes for each pipet are different, each pipet needs to be

   calibrated to correct for the different-sized drops.

7. Write the chemical equation for each titration reaction you carried out in this experiment.

   $NaOH + HCl \rightarrow NaCl + HOH$.

   $NaOH + HNO_3 \rightarrow NaNO_3 + HOH$.

   $NaOH + CH_3COOH \rightarrow CH_3COONa + HOH$.

8. Write the balanced equation for the reaction of sulfuric acid, H_2SO_4, with sodium hydroxide, NaOH. How is it different from the equations you wrote for the reactions of HCl, HNO_3, and CH_3COOH with NaOH?

   $2NaOH + H_2SO_4 \rightarrow Na_2SO_4 + 2HOH$.

   The mole ratio for base to acid is 2:1 rather than 1:1.

9. Sulfuric acid, H_2SO_4, is an example of a diprotic acid. Explain what this means. Give an example of a triprotic acid. Give two examples of monoprotic acids.

An acid that has two acidic hydrogens. H_3PO_4 is triprotic. HCl, HNO_3, and

CH_3COOH are monoprotic.

NOW IT'S YOUR TURN!

1. Let's explore titration a little further. To carry out a "serial titration," add four drops of HCl + one drop phen to a 1×12 well plate as shown below.

1	2	3	4	5	6	7	8	9	10	11	12

Then add: 1 2 3 4 5 6 7 8 9 10 11 12 drops of NaOH.

(Add the number of drops of NaOH equal to the well number.) Record your results.

a. Which wells have more acid than base? Which have more base than acid?

The colorless ones. The pink ones.

b. The end point is the point at which the indicator changes colors. Which well represents the end point of the titration?

The first pink well, which should be number 8 or number 9.

c. The equivalence point is the point at which enough base is added to just neutralize the acid. (The moles of base are "equal" to the moles of acid.) Which well represents the equivalence point?

Somewhere between the last colorless well and the first pink well.

d. How does the equivalence point differ from the end point? By how many drops, at most, is the equivalence point different from the end point?

The equivalence point is where the acid is exactly neutralized by the base.

The end point is where the indicator changes color. One drop.

2. Design titration experiments to determine the molar concentration of H_2SO_4. Be sure to calibrate each pipet you use and run each experiment at least twice so you can be confident of your answers. If you calculate the molar concentration of H_2SO_4 in the same way as the other acids, your result will be off by a factor of 2. Where does the factor of 2 go in the molarity calculation?

3. Some toilet-bowl cleaners are water solutions containing hydrochloric acid, HCl. Vinegar is a water solution of ethanoic acid, CH_3COOH. Design experiments to determine the molar concentrations of HCl in various household products and of ethanoic acid, CH_3COOH, in vinegar. Be sure to calibrate the pipets you use. Organize your results into a table like Table 18.3 and report your calculations in your laboratory notebook. (**Note:** Because some of the solutions are highly colored, the end point might not be pink. Try using three drops phen and look for the end point to be a distinct color change.)

19 MASS TITRATIONS: MEASURING MOLAR CONCENTRATIONS

Small-Scale Experiment for text Section 12.2

For your course planning, you may not want to use this lab until Chapter 19.

OBJECTIVES

- **Measure** the molar concentration of acids, using weight titrations.
- **Compare** the accuracy of mass titrations with that of volumetric titrations.
- **Identify** unknown solutions by applying both qualitative and quantitative analysis.

INTRODUCTION

A *mass titration* is a method of finding molar concentration by measuring the mass of solutions. A mass titration is often more accurate than a volumetric titration because a balance is usually a more accurate instrument than a pipet. The result of a mass titration depends only on masses determined directly from the balance and not on volumes determined from pipets.

You can use the balance to determine the volumes of solutions. You know that the density of water is one gram per cubic centimeter or one milligram per microliter. The densities of dilute aqueous solutions are assumed to be equal to the density of water. This means that if you measure the mass of a solution in milligrams, it has the same numerical volume in microliters.

PURPOSE

In this experiment, you will carry out a mass titration. You will measure the mass of a sample of acid and add an indicator. Then you will determine the mass of NaOH you need to add to reach the end point. To do this using a small-scale balance, you will zero your balance with a pipet full of NaOH. There is no need to find the mass of the pipet because you only need to know the *difference* in mass before and after the titration. Next, you will add NaOH to the acid solution until the indicator changes. Finally, you will determine the mass of the NaOH needed for the titration by placing the pipet back on the small-scale balance and adding weights to make up for the NaOH you used. The total mass you add is the mass of the NaOH that was used in the titration.

SAFETY 🥽 🧥 ☠ 🧪 🫁

- Wear safety goggles, an apron, and gloves when working with corrosive chemicals.
- Use full small-scale pipets only for the controlled delivery of liquids.
- Don't chew gum, drink, or eat in the laboratory. Never taste a chemical in the laboratory.
- Avoid inhaling substances that can irritate your respiratory system.

MATERIALS

Small-scale pipets of the following solutions:
phenolphthalein (phen)
sodium hydroxide (NaOH)
nitric acid (HNO$_3$)
sulfuric acid (H$_2$SO$_4$)
ethanoic acid (CH$_3$COOH)
hydrochloric acid (HCl)

EQUIPMENT

balance
plastic cup

EXPERIMENTAL PROCEDURE

1. Measure 500 mg of acid solution on your small-scale balance as follows:

   a. Place a 500-mg weight in a clean, dry cup.

   b. Set the balance so the pointer reads zero.

   c. Remove the weight and add acid until the pointer again reads zero.

2. Add five drops of phen.

3. Tare two full NaOH pipets.

   a. Place two pipets of NaOH in a second clean, dry cup.

   b. Set the balance so it reads zero. (Use two pipets just to make sure you have enough NaOH.)

4. Titrate the acid solution in the first cup with NaOH from one of the pipets until *one drop* turns the solution to a stable pink color.

5. Determine the mass of the NaOH you used for the titration. Record this mass in Table 19.1.

   a. Return both of the NaOH pipets to the second cup.

   b. Add weights until the balance pointer again reads zero. The sum of the added weights is the mass of the NaOH used in the titration.

6. Repeat Steps 1–5 until you obtain consistent results. (The only way to tell whether your result is reliable is to reproduce it!)

7. Design and carry out mass titrations to determine the molar concentrations of nitric acid, HNO$_3$; sulfuric acid, H$_2$SO$_4$; and ethanoic acid, CH$_3$COOH. Titrate each acid at least twice.

EXPERIMENTAL DATA

Record your results in Table 19.1 or in a copy of the table in your notebook.

Table 19.1 Molarity of Acids

	HCl	HCl	HNO₃	HNO₃	H₂SO₄	H₂SO₄	CH₃COOH	CH₃COOH
Mass of acid (mg)	500	500	500	500	500	500	500	500
Mass of NaOH (mg)	1000	1000	1000	1000	2000	2000	900	900
Molarity of acid (M)	1.0	1.0	1.0	1.0	1.0	1.0	1.0	1.0

Calculate the molar concentration of HCl in each sample. Record your data in Table 19.1. Do the same calculation for the titrations of HNO_3, H_2SO_4, and CH_3COOH. (**Note:** When calculating the molar concentration of H_2SO_4, you must divide your result by 2 because there are 2 moles of hydrogen per mole of sulfuric acid.)

$$\text{Molarity of acid} = \frac{(\text{molarity of NaOH})(\text{mass of NaOH in mg})}{(\text{mass of HCl in mg})}$$

In this experiment the molarity of NaOH is 0.5M.

Here we assume that the densities of the solutions are all 1.00 g/mL or (1000 mg/mL) and that the stoichiometry of the acid–base reactions are all 1:1.

CLEANING UP

Avoid contamination by cleaning up in a way that protects you and your environment. Carefully clean the plastic cup by disposing of the liquid contents, rinsing the cup thoroughly with water, and drying it with a paper towel. Dispose of the paper towels in the waste bin. Wash your hands thoroughly with soap and water.

QUESTIONS FOR ANALYSES

Use what you learned in this experiment to answer the following questions.

1. Why is it that when you measure the mass of a dilute solution, the number of milligrams of solution is equal to the number of microliters of solution?

   The densities of dilute aqueous solutions are assumed to be equal to the

   density of water, 1 g/mL.

2. When using a small-scale balance, why is it not necessary to find the mass of the NaOH pipet before you begin titrating?

   You need to know only the difference in the mass of the NaOH pipet to determine how much

   NaOH was used in the titration.

3. Why is it not important to expel the air bubble or hold the pipet at a vertical angle when you titrate?

   You are not measuring the volume of drops.

4. Explain how you can determine the mass of the NaOH used in the titration without ever knowing the mass of the pipet or its contents.

   You can tare the balance with the pipets before the titration, add weights

   to balance it afterwards, and sum the amount of added mass to find out

   how much NaOH you used.

NOW IT'S YOUR TURN!

1. Your teacher will give you a list of consumer products to titrate. Use the Experimental Procedure in this experiment to titrate each consumer product at least twice, or until you obtain consistent results. Substitute the HCl in this experiment for the consumer product containing HCl or another acid. Make a table in which to record your data and report the name of the product, the mass of the product sample, the mass of the NaOH needed to titrate it, and the calculated molar concentration of HCl or other acid in the product.

   a. Use your data for the titration of household products to calculate the % HCl in each household product, and record it in a table.

   $$\% \ HCl = \frac{g \ HCl}{100 \ g \ soln} = \frac{mol \ HCl}{1 \ L \ soln} \times \frac{36.5 \ g \ HCl}{mol \ HCl} \times \frac{1 \ L \ soln}{1000 \ g \ soln} \times 100$$

   (The molar mass of HCl is 36.5 g/mol. The density of each solution is taken to be 1000 g/L.)

   b. Read each household product's label and find the % HCl listed. Compare each value to your calculated values. Calculate the % error for each product.

   $$\% \ error = \frac{|calculated \ value - product \ label \ value|}{product \ label \ value} \times 100$$

   c. Are your calculated values necessarily in error? Explain. What factors might account for the differences?

   No. Evaporation or dilution of an older bottle might contribute to the errors.

   d. Use your data for the titration of vinegar to calculate the % CH_3COOH in vinegar and record it in a table.

   $$\% \ CH_3OOH = \frac{g \ CH_3COOH}{100 \ g \ soln} = \frac{mol \ CH_3COOH}{1 \ L \ soln} \times \frac{60 \ g \ CH_3COOH}{mol \ CH_3COOH} \times \frac{1 \ L \ soln}{1000 \ g \ soln} \times 100$$

   (The molar mass of CH_3COOH is 60 g/mol. The density of each solution is taken to be 1000 g/L.)

   e. Calculate the percent error for ethanoic acid, CH_3COOH, in vinegar.

2. Now you know how to determine the molar concentration of an acid. This is *quantitative analysis.* Quantitative analysis answers the question, "How much?" However, you also need to know what the acid is. *Qualitative analysis* answers the question, "What is it?"

a. Below is a design for an experiment to study and compare the reactions of various acids. You can use their differences to identify what they are.

Mix one drop of each of these compounds in the indicated space.

	BTB	UI	Na_2CO_3	$Pb(NO_3)_2$	$AgNO_3$	$CaCl_2$
HCl	yellow	red	bubbles	white ppt X	white ppt X	NVR X
HNO_3	yellow	red	bubbles	NVR X	NVR X	NVR X
H_2SO_4	yellow	red	bubbles	white ppt X	NVR X	white ppt X
CH_3COOH	yellow	orange	bubbles	NVR X	NVR X	NVR X

Which reactions are the same for all the acids? Which reactions are different and therefore afford a way to distinguish the acids?

b. Obtain three unknown acids from your teacher. Design some experiments to identify the acids (qualitative analysis) and to determine their molar concentrations (quantitative analysis.) Report your results as instructed.

20 ABSORPTION OF WATER BY PAPER TOWELS: A CONSUMER LAB

Small-Scale Experiment for text Section 13.2

OBJECTIVES

- **Measure** the amounts of water absorbed by different commercial paper towels.
- **Measure** the strengths of different brands of paper towels when wet.
- **Measure** the time it takes paper towels to absorb water.
- **Compare** the properties of different brands of paper towels.
- **Determine** the best brand for the money.

INTRODUCTION

Each paper-towel manufacturer goes to great lengths to persuade consumers that its brand is better than all the others. Eye-catching packaging and decorator designs compete for your attention on the supermarket shelves. At certain times of the year, you can even buy paper towels with holiday themes. Television commercials pitch the properties of paper towels: how much moisture they absorb, how fast they do it, and how strong they are when wet.

Is one paper towel really better than another? Does price reflect quality? What does it mean to be better? Stronger? Faster? More absorbent?

PURPOSE

In this experiment, you will attempt to answer some of these questions and along the way you will formulate even more questions. You will begin by examining several properties of paper towels. You will determine the mass of a dry paper towel, wet it, and determine its mass again to see how much water it absorbed. You will test the rate at which the water is absorbed by measuring the time it takes to absorb a certain amount of water. Finally, you will test the wet strength of paper towels to determine how well they hold up to tough jobs. You will then compile your results and compare these results with the price of each product to try to determine the best buy in the paper-towel market.

SAFETY ✂

- Behave in a way that is consistent with a safe laboratory.
- To avoid a puncture wound, use scissors or other sharp objects only as intended.

EQUIPMENT

5-cm × 10-cm poster-board card	plastic cup
several brands of paper towels	water
with their labels	soda straws
scissors	1/4-inch hole punch
balance	clothespins

EXPERIMENTAL PROCEDURE

Part A. How much water does each towel absorb?

1. Use the card as a template to cut a 5-cm × 10-cm piece of paper towel. Determine the mass of the towel dry. Record the mass in Table 20.1.

2. Fold the paper towel in half the long way and wet it thoroughly in a cup half full of water.

3. When removing the towel from the water, skim it across the lip of the cup to remove excess water. Determine the mass of the wet towel. Record the mass in Table 20.1.

4. Repeat this procedure for several brands of paper towels.

Part B. How quickly does each towel absorb water?

clothespin

straw

5-cm × 10-cm paper towel

2.0-cm mark

1.0-cm mark

3-oz cup with H_2O

balance base

5. Make a straw stand on your balance base to hang paper towels, as shown in Figure 20.1. Hang a 5-cm × 10-cm piece of paper towel from the stand by a clothespin so that it is immersed in a cup of water to a depth of 1 cm. Measure the time it takes for the water to travel 2 cm up the paper. Repeat the procedure for the other brands of towels. Record your results in Table 20.2.

Figure 20.1 *Straw stand for paper towels*

Part C. How strong is each wet towel?

6. Attach two clothespins, one to each end of a 1-cm × 10-cm piece of paper towel, and wet the towel in the middle. Be sure the wet part does not touch either clothespin. Hold one clothespin in your hand and attach clothespins, one at a time, to the other clothespin. Count the number of clothespins that are needed to break the wet towel. Record your results in Table 20.3.

Part D. How do the paper towels compare in price?

7. Read the labels on each brand of paper towel you measured. Find the following data and record it in Table 20.4.

   a. The price per roll.

   b. The number of square feet of paper per roll.

   c. The number of square feet you can buy for a penny.

$$x = \frac{\text{sq ft}}{\text{penny}} = \frac{\text{number of sq ft}}{\text{roll}} \times \frac{1 \text{ roll}}{\text{price per penny}}$$

   d. Calculate the milligrams of water absorbed per penny.

$$x = \frac{\text{mg}}{\text{penny}} = \frac{\text{sq ft}}{\text{penny}} \times \frac{929 \text{ cm}^2}{\text{sq ft}} \times \frac{\text{mg absorbed}}{50 \text{ cm}^2}$$

EXPERIMENTAL DATA

Record your results in Tables 20.1, 20.2, 20.3 and 20.4 or in copies of the tables in your notebook.

Table 20.1   How much water does each towel absorb?

Brand of towel	A	B	C	D	E
Wet mass (mg)	1677	1863	3135	1045	1977
Dry mass (mg)	287	288	250	215	290
Water mass (mg)	1390	1575	2885	830	1687
Relative water mass	1.67	1.90	3.47	1.00	2.03

To find the mass of the water, subtract the dry mass from the wet mass. To find the "relative water mass," divide all the "water masses" by the lowest "water mass." This will tell you how many times better each towel is at picking up water compared to the towel that is the least absorbent.

Table 20.2   How quickly does each towel absorb water?

Brand of towel	A	B	C	D	E
Time to absorb water to a depth of 2 cm (s)	42	55	15	205	45

Table 20.3   How strong is each wet towel?

Brand of towel	A	B	C	D	E
Number of clothespins	15	12	26	7	16

Name _____ Date _____ Class _____

Table 20.4   How do the paper towels compare in price?

Brand of towel	A	B	C	D	E
Price per roll ($)	0.67	0.69	0.99	0.49	0.79
Square feet per roll	69	85	67	66	63
Square feet per penny	1.0	1.2	0.68	1.3	0.80
Milligrams water absorbed per ¢	26,000	35,000	36,000	20,000	25,000

CLEANING UP

Avoid contamination by cleaning up in a way that protects you and your environment. Please recycle all usable pieces of paper towels. Dispose of unusable scraps in the waste bin.

QUESTIONS FOR ANALYSES

Use what you learned in this experiment to answer the following questions.

1. Which paper towel is the most absorbent? The least?

   The ones with the largest and smallest "water masses," respectively.

2. Which paper towel absorbed water faster than all the others? Slower than all the others?

   The times vary from several seconds to several minutes.

3. Which is the strongest paper towel? Which is the weakest?

   Answers will vary.

NOW IT'S YOUR TURN!

1. Why is it important to do the strength test in Step 6 with clothespins touching only dry parts of the towel? Repeat the experiment with the clothespins touching the wet part of the towel.

   With the clothespins touching the wet part of the towel, the towel always breaks at this

   weakest point. This is not a good indication of the wet strength of the paper.

2. What other types of paper can you test at home?

   Typing paper, computer paper, facial tissue, toilet tissue, and napkins.

21 SYNTHESIS AND QUALITATIVE ANALYSIS OF GASES

Small-Scale Experiment for text Section 14.4

OBJECTIVES

- **Carry out** chemical reactions that produce gases.
- **Detect** the gases produced by reactions of aqueous solutions, using indicators.
- **Identify** unknown gases and the solutions that produce them.

INTRODUCTION

Gases are found everywhere. Open a can or bottle of a carbonated soft drink, and carbon dioxide, CO_2, bubbles appear. Balloons are commonly filled with helium, He. On average, you inhale and exhale a mixture of gases about 12 times a minute. The air you inhale is mainly nitrogen and oxygen—about 78% nitrogen and 21% oxygen. The final 1% includes argon and other noble gases; carbon dioxide and water vapor; and oxides of sulfur and nitrogen.

Sulfur and nitrogen oxides are the main pollutants in air. Sulfur dioxide, SO_2, is produced when fuels such as coil or oil, which can contain some sulfur compounds, are burned. Sulfur dioxide released into the atmosphere can react with oxygen and form sulfur trioxide, SO_3. When sulfur dioxide and sulfur trioxide dissolve in water vapor, they produce acid precipitation. This precipitation is harmful to organisms and to the surfaces of buildings and other outdoor structures. The oxides of nitrogen are a family of compounds that are commonly represented by the general formula NO_x (NO_2, NO, N_2O_5, and N_2O). A large concentration of NO_x compounds in the atmosphere is a trigger for smog.

PURPOSE

In this experiment, you will observe some chemical reactions that produce gases. You will produce each gas by mixing two aqueous solutions on a small-scale reaction surface. You will surround each mixture with indicators that change color in the presence of the gas. You will cover each mixture with a clear plastic cup while the gas diffuses into the indicators. Later, you will use the color changes that you observe and record to identify samples of unknown gases.

SAFETY 🗱 🗱 🗱 🗱 🗱

- Wear safety goggles, an apron, and gloves when working with corrosive chemicals.
- Use full small-scale pipets only for the controlled delivery of liquids.
- Don't chew gum, drink, or eat in the laboratory. Never taste a chemical in the laboratory.
- Avoid inhaling substances that can irritate your respiratory system.

MATERIALS

Small-scale pipets of the following solutions:

potassium iodide (KI)   sodium nitrite (NaNO$_2$)
starch   sodium hydroxide (NaOH)
bromthymol blue (BTB)   sodium hydrogen carbonate (NaHCO$_3$)
hydrochloric acid (HCl)   hydrogen peroxide (H$_2$O$_2$)
sodium hypochlorite (NaClO)   potassium permanganate (KMnO$_4$)
sodium hydrogen sulfite (NaHSO$_3$)   ammonium chloride (NH$_4$Cl)

EQUIPMENT

two clear plastic cups
small-scale reaction surface

Name _____ Date _____ Class _____

EXPERIMENTAL PAGE

1. Place one drop of each indicator solution in the four squares near the edge of each circle. Place one drop of each reactant solution together in the center of each circle. Then quickly cover the entire circle with a cup. Be sure the cup does not touch any of the solutions.

2. Observe any changes that take place over several minutes. Note whether any bubbles appear in the reaction mixture. Gases produced by the mixing of the reactants in the center will cause some of the indicators to change color. Record your results in Table 21.1.

a.

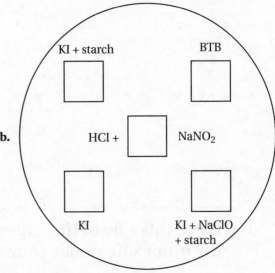

b.

3. Add a few drops of NaOH to each of the reaction mixtures. Then clean the small-scale reaction surface with a *damp* paper towel, and dry it. Clean the cups with a *dry* paper towel to absorb stray gases.

4. Repeat Steps 1 and 2 with the reactant mixtures shown in circles **c** and **d**.

c.

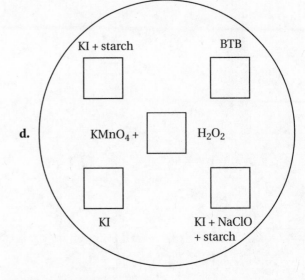

d.

5. Repeat Step 3. Then turn to page 149 and continue with the experiment.

Place this side of the Experimental Page facedown. Use the other side under your small-scale reaction surface.

6. Repeat Steps 1 and 2 with the reaction mixtures shown in circles **e** and **f**.

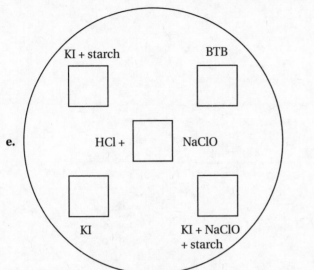

e.

KI + starch   BTB

HCl +   NaClO

KI   KI + NaClO + starch

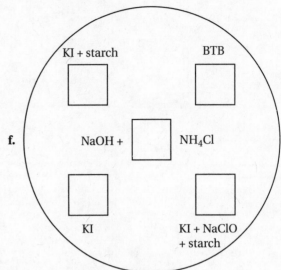

f.

KI + starch   BTB

NaOH + NH_4Cl

KI   KI + NaClO + starch

7. Add a few drops of NaOH to each reaction mixture. Then clean the small-scale reaction surface with a *damp* paper towel, and dry it. Clean the cups with a *dry* paper towel to absorb stray gases.

Place this side of the Experimental Page facedown. Use the other side under your small-scale reaction surface.

Name _____ Date _____ Class _____

EXPERIMENTAL DATA

Record your results in Table 21.1 or in a copy of the table in your notebook.

Table 21.1   Observations of Gases

Mixture	Bubbles?	BTB (Green)	KI + Starch (Colorless)	KI + NaClO + Starch (Black)	KI (Colorless)
a. $NaHSO_3$ + HCl	no	yellow	no change	colorless	no change
b. $NaNO_2$ + HCl	no	yellow	black	no change	yellow
c. $NaHCO_3$ + HCl	yes	no change	no change	no change	no change
d. H_2O_2 + $KMnO_4$	yes	no change	no change	no change	no change
e. NaClO + HCl	yes	yellow	black	no change	yellow
f. NH_4Cl + NaOH	no	blue	no change	no change	no change

CLEANING UP

Avoid contamination by cleaning up in a way that protects you and your environment. Carefully clean the plastic cups by wiping them with a dry paper towel. Clean the small-scale reaction surface by absorbing the contents onto a paper towel, rinse the small-scale reaction surface with a damp paper towel, and dry it. Dispose of the paper towels in the waste bin. Wash your hands thoroughly with soap and water.

QUESTIONS FOR ANALYSIS

Use your experimental data and what you learned in this experiment to answer the following questions.

1. Describe an observed change or changes that could be used to identify each gas produced.

   Gas a turns I_2 reagent colorless. Gas b does not bubble and turns

   KI + starch black. No color change with any indicator solution. The reaction mixture

   ($KMnO_4$) changes from purple to colorless as gas d is formed. Gas e forms bubbles

   and turns KI + starch black. Gas f turns BTB blue.

2. Gas **d** was oxygen. What evidence from your procedure might have led you to identify this gas as oxygen or nitrogen?

   Air is composed of mostly nitrogen and oxygen. The indicators didn't change

   in air, so they shouldn't change in the presence of nitrogen or oxygen.

3. Given the word equations below, write and balance chemical equations to describe the formation of each gas produced in the experiment.

a. Sodium hydrogen sulfite reacts with hydrochloric acid to produce sulfur dioxide gas, water, and sodium chloride.

$NaHSO_3 + HCl \rightarrow SO_2(g) + H_2O + NaCl.$

b. Sodium nitrite reacts with hydrochloric acid to produce nitrogen monoxide gas, water, sodium chloride, and sodium nitrate.

$3NaNO_2 + 2HCl \rightarrow 2NO(g) + H_2O + 2NaCl + NaNO_3.$

Nitrogen monoxide gas reacts with oxygen gas in the air to produce nitrogen dioxide gas.

$2NO(g) + O_2(g) \rightarrow 2NO_2(g).$

c. Sodium hydrogen carbonate reacts with hydrochloric acid to produce carbon dioxide gas, water, and sodium chloride.

$HCl + NaHCO_3 \rightarrow CO_2(g) + H_2O + NaCl.$

d. Hydrogen peroxide reacts with permanganate ion and hydrogen ion to produce oxygen gas, manganese(II) ion, and water.

$5H_2O_2 + 2MnO_4^- + 6H^+ \rightarrow 5O_2(g) + 2Mn^{2+} + 8H_2O.$

e. Chlorine gas, water, and sodium chloride are produced when hydrochloric acid is added to sodium hypochlorite, NaClO.

$NaClO + 2HCl \rightarrow Cl_2(g) + NaCl + H_2O.$

f. Sodium hydroxide reacts with ammonium chloride to produce ammonia gas, water, and sodium chloride.

$NH_4Cl + NaOH \rightarrow NH_3(g) + H_2O + NaCl.$

4. Given the word equations below, write and balance chemical equations to describe each reaction of a gas with an indicator or the water in an indicator solution. In each case describe the change in the indicator. The letter of each word equation corresponds to a letter on the Experimental Pages.

a. Sulfur dioxide gas reacts with water in the BTB indicator to produce sulfurous acid. (**Hint:** The formula for sulfurous acid has one fewer oxygen atom than the formula for sulfuric acid.)

$SO_2(g) + H_2O \rightarrow H_2SO_3.$ The sulfurous acid turns BTB yellow.

Sulfur dioxide gas reacts with iodine and water to form iodide ion, sulfate ion, and hydrogen ion.

$2H_2O + SO_2(g) + I_2 \rightarrow SO_4^{2-} + 2I^- + 4H^+.$ As I_2 reacts, the black color fades.

b. Nitrogen dioxide gas reacts with water in the BTB indicator to produce nitric acid and nitrous acid.

$2NO_2(g) + H_2O \rightarrow HNO_2 + HNO_3.$ The acids produced turn BTB yellow.

c. Chlorine gas reacts with iodide ion to form iodine and chloride ion.

$Cl_2(g) + 2I^- \rightarrow I_2 + 2Cl^-$. As I_2 forms, its yellow color in aqueous solution

becomes apparent, and the starch + KI turns black.

Chlorine gas reacts with water in the BTB solution to form hydrochloric acid and hypochlorous acid.

$Cl_2(g) + H_2O \rightarrow HCl + HClO$. The acids produced turn BTB yellow.

d. Ammonia gas reacts with water in the BTB solution to produce hydroxide ion and ammonium ion.

$NH_3(g) + HOH \rightarrow NH_4^+ + OH^-$. The hydroxide ions turn BTB blue.

NOW IT'S YOUR TURN!

1. Obtain six unknown solutions from your teacher and apply the technique you used in this experiment to identify the solutions and the gases they produce when mixed. Make a table similar to Table 21.1 to record which solutions you mixed and what you observed. Then identify the solutions and gases produced.

Students should look for distinguishing changes in the indicators as described in

Question 1 in the Questions for Analyses section.

2. Acids such as ethanoic acid, CH_3COOH, and hydrochloric acid, HCl, are volatile. That is, they readily evaporate from solution. Design a way of detecting aqueous solutions of these acids. After you have your teacher's approval, do the experiment. Can your method distinguish these acids from sulfuric and nitric acids? Can it distinguish these acids from one another?

Place one drop of acid and one drop of BTB next to each other under a cup.

Watch the green BTB turn yellow after time. H_2SO_4 and HNO_3 will not

produce a sufficient quantity of gas to produce a change in the indicators. HCl

will change universal indicator to a much deeper red color than will ethanoic acid.

Chapter 15 • *Water and Aqueous Systems*   **SMALL-SCALE EXPERIMENT**

22 REACTIONS OF AQUEOUS IONIC COMPOUNDS

Small-Scale Experiment for text Section 15.2

OBJECTIVES

- **Observe** a number of chemical reactions by mixing solutions of ionic compounds.
- **Classify** data efficiently, using a matrix.
- **Identify** unknown chemicals by using information in the data matrix.

INTRODUCTION

Science progresses through the process of experimentation: *asking questions, finding ways to answer them, and generating more questions.* As a student of chemistry, you make many observations in the process of designing and carrying out experiments. You organize your observations in tables so that they are clearly available for answering questions and solving problems. Then you can compare your well-organized data in order to answer questions and solve problems. You consider all the data so you can make correlations that would not be possible if each observation was considered alone. Your correlations may raise more questions than they answer. But these new questions promote further experimentation.

All of the steps in the process of experimentation depend on careful observations. The prerequisite to answering any chemical question or to solving any chemical problem is the accumulation of sufficient, accurate, and well-organized observations.

PURPOSE

In this experiment, you will solve a chemical logic problem. You will mix 13 solutions of known ionic compounds in all possible binary (two at a time) combinations. You will record your observations in such a way that comparisons of the chemical behavior of the various mixtures can be made easily. You will study the similarities and differences between the reactions of ionic compounds, and you will use your record of observations to determine the identity of various unknown solutions. In Small-Scale Experiment 23, you will use the data obtained in this experiment to identify eight unknown solutions chosen at random from the original 13.

SAFETY 🦺 🧤 ☠️ 🧪 ⚗️

- Wear your safety goggles, an apron, and gloves when working with corrosive chemicals.
- Use full small-scale pipets only for the controlled delivery of liquids.
- Don't chew gum, drink, or eat in the laboratory. Never taste a chemical in the laboratory.
- Avoid inhaling substances that can irritate your respiratory system.

MATERIALS

Small-scale pipets of the following solutions:

lead(II) nitrate (Pb(NO$_3$)$_2$)	sodium hydroxide (NaOH)
ammonia (NH$_3$)	sulfuric acid (H$_2$SO$_4$)
iron(III) chloride (FeCl$_3$)	copper(II) sulfate (CuSO$_4$)
sodium carbonate (Na$_2$CO$_3$)	potassium iodide (KI)
nitric acid (HNO$_3$)	sodium phosphate (Na$_3$PO$_4$)
calcium chloride (CaCl$_2$)	hydrochloric acid (HCl)
silver nitrate (AgNO$_3$)	

EQUIPMENT

small-scale reaction surface
empty pipet for stirring

EXPERIMENTAL PAGE

Place one drop of $Pb(NO_3)_2$ on each **X** in the first column. Add one drop of each of the other solutions to the $Pb(NO_3)_2$. Stir each mixture by blowing air with a clean, empty pipet. Repeat the procedure for each column. Record your results in Table 22.1.

	$Pb(NO_3)_2$	HCl	Na_3PO_4	KI	$CuSO_4$	H_2SO_4	NaOH	$AgNO_3$	$CaCl_2$	HNO_3	Na_2CO_3	$FeCl_3$	
NH_3	X	X	X	X	X	X	X	X	X	X	X	X	NH_3
$FeCl_3$	X	X	X	X	X	X	X	X	X	X	X		$FeCl_3$
Na_2CO_3	X	X	X	X	X	X	X	X	X	X			Na_2CO_3
HNO_3	X	X	X	X	X	X	X	X	X				HNO_3
$CaCl_2$	X	X	X	X	X	X	X	X					$CaCl_2$
$AgNO_3$	X	X	X	X	X	X	X						$AgNO_3$
NaOH	X	X	X	X	X	X							NaOH
H_2SO_4	X	X	X	X	X								H_2SO_4
$CuSO_4$	X	X	X	X									$CuSO_4$
KI	X	X	X										KI
Na_3PO_4	X	X											Na_3PO_4
HCl	X												HCl
	$Pb(NO_3)_2$												

EXPERIMENTAL DATA

Record your results in Table 22.1 or in a copy of the table in your notebook.

Table 22.1 Reactions of Aqueous Ionic Compounds

	Pb(NO$_3$)$_2$	HCl	Na$_3$PO$_4$	KI	CuSO$_4$	H$_2$SO$_4$	NaOH	AgNO$_3$	CaCl$_2$	HNO$_3$	Na$_2$CO$_3$	FeCl$_3$	
NH$_3$	white ppt	NVR	NVR	NVR	blue ppt	NVR	NVR	light white ppt	NVR	NVR	NVR	orange ppt	NH$_3$
FeCl$_3$	white ppt	NVR	orange ppt	amber soln	NVR	NVR	orange ppt	white ppt	NVR	NVR	orange ppt	FeCl$_3$	
Na$_2$CO$_3$	white ppt	bubbles	NVR	NVR	blue ppt	bubbles	NVR	tan ppt	white ppt	bubbles	Na$_2$CO$_3$		
HNO$_3$	NVR	NVR	NVR	NVR	NVR	NVR	NVR	NVR	NVR	HNO$_3$			
CaCl$_2$	white ppt	NVR	white ppt	NVR	NVR	slow white ppt	white ppt	white ppt	CaCl$_2$				
AgNO$_3$	NVR	white ppt	tan ppt	light green ppt	NVR	NVR	muddy brown ppt	AgNO$_3$					
NaOH	white ppt	NVR	NVR	NVR	blue ppt	NVR	NaOH						
H$_2$SO$_4$	white ppt	NVR	NVR	NVR	NVR	H$_2$SO$_4$							
CuSO$_4$	white ppt	NVR	blue ppt	brown ppt	CuSO$_4$								
KI	bright yellow ppt	NVR	NVR	KI									
Na$_3$PO$_4$	white ppt	NVR	Na$_3$PO$_4$										
HCl	white ppt	HCl											
Pb(NO$_3$)$_2$													

CLEANING UP

Avoid contamination by cleaning up in a way that protects you and your environment. Carefully clean the small-scale reaction surface by absorbing the contents onto a paper towel. Rinse the small-scale reaction surface with a damp paper towel and dry it. Dispose of the paper towels in the waste bin. Wash your hands thoroughly with soap and water.

QUESTIONS FOR ANALYSES

Use what you learned in this experiment to answer the following questions.

1. Write and balance chemical equations for each precipitation reaction you observed for lead(II) nitrate. For example, lead(II) nitrate ($Pb(NO_3)_2$), and potassium iodide (KI), react to form a very bright yellow precipitate:

$$Pb(NO_3)_2 + 2KI \rightarrow PbI_2(s) + 2KNO_3$$

(**Hint:** Use NH_4OH for NH_3. See Question 2.)

$Pb(NO_3)_2 + 2NH_4OH \rightarrow Pb(OH)_2(s) + 2NH_4NO_3$ $\qquad$ $Pb(NO_3)_2 + H_2SO_4 \rightarrow PbSO_4(s) + 2HNO_3$

$3Pb(NO_3)_2 + 2FeCl_3 \rightarrow 3PbCl_2(s) + 2Fe(NO_3)_3$ $\qquad$ $Pb(NO_3)_2 + CuSO_4 \rightarrow PbSO_4(s) + Cu(NO_3)_2$

$Pb(NO_3)_2 + Na_2CO_3 \rightarrow PbCO_3(s) + 2NaNO_3$ $\qquad$ $3Pb(NO_3)_2 + 2Na_3PO_4 \rightarrow Pb_3(PO_4)_2(s) + 6NaNO_3$

$Pb(NO_3)_2 + CaCl_2 \rightarrow PbCl_2(s) + Ca(NO_3)_2$ $\qquad$ $Pb(NO_3)_2 + 2HCl \rightarrow PbCl_2(s) + 2HNO_3$

$Pb(NO_3)_2 + 2NaOH \rightarrow Pb(OH)_2(s) + 2NaNO_3$

2. You may have noticed that some chemicals formed precipitates when mixed with ammonia (NH_3). This is because ammonia reacts with water to produce ammonium hydroxide, NH_4OH:

$$NH_3 + H_2O \rightarrow NH_4OH$$

To write the chemical equations for the precipitations with ammonia, you need to replace NH_3 with NH_4OH. For example,

$$Pb(NO_3)_2 + 2NH_4OH \rightarrow Pb(OH)_2(s) + 2NH_4NO_3$$

Write chemical equations for all the other precipitation reactions you observed with NH_3.

$CuSO_4 + 2NH_4OH \rightarrow Cu(OH)_2(s) + (NH_4)_2SO_4.$

$Pb(NO_3)_2 + 2NH_4OH \rightarrow Pb(OH)_2(s) + 2NH_4NO_3.$

$FeCl_3 + 3NH_4OH \rightarrow Fe(OH)_3(s) + 3NH_4Cl.$

$AgNO_3 + NH_4OH \rightarrow AgOH(s) + NH_4NO_3.$

3. Which reactions gave distinctive bubbles? What chemicals do all these reactions have in common? Write chemical equations to describe all the reactions that produced bubbles.

Na_2CO_3 produces bubbles with the three acids, HCl, HNO_3, and H_2SO_4.

Na_2CO_3 + 2HCl → 2NaCl + $CO_2(g)$ + H_2O.

Na_2CO_3 + $2HNO_3$ → $2NaNO_3$ + $CO_2(g)$ + H_2O.

Na_2CO_3 + H_2SO_4 → Na_2SO_4 + $CO_2(g)$ + H_2O.

4. Which reactions gave color changes but no precipitate?

KI + $FeCl_3$.

5. Which mixings could you have predicted in advance would not result in a reaction?

Any with a common cation or a common anion.

NOW IT'S YOUR TURN!

1. Investigate further the reaction of $CuSO_4$ with NH_3. Try one drop of NH_3 with several drops of $CuSO_4$. Then try one drop of $CuSO_4$ with several drops of NH_3. What is distinctive about this reaction?

Excess copper sulfate produces a light blue precipitate that dissolves in

excess ammonia to give a clear, dark blue solution.

2. Investigate further the reaction of $AgNO_3$ with NH_3. Try one drop of NH_3 with several drops of $AgNO_3$. Then try one drop of $AgNO_3$ with several drops of NH_3. What is distinctive about this reaction?

Excess silver nitrate produces a light white precipitate that dissolves in

excess ammonia.

3. Investigate further the reaction of $Pb(NO_3)_2$ with NaOH. Try one drop of NaOH with several drops of $Pb(NO_3)_2$. Then try one drop of $Pb(NO_3)_2$ with several drops of NaOH. What is distinctive about this reaction?

Excess lead nitrate produces a white precipitate that dissolves in excess

NaOH.

4. A very distinctive precipitate is formed when H_2SO_4 and $CaCl_2$ are mixed. Repeat the reaction between sulfuric acid (H_2SO_4) and calcium chloride ($CaCl_2$). What is so distinctive about this precipitate?

It takes 20 to 30 seconds of stirring for the precipitate to form.

5. Challenge a classmate. Hide the label and place one drop of either the top or bottom solution on your classmate's grid (below). Ask him or her to identify it by using just one drop of any of the 13 chemicals. Repeat for each space.

$AgNO_3$	$CuSO_4$	Na_2CO_3	$FeCl_3$	$NaOH$	HCl	H_2SO_4	HNO_3
X	X	X	X	X	X	X	X
$Pb(NO_3)_2$	$CaCl_2$	Na_3PO_4	KI	NH_3	H_2SO_4	HNO_3	HCl

6. Ask a third classmate to line up 12 separate drops of any unknown chemical on your small-scale reaction surface. You go first. Add any chemical to the first drop and guess what the unknown is. The second classmate adds any chemical to the second drop and makes a guess. It's your turn again. Continue until there is a winner. Play this game several times until you can identify the unknown in just a few drops.

7. Choose a chemical and place one drop in each of the 11 spaces on a classmate's grid (below). Challenge him or her to devise a way to uncover its identity in fewer drops than you used to identify his or her unknown.

1	2	3	4	5	6	7	8	9	10	11
X	X	X	X	X	X	X	X	X	X	X

Chapter 15 • *Water and Aqueous Systems*   **SMALL-SCALE EXPERIMENT**

23 IDENTIFICATION OF EIGHT UNKNOWN SOLUTIONS

Small-Scale Experiment for text Section 15.2

OBJECTIVE

• **Identify** eight unknown solutions, using known data and logical thinking.

INTRODUCTION

The art of logical thinking is essential to mastering chemistry. Although it is important to be familiar with many chemical facts so that you can utilize the language of chemistry effectively, it is even more important to be able to assimilate these facts and organize them in logical ways so they can be used to solve problems. The art of logical thinking is not difficult to acquire, but it does require practice. Try out your own ability on the following logic problem.

During a chemistry class, five pairs of students are working on five different experiments at a row of lab stations numbered 1–5 consecutively. From the information given below, can you tell what each student's experiment is, at which lab station he or she is working, and who his or her lab partner is?

Clues:

1. The halogens experiment and all the other experiments are performed by lab partners of the opposite sex. For example, Ann Ion's lab partner is a boy.

2. Milli Liter and Ben Zene work together.

3. Charles Law does not work at lab station #2.

4. Molly Cool and her partner work between station #3 and the station occupied by Barry Um.

5. Phyllis Pipet, building a spectroscope, is not at #4.

6. Milli Liter does not work next to Molly Cool.

7. Earl N. Meyer works at #4.

8. Ionic reactions are being carried out at #5.

9. Hal Ogen is building a small-scale balance.

10. Only one of the Um twins, Francie or Barry, works at station #1, doing an acid–base titration.

Answers:

Lab Station	Boy	Girl	Experiment
1	Barry Um	Ann Ion	Acid–Base Titration
2	Hal Ogen	Molly Cool	Small-Scale Balance
3	Charles Law	Phyllis Pipet	Spectroscope
4	Earl N. Meyer	Francie Um	Halogens
5	Ben Zene	Milli Liter	Ionic Reactions

Name _____ Date _____ Class _____

PURPOSE

In this experiment, you will mix eight unknown solutions two at a time just as you did in Small-Scale Experiment 22. The eight unknown solutions have been chosen at random from the original 13. You will compare your results with those you obtained in Small-Scale Experiment 22 and identify the eight unknown solutions through logical reasoning as you did in solving the above problem. A successful conclusion to this lab does not require a Ph.D. in chemistry. It does require good organization, clear logical thinking, and good data.

SAFETY 🦺 ☠️ 🧪 🫁

- Wear safety goggles, an apron, and gloves when working with corrosive chemicals.
- Use full small-scale pipets only for the controlled delivery of liquids.
- Don't chew gum, drink, or eat in the laboratory. Never taste a chemical in the laboratory.
- Avoid inhaling substances that can irritate your respiratory system.

MATERIALS

Small-scale pipets of the following solutions:

lead(II) nitrate ($Pb(NO_3)_2$)   sodium hydroxide (NaOH)
ammonia (NH_3)   sulfuric acid (H_2SO_4)
iron(III) chloride ($FeCl_3$)   copper(II) sulfate ($CuSO_4$)
sodium carbonate (Na_2CO_3)   potassium iodide (KI)
nitric acid (HNO_3)   sodium phosphate (Na_3PO_4)
calcium chloride ($CaCl_2$)   hydrochloric acid (HCl)
silver nitrate ($AgNO_3$)

Eight small-scale pipets of unknown solutions labeled with different numbers.

EQUIPMENT

small-scale reaction surface
empty pipet for stirring

EXPERIMENTAL PAGE

1. Obtain eight small-scale pipets labeled with numbers from your teacher. The eight pipets contain eight of the original 13 solutions from Small-Scale Experiment 22. Write the numbers of the unknowns along the horizontal in Table 23.1 and in reverse order along the vertical. Mix one drop of each solution on the indicated **X,** just as you did in the last experiment. Stir each mixture by blowing air with an empty pipet. Record your results in Table 23.1.

Unknown
numbers: ____ ____ ____ ____ ____ ____ ____

____ | X | X | X | X | X | X | X | ____

____ | X | X | X | X | X | X |

____ | X | X | X | X | X |

____ | X | X | X | X |

____ | X | X | X |

____ | X | X |

____ | X |

____

2. Compare your unknown reactions to those of the 13 solutions in Small-Scale Experiment 22, and see how many unknowns you can identify.

3. Devise a way to use the original 13 solutions to correctly identify your unknowns. To do this, you should mix each unknown with several knowns, one at a time.

Place this side of the Experimental Page facedown. Use the other side under your small-scale reaction surface.

EXPERIMENTAL DATA

Record your results in Tables 23.1 and 23.2 or in copies of the tables in your notebook.

Table 23.1   Eight Unknowns

Unknown
numbers: _____ _____ _____ _____ _____ _____ _____

_____ | X | X | X | X | X | X | X | _____

_____ | X | X | X | X | X | X | _____

_____ | X | X | X | X | X | _____

_____ | X | X | X | X | _____

_____ | X | X | X | _____

_____ | X | X | _____

_____ | X | _____

_____

Table 23.2   Numbers, Formulas, and Names of Eight Unknown Solutions

Number								
Formula								
Name								

CLEANING UP

Avoid contamination by cleaning up in a way that protects you and your environment. Carefully clean the small-scale reaction surface by absorbing the contents onto a paper towel. Rinse the small-scale reaction surface with a damp paper towel and dry it. Dispose of the paper towels in the waste bin. Wash your hands thoroughly with soap and water.

QUESTIONS FOR ANALYSES

Use what you learned in this experiment to answer the following questions.

1. What is the identity (name and formula) of each unknown you used in this experiment?

   _____

2. Describe the logical thought process by which you arrived at your conclusions.

   _____

NOW IT'S YOUR TURN!

1. Obtain another set of eight unknown solutions. Devise a way to correctly identify your unknowns *without using known solutions*. (**Hint:** Design an 8 × 8 grid similar to the one on the Experimental Page. Mix the unknowns with each other two at a time.) Compare your unknown reactions to the data you collected from the 13 solutions in the last experiment. This time you may not use your known solutions to identify the unknowns.

2. Report the results as you did before. Describe the logical thought process by which you arrived at your conclusions. Check your results with your teacher.

Chapter 15 • *Water and Aqueous Systems* **SMALL-SCALE EXPERIMENT**

24 ELECTROLYTES

Small-Scale Experiment for text Section 15.2

OBJECTIVES

- **Observe** and **record** the electrical conductivity of water solutions and solid compounds.
- **Classify** substances as strong electrolytes, weak electrolytes, or nonelectrolytes, using conductivity data.
- **Observe** the phenomena of *deliquescence* and *water of hydration*.

INTRODUCTION

Electrolytes are compounds that exist as dissolved ions in water solutions. A distinguishing macroscopic property of electrolyte solutions is that they conduct electricity. Molten electrolytes also conduct electricity. The submicroscopic interpretation is that in the molten state or in solution, ions are free to move. These charged particles carry the electrical current.

PURPOSE

In this experiment, you will investigate water solutions of chemicals by testing them for conductivity. You will then evaporate the water and test the remaining solids. You will interpret your results in terms of the submicroscopic behavior of atoms and molecules. Finally, you will test various solutions to determine their relative tendencies to conduct electricity, and again interpret your results in terms of atoms and molecules. You will classify solutions as *strong electrolytes*, those that readily conduct electricity; *weak electrolytes*, those that conduct electricity only weakly; and *nonelectrolytes*, those that do not conduct electricity.

A small-scale conductivity apparatus is shown in Figure 24.1. When the two leads are immersed in a drop of solution or in a solid that conducts electricity, the light emitting diode (LED) will glow.

Figure 24.1 *Conductivity apparatus*

SAFETY 🖾 🖾 🖾 🖾 🖾 🖾

- Wear safety goggles, an apron, and gloves when working with corrosive chemicals.
- Use full small-scale pipets only for the controlled delivery of liquids.
- Don't chew gum, drink, or eat in the laboratory. Never taste a chemical in the laboratory.
- Do not touch hot glassware or equipment.
- Avoid inhaling substances that can irritate your respiratory system.

MATERIALS

Small-scale pipets of the following solutions:

calcium chloride ($CaCl_2$)	zinc chloride ($ZnCl_2$)
sodium hydrogen sulfate ($NaHSO_4$)	sodium carbonate (Na_2CO_3)
sodium hydroxide (NaOH)	water
sodium phosphate (Na_3PO_4)	ethanol (CH_3CH_2OH)
sodium hydrogen carbonate ($NaHCO_3$)	2-propanol ($CH_3CHOHCH_3$)
iron(III) chloride ($FeCl_3$)	methanol (CH_3OH)
copper(II) sulfate ($CuSO_4$)	hydrogen peroxide (H_2O_2)
aluminum chloride ($AlCl_3$)	

Solids:

sodium chloride (NaCl)	calcium chloride ($CaCl_2$)
potassium chloride (KCl)	sodium carbonate (Na_2CO_3)
potassium iodide (KI)	sucrose ($C_{12}H_{22}O_{11}$)

EQUIPMENT

glass slide
conductivity apparatus
hot plate
spatulas
small-scale reaction surface

Name _____ Date _____ Class _____

EXPERIMENTAL PAGE

Part A. Conductivity of Ionic Compounds

1. Place one drop of each indicated chemical solution on a glass slide in the arrangement shown, and test each drop for conductivity with the conductivity apparatus. Be sure to *clean and dry* the conductivity leads after each test.

$CaCl_2$	$NaHSO_4$	$NaOH$	Na_3PO_4	$NaHCO_3$
x	x	x	x	x
x	x	x	x	x
$FeCl_3$	$CuSO_4$	$AlCl_3$	$ZnCl_2$	Na_2CO_3

2. Now evaporate water from the droplets by putting the glass slide on a hot plate. Test for conductivity again. **CAUTION:** *The glass will be hot. Handle with tongs or a plastic spatula.*

3. Allow the slide to cool and observe any changes over time. Meanwhile, go on to Part B.

Part B. Conductivity of Solids

4. Place one grain of each solid (s) in the indicated place and test each for conductivity. Then add one drop of water to each and test the "wet" mixture for conductivity.

$NaCl(s)$	$KCl(s)$	$KI(s)$	$CaCl_2(s)$	$Na_2CO_3(s)$	$C_{12}H_{22}O_{11}(s)$
salt	"lite" salt	in iodized salt	ice-melter	washing soda	table sugar

Part C. Conductivity of Liquids

5. Place one drop of each liquid (l) in the indicated place and test each for conductivity. Then add one drop of water and test the "wet" mixture for conductivity.

$H_2O(l)$	$CH_3CH_2OH(l)$	$CH_3CHOHCH_3(l)$	$CH_3OH(l)$	$H_2O_2(l)$
water	ethanol grain alcohol	2-propanol rubbing alcohol	methanol wood alcohol	hydrogen peroxide a disinfectant

Place this side of the Experimental Page facedown. Use the other side under your small-scale reaction surface.

Name _____ Date _____ Class _____

EXPERIMENTAL DATA

Record your results in Tables 24.1, 24.2, and 24.3. or in copies of the tables in your notebook.

Table 24.1 Conductivity of Ionic Compounds

	In Solution	After Water Evaporates			In Solution	After Water Evaporates
$CaCl_2$	yes	no		$FeCl_3$	yes	no
$NaHSO_4$	yes	no		$CuSO_4$	yes	no
$NaOH$	yes	no		$AlCl_3$	yes	no
Na_3PO_4	yes	no		$ZnCl_2$	yes	no
$NaHCO_3$	yes	no		Na_2CO_3	yes	no

Which of the solutions seemed to be slow to evaporate? Which of the compounds absorbed waer upon standing in air?

NaOH, NaHSO₄, AlCl₃, ZnCl₂.

Table 24.2 Conductivity of Solids

	$NaCl(s)$	$KCl(s)$	$KI(s)$	$CaCl_2(s)$	$Na_2CO_3(s)$	$C_{12}H_{22}O_{11}(s)$
Dry	no	no	no	no	no	no
Wet	yes	yes	yes	yes	yes	no

Table 24.3 Conductivity of Liquids

	$H_2O(l)$	$CH_3CH_2OH(l)$	$CH_3CHOHCH_3(l)$	$CH_3OH(l)$	$H_2O_2(l)$
Alone	no	no	no	no	no
Water added	no	no	no	no	no

CLEANING UP

Avoid contamination by cleaning up in a way that protects you and your environment. Carefully clean the small-scale reaction surface by absorbing the contents onto a paper towel. Rinse the small-scale reaction surface with a damp paper towel and dry it. Dispose of the paper towels in the waste bin. Clean the glass slide by rinsing it with water and drying it with a paper towel. Wash your hands thoroughly with soap and water.

QUESTIONS FOR ANALYSES

Use what you learned in this experiment to answer the following questions.

1. **a.** Do any of the solids in any part of this experiment conduct electricity?
   b. What must be added before a solid will conduct electricity?
   c. Does this work every time? Give an example.

   a. No   b. Water   c. No. Table sugar ($C_{12}H_{22}O_{11}$) does not conduct

   when wet.

2. A substance exhibits *deliquescence* when it absorbs enough water from the air to completely dissolve. Which solutions in Part A are deliquescent? (**Hint:** They seemed sluggish in evaporating or became wet upon standing in air.)

   NaOH, NaHSO$_4$, AlCl$_3$, ZnCl$_2$.

3. Water molecules that are fixed in the lattice of an ionic compound when it is in the solid state are called *water of hydration*. Water of hydration can be driven off by strong heating, often with a dramatic change in color. Which solids in Part A, Step 2, contain water of hydration?

   CuSO$_4$.

4. You can picture solid sodium chloride as a regular ordered arrangement of atoms called an ionic lattice (Figure 24.2). Solid KCl and KI are similar to NaCl. Draw them and explain the result of the conductivity test in terms of your drawing.

Figure 24.2 *Ionic lattice of NaCl*

The ionic solids do not conduct because their ions are locked in fixed

positions in the ionic lattice of the solid.

5. You know that solutions that conduct electricity do so because they contain ions that are free to move about in solution. For example, a solution of aqueous sodium chloride can be pictured as in Figure 24.3. On a separate sheet of paper, draw pictures to represent the solutions of KI and KCl. Explain the conductivity test in terms of your pictures.

Figure 24.3 *Drop of aqueous NaCl*

The solution process causes the ionic lattice to break apart, freeing the
_____

ions to move and conduct electricity.
_____

6. Which of the liquids in Part C conduct electricity? Which conduct electricity when water is added?

None conduct, with or without water.
_____

7. a. Make a list of electrolytes and another list of nonelectrolytes.

Electrolytes					Nonelectrolytes	
$CaCl_2$	$FeCl_3$	Na_3PO_4	$AlCl_3$	KI	H_2O	CH_3CH_2OH
$NaHSO_4$	$CuSO_4$	$NaHCO_3$	Na_2CO_3		$CH_3CHOHCH_3$	CH_3OH
NaOH	$ZnCl_2$	NaCl	KCl		H_2O_2	$C_{12}H_{22}O_{11}$

b. Pure water is a nonelectrolyte. Predict what will happen if you test tap water for conductivity.

The light will glow dimly. Tap water is a weak electrolyte because it
_____

contains ions from dissolved minerals.
_____

8. Study the chemical formulas of the electrolytes and nonelectrolytes. What chemical species do all electrolytes contain? How are the nonelectrolytes different? Draw a conclusion based on your answers to these questions.

Ions. Nonelectrolytes do not contain ions. Aqueous solutions of ionic compounds
_____

are electrolytes. Covalent compounds generally are not electrolytes.
_____

9. You know that when an ionic solid dissolves in water, water molecules attract the ions, causing them to come apart or dissociate. The resulting dissolved ions are electrically charged particles that allow the solution to conduct electricity. Chemical equations that represent this phenomenon are written like this:

$$NaCl(s) \rightarrow Na^+(aq) + Cl^-(aq) \text{ or } CaCl_2(s) \rightarrow Ca^{2+}(aq) + 2Cl^-(aq)$$

Write a similar chemical equation for each electrolyte you observed in this experiment.

$ZnCl_2(s) \rightarrow Zn^{2+}(aq) + 2Cl^-(aq)$	$KCl(s) \rightarrow K^+(aq) + Cl^-(aq)$
$CuSO_4(s) \rightarrow Cu^{2+}(aq) + SO_4^{2-}(aq)$	$KI(s) \rightarrow K^+(aq) + I^-(aq)$
$FeCl_3(s) \rightarrow Fe^{3+}(aq) + 3Cl^-(aq)$	$Na_3PO_4(s) \rightarrow 3Na^+(aq) + PO_4^{3-}(aq)$
$NaHSO_4(s) \rightarrow Na^+(aq) + HSO_4^-(aq)$	$NaOH(s) \rightarrow Na^+(aq) + OH^-(aq)$
$NaHCO_3(s) \rightarrow Na^+(aq) + HCO_3^-(aq)$	$AlCl_3(s) \rightarrow Al^{3+}(aq) + 3Cl^-(aq)$
$Na_2CO_3(s) \rightarrow 2Na^+(aq) + CO_3^{2-}(aq)$	

NOW IT'S YOUR TURN!

1. Using a soda straw, obtain small samples of these household products: a solid toilet-bowl cleaner, a small piece of seltzer tablet, baking powder (not soda!). Add a drop of water to each. What do you observe? Test for conductivity. Explain why these substances do not react until water is added.

They all fizz. All solutions conduct. They react only when water breaks the

ionic lattices, thereby freeing the ions.

2. Test these aqueous solutions for conductivity:

One drop each:	One drop each:	One drop each:	One drop each:
HCl	NaOH	HNO_3	KOH
CH_3COOH	NH_3	H_3PO_4	H_2SO_4

Solutions that cause the LED to glow brightly are called *strong electrolytes*. Those that make it glow less brightly are called *weak electrolytes*. Make a list of the strong and weak electrolytes, and propose an explanation for the difference in the brightness of the LED.

Strong: HCl, HNO_3, H_2SO_4, NaOH, KOH. Weak: CH_3COOH, NH_3, H_3PO_4.

Weak electrolytes provide fewer ions in solution, so they do not conduct

electricity as well as strong electrolytes.

25 | HARD AND SOFT WATER

Small-Scale Experiment for text Section 15.3

OBJECTIVES

- **Measure** the total hardness of water in various water samples.
- **Apply** the ion exchange process to "soften" hard water.

INTRODUCTION

Hard water contains dissolved salts, especially those of calcium, magnesium, and iron. Most of the dissolved calcium ions in the waters of rivers, lakes, and streams originate from limestone, which is principally calcium carbonate ($CaCO_3$). Limestone is dissolved by rainwater or by water contaminated by mining and industrial wastes containing hydrochloric and sulfuric acids.

$$CaCO_3(s) + H^+(aq) \rightarrow Ca^{2+}(aq) + HCO_3^-(aq)$$

The reaction of water with atmospheric carbon dioxide makes precipitation slightly acidic. Acidic precipitation can also result from the reaction of atmospheric water with industrial pollutants such as sulfur dioxide and nitrogen dioxide.

$$H_2O(l) + CO_2(g) \rightarrow H_2CO_3(aq)$$
$$H_2O(l) + SO_2(g) \rightarrow H_2SO_3(aq)$$
$$H_2O(l) + 2NO_2(g) \rightarrow HNO_2(aq) + HNO_3(aq)$$

The location of limestone deposits varies throughout the country, as do the amounts of industrial acids contaminating rivers and contributing to the acidity of precipitation. Thus, the amount of dissolved calcium ion varies from place to place and so does the resultant hardness of water.

Calcium ions, while nontoxic, present a number of household and industrial problems. For example, calcium ion reacts with the ingredients of many soaps and shampoos to form an insoluble scum that you can observe as a "bathtub ring." The formation of this precipitate causes soap to lose some of its effectiveness.

$$Ca^{2+}(aq) + 2CH_3(CH_2)_{16}COONa(aq) \rightarrow 2Na^+(aq) + (CH_3(CH_2)_{16}COO)_2Ca(s)$$

sodium stearate   calcium stearate
a typical soap   an insoluble scum

Hard water also accounts for the buildup of boiler scale on the insides of teapots, water heaters, and industrial boilers. The scale consists mainly of calcium carbonate that has precipitated from hard water upon heating:

$$Ca(HCO_3)_2(aq) + heat \rightarrow CaCO_3(s) + CO_2(g) + H_2O$$

Calcium carbonate scale must be removed periodically because it reduces heating efficiency by acting as an insulator. Calcium carbonate also promotes corrosion and blocks pipes.

PURPOSE

In this experiment, you will measure the total amount of calcium and magnesium ions in various water samples from around the country and/or from your area. You will add a particular kind of solution, called a buffer, to each water sample, which will maintain the pH at about 10.5. You will then titrate each sample with ethylenediamine tetraacetic acid, EDTA, until the indicator Ero-T turns from wine red to sky blue at the end point.

You will report the results as parts per million (ppm) of calcium carbonate, $CaCO_3$, even though some of the hardness may be due to the presence of magnesium ions. A part per million is a milligram of calcium carbonate per liter of water sample. The higher the parts per million of $CaCO_3$, the more calcium ions are in the water, and the harder the water is.

SAFETY

- Wear safety goggles, an apron, and gloves when working with corrosive chemicals.
- Use full small-scale pipets only for the controlled delivery of liquids.
- Don't chew gum, drink, or eat in the laboratory. Never taste a chemical in the laboratory.
- Avoid inhaling substances that can irritate your respiratory system.

MATERIALS

Small-scale pipets of the following solutions:
various water samples (labeled)
deionized water
ammonia/ammonium chloride
  (buffer)

Solids: eriochrome black T indicator
  (Ero-T)
ethylenediamine tetraacetic acid
  (EDTA)

EQUIPMENT

small-scale balance with extra pan, or other balance

EXPERIMENTAL PROCEDURE

Determine the hardness of each water sample by the following method:

1. Obtain the mass of about 2500 mg of a water sample in a plastic cup.

   a. Place a 2500-mg weight in your small-scale balance pan, and adjust the balance beam and counterweight until the pointer indicates the zero point.

   b. Remove the weight and drop in enough water sample to return the pointer to the zero point.

2. Add 15 drops of buffer.

3. Add Ero-T indicator until the color is medium to dark wine red.

4. Mass or tare a full pipet of EDTA.

   a. Place a full pipet in a second small-scale balance pan.

   b. Adjust the small-scale balance to read zero.

5. Titrate the water sample with EDTA until the last tinges of red turn blue.

6. Find the mass of EDTA that was lost.

   a. Return the used EDTA pipet to the small-scale balance.

   b. Add weights until the pointer again reads zero.

7. Repeat the above steps for each of the other water samples including tap water and distilled water. Compare the hardness of water in the various other samples available in your lab.

8. Calculate the parts per million (ppm) of $CaCO_3$ in the water sample. (1 ppm = 1 mg $CaCO_3$/L of water.) Record your results in Table 25.1. To do the calculation, you will need the following pieces of information:

   a. The mass loss of EDTA used in the titration in mg.

   b. The mass of the water sample in mg.

   c. The density of EDTA solution = 1000 mg/1 mL.

   d. The density of water = 1000 mg/1 mL.

   e. 1000 mL = 1 L or 1000 mL/1 L.

   f. The concentration of EDTA solution = 0.002 mmol/mL.

   g. The overall stoichiometry of the reaction = 1 mmol $CaCO_3$/1 mmol EDTA.

   h. The molar mass of $CaCO_3$ = 100 mg/mmol.

$$\text{ppm } CaCO_3 = \text{mg } CaCO_3/\text{L } H_2O = \frac{a}{b} \times \frac{d}{c} \times e \times f \times g \times h$$

To be sure you understand the calculation, substitute each quantity (number and units) into the equation and cancel the units. For subsequent calculations, simplify the equation by combining terms that are always constant.

The indicator is red in the presence of Mg^{2+}. EDTA reacts with both Ca^{2+} and Mg^{2+}. The indicator turns blue when all of the Mg^{2+} and Ca^{2+} are combined with EDTA.

Equations:

$$Mg^{2+} + 2In^- = MgIn_2$$
$$\text{blue} \qquad\qquad \text{red}$$

$$EDTA^{2-} + Ca^{2+} \rightarrow CaEDTA$$
$$EDTA^{2-} + Mg^{2+} \rightarrow MgEDTA$$

Name _____ Date _____ Class _____

EXPERIMENTAL DATA

Record your results in Table 25.1 or in a copy of the table in your notebook.

Table 25.1   Titration Data for Water Samples

Water Sample	Mass of Sample (mg)	Mass Loss of EDTA (mg)	ppm CaCO$_3$
	2550	600	47
	2550	1400	110
	2550	2420	190
	2550	395	31
	2550	2805	220

CLEANING UP

Avoid contamination by cleaning up in a way that protects you and your environment. Carefully clean the plastic balance cup by rinsing the contents down the drain. Rinse the cup and dry it with a paper towel. Dispose of the paper towels in the waste bin. Wash your hands thoroughly with soap and water.

QUESTIONS FOR ANALYSES

Use what you learned in this experiment to answer the following questions.

1. Which sample is the hardest water you titrated? Which is the softest? What does it mean for water to be "hard" or "soft"?

   The hardest water is the one with the highest ppm of CaCO$_3$. The

   softest water is the one with the lowest ppm CaCO$_3$. Hard water contains

   comparatively more calcium ions.

2. What is a part per million?

   One milligram per liter.

3. In the titration, why did you not need to know the mass of the full EDTA pipet?

   Only the amount of EDTA needs to be known.

4. Write a balanced equation for the titration of calcium ion with EDTA.

   EDTA^{2-} + Ca^{2+} → CaEDTA.

5. EDTA is commonly used as an additive in foods. The function of the EDTA is to tie up metal cations that may cause clouding of the product. Read some labels at home and find some foods that contain EDTA in some form. List them here.

Answers will vary. Some bottled salad dressings and carbonated soft drinks contain EDTA.

NOW IT'S YOUR TURN!

1. When water is passed through an ion exchange buret, it becomes acidic because Ca^+ ions are exchanged for H^+ ions. The equation for the ion exchange reaction follows:

$$Ca^{2+} + H^+H^+ \rightarrow Ca^{2+} + 2H^+$$

R   R   R = ion exchange "resin"

This principle is used in a practical everyday setting in a home water softener.

a. Recharge an acid resin ion exchanger with a small amount of HCl.

b. Drain it thoroughly and rinse it twice with deionized water. Expel as much of the rinse water as possible.

c. Draw a few drops of hard water into the exchanger and shake gently for 15 seconds. Add five drops of this water to one drop of BTB and record the color. What color does each water sample that was treated in the ion exchanger turn BTB? What ions are present in these samples?

Yellow. Hydrogen ions.

d. Expel five more drops from the exchanger, shake in a few grains of Ero-T indicator, and add a few drops of buffer. Record the color.

e. Repeat for the other water samples.
What color does each water sample that was treated with the ion exchanger turn Ero-T? What does this tell you about the presence of calcium ion? Explain.

All turn blue. There is no calcium ion present. The calcium ion was

replaced by the hydrogen ion in the ion exchanger.

26 SOLUBILITY RULES

Small-Scale Experiment for text Section 16.1

OBJECTIVES

- **Observe** and **record** chemical changes that form precipitates.
- **Derive** general solubility rules from experimental data.
- **Describe** precipitation reactions by writing net ionic equations.

INTRODUCTION

In the study of chemical reactions, it is helpful to know when to expect a precipitate to form. A *soluble* compound will dissolve readily in water and, therefore, will *not* form a precipitate. An *insoluble* compound will not dissolve readily in water and, therefore, *will* form a precipitate.

How do you know which ionic compounds form precipitates and which do not? To find out, you can make a large number of mixings involving many different cations and anions. By observing the results and correlating them in a logical fashion, you can formulate some general solubility rules.

These rules can be used to describe the behavior of ionic compounds in solution and determine which combinations of compounds will form precipitates. For example, if a sodium ion is used as a probe and a large number of observations indicate that no precipitates containing the sodium ion are formed in aqueous solution, one conclusion might be: "All sodium salts are soluble in water. They do not form precipitates." In fact, a large number of such observations have been made, and it is well known that sodium salts are water-soluble. There are no common exceptions to this rule.

PURPOSE

In this experiment, you will mix a number of cation solutions and anion solutions two by two. Each anion solution will be used as a probe to determine which cations form precipitates with that anion. Using your data, you can derive some general solubility guidelines or rules.

Careful selection of compounds to represent cations and anions is important. For example, the solutions to represent anions are chosen to be compounds of sodium because we know that all sodium compounds are soluble in water, so any precipitate we see will be typical of the anion. Sodium ion (Na^+) will always be a "spectator ion," that is, it will not take part in a precipitation chemical reaction.

Keep in mind that you need not perform mixings between solutions having a common ion. For example, it should be obvious that $CuSO_4$ will not react with Na_2SO_4 because both compounds contain the sulfate ion. Thus, with a little planning, you can avoid any unnecessary mixings.

Name _____ Date _____ Class _____

SAFETY

- Wear safety goggles, an apron, and gloves when working with corrosive chemicals.
- Use full small-scale pipets only for the controlled delivery of liquids.
- Don't chew gum, drink, or eat in the laboratory. Never taste a chemical in the laboratory.

MATERIALS

Small-scale pipets containing solutions representing cations:

aluminum chloride ($AlCl_3$)   lead(II) nitrate ($Pb(NO_3)_2$)

ammonium chloride (NH_4Cl)   magnesium sulfate ($MgSO_4$)

calcium chloride ($CaCl_2$)   potassium iodide (KI)

copper(II) sulfate ($CuSO_4$)   silver nitrate ($AgNO_3$)

sodium chloride (NaCl)   zinc chloride ($ZnCl_2$)

iron(III) chloride ($FeCl_3$)

Small-scale pipets containing solutions representing anions:

sodium carbonate (Na_2CO_3)   sodium nitrate ($NaNO_3$)

sodium chloride (NaCl)   sodium phosphate (Na_3PO_4)

sodium hydroxide (NaOH)   sodium sulfate (Na_2SO_4)

EQUIPMENT

small-scale reaction surface

empty pipet for stirring

Name _____ Date _____ Class _____

EXPERIMENTAL PAGE

Mix one drop of each. Stir by gently blowing air through a clean, dry pipet.

	Na$_2$CO$_3$ (CO$_3^{2-}$)	NaCl (Cl$^-$)	NaOH (OH$^-$)	NaNO$_3$ (NO$_3^-$)	Na$_3$PO$_4$ (PO$_4^{3-}$)	Na$_2$SO$_4$ (SO$_4^{2-}$)
Anions						
Cations						
AlCl$_3$ (Al^{3+})	X	X	X	X	X	X
NH$_4$Cl (NH$_4^+$)	X	X	X	X	X	X
CaCl$_2$ (Ca^{2+})	X	X	X	X	X	X
CuSO$_4$ (Cu^{2+})	X	X	X	X	X	X
NaCl (Na$^+$)	X	X	X	X	X	X
FeCl$_3$ (Fe^{3+})	X	X	X	X	X	X
Pb(NO$_3$)$_2$ (Pb^{2+})	X	X	X	X	X	X
MgSO$_4$ (Mg^{2+})	X	X	X	X	X	X
KI (K$^+$)	X	X	X	X	X	X
AgNO$_3$ (Ag$^+$)	X	X	X	X	X	X
ZnCl$_2$ (Zn^{2+})	X	X	X	X	X	X

Place this side of the Experimental Page facedown. Use
the other side under your small-scale reaction surface.

EXPERIMENTAL DATA

Record your results in Table 26.1 or in a copy of the table in your notebook.

Table 26.1   Anion-Cation Mixings

Anions Cations	Na_2CO_3 (CO_3^{2-})	$NaCl$ (Cl^-)	$NaOH$ (OH^-)	$NaNO_3$ (NO_3^-)	Na_3PO_4 (PO_4^{3-})	Na_2SO_4 (SO_4^{2-})
$AlCl_3$ (Al^{3+})	white ppt	NVR	white ppt	NVR	white ppt	NVR
NH_4Cl (NH_4^+)	NVR	NVR	NVR	NVR	NVR	NVR
$CaCl_2$ (Ca^{2+})	white ppt	NVR	white ppt	NVR	white ppt	NVR
$CuSO_4$ (Cu^{2+})	blue ppt	NVR	blue ppt	NVR	blue ppt	NVR
$NaCl$ (Na^+)	NVR	NVR	NVR	NVR	NVR	NVR
$FeCl_3$ (Fe^{3+})	orange ppt	NVR	orange ppt	NVR	orange ppt	NVR
$Pb(NO_3)_2$ (Pb^{2+})	white ppt	white ppt	white ppt	NVR	white ppt	white ppt
$MgSO_4$ (Mg^{2+})	white ppt	NVR	white ppt	NVR	white ppt	NVR
KI (K^+)	NVR	NVR	NVR	NVR	NVR	NVR
$AgNO_3$ (Ag^+)	tan ppt	white ppt	brown ppt	NVR	tan ppt	NVR
$ZnCl_2$ (Zn^{2-})	white ppt	NVR	white ppt	NVR	white ppt	NVR

CLEANING UP

Avoid contamination by cleaning up in a way that protects you and your environment. Carefully clean the small-scale reaction surface by absorbing the contents onto a paper towel. Rinse the small-scale reaction surface with a damp paper towel and dry it. Dispose of the paper towels in the waste bin. Wash your hands thoroughly with soap and water.

Name _____ Date _____ Class _____

QUESTIONS FOR ANALYSES

Use what you learned in this experiment to answer the following questions.

1. Examine your data for each column of anions. Which anions generally form precipitates? What are the exceptions? Which anions generally do not form precipitates? What are the exceptions?

   Carbonate, hydroxide, and phosphate generally form precipitates, except

   with sodium, potassium, and ammonium. Chloride, nitrate, and sulfate

   generally do not form precipitates, except $AgCl(s)$, $PbCl_2(s)$, and $PbSO_4(s)$.

2. Examine your data for each row of cations. Which cations generally do not form precipitates?

   Potassium ion (K^+), sodium ion (Na^+), and ammonium ion (NH_4^+).

3. You have seen that precipitation reactions can be written as double-replacement reactions in which the ions of the reactants switch partners to form products. For example, aluminum chloride reacts with sodium hydroxide to form a precipitate of aluminum hydroxide and sodium chloride:

$$AlCl_3 + 3NaOH \rightarrow Al(OH)_3(s) + 3NaCl$$

   Write and balance complete chemical equations for the other precipitation reactions you observed for aluminum chloride and those you observed for copper sulfate.

   *Because of the acidity of Al^{3+} and Fe^{3+}, the carbonates of these cations do not exist. Hydroxides are produced instead.

   $2AlCl_3 + 3Na_2CO_3 \rightarrow Al_2(CO_3)_3(s) + 6NaCl^*$.

   $AlCl_3 + Na_3PO_4 \rightarrow AlPO_4(s) + 3NaCl$.

   $CuSO_4 + 2NaOH \rightarrow Cu(OH)_2(s) + Na_2SO_4$.

   $CuSO_4 + Na_2CO_3 \rightarrow CuCO_3(s) + Na_2SO_4$.

   $3CuSO_4 + 2Na_3PO_4 \rightarrow Cu_3(PO_4)_2(s) + 3Na_2SO_4$.

4. Ionic compounds are electrolytes in water solution because their ionic lattices break apart in water, and the separated ions can carry an electric current. For example, $AlCl_3$ exists in water solution as Al^{3+} and Cl^- ions. Similarly, sodium hydroxide exists in water as Na^+ and OH^- ions. Therefore, when aqueous aluminum chloride and aqueous sodium hydroxide react, the reactants are really these ions: Al^{3+}, Cl^-, Na^+, and OH^-. The sodium chloride product also exists as ions because it does not precipitate. The ionic equation for the reaction between aluminum chloride and sodium hydroxide is this:

$$Al^{3+} + 3Cl^- + 3Na^+ + 3OH^- \rightarrow Al(OH)_3(s) + 3Na^+ + 3Cl^-$$

   The net ionic equation is obtained by eliminating the ions common to both sides of the equation:

$$Al^{3+} + 3OH^- \rightarrow Al(OH)_3(s)$$

Write net ionic equations to describe all the reactions you observed that formed precipitates. Begin by identifying the precipitate and working backwards. The net ionic equations for the three precipitation reactions involving the aluminum ion are written like this:

$$2Al^{3+} + 3CO_3^{2-} \rightarrow Al_2(CO_3)_3(s) \text{ (white)}^*$$

$$Al^{3+} + 3OH^- \rightarrow Al(OH)_3(s) \text{ (white)}$$

$$Al^{3+} + PO_4^{3-} \rightarrow AlPO_4(s) \text{ (white)}$$

$Ca^{2+} + CO_3^{2-} \rightarrow CaCO_3(s)$ (white)	$Pb^{2+} + 2Cl^- \rightarrow PbCl_2(s)$ (white)
$Ca^{2+} + 2OH^- \rightarrow Ca(OH)_2(s)$ (white)	$Pb^{2+} + SO_4^{2-} \rightarrow PbSO_4(s)$ (white)
$3Ca^{2+} + 2PO_4^{3-} \rightarrow Ca_3(PO_4)_2(s)$ (white)	$Mg^{2+} + CO_3^{2-} \rightarrow MgCO_3(s)$ (white)
$Cu^{2+} + CO_3^{2-} \rightarrow CuCO_3(s)$ (blue)	$Mg^{2+} + 2OH^- \rightarrow Mg(OH)_2(s)$ (white)
$Cu^{2+} + 2OH^- \rightarrow Cu(OH)_2(s)$ (blue)	$3Mg^{2+} + 2PO_4^{3-} \rightarrow Mg_3(PO_4)_2(s)$ (white)
$3Cu^{2+} + 2PO_4^{3-} \rightarrow Cu_3(PO_4)_2(s)$ (blue)	$2Ag^+ + CO_3^{2-} \rightarrow Ag_2CO_3(s)$ (tan)
$2Fe^{3+} + 3CO_3^{2-} \rightarrow Fe_2(CO_3)_3(s)$ (orange)*	$Ag^+ + OH^- \rightarrow AgOH(s)$ (brown)**
$Fe^{3+} + 3OH^- \rightarrow Fe(OH)_3(s)$ (orange)	$3Ag^+ + PO_4^{3-} \rightarrow Ag_3PO_4(s)$ (tan)
$Fe^{3+} + PO_4^{3-} \rightarrow FePO_4(s)$ (orange)	$Ag^+ + Cl^- \rightarrow AgCl(s)$ (white)
$Pb^{2+} + CO_3^{2-} \rightarrow PbCO_3(s)$ (white)	$Zn^{2+} + CO_3^{2-} \rightarrow ZnCO_3(s)$ (white)
$Pb^{2+} + 2OH^- \rightarrow Pb(OH)_2(s)$ (white)	$Zn^{2+} + 2OH^- \rightarrow Zn(OH)_2(s)$ (white)
$3Pb^{2+} + 2PO_4^{3-} \rightarrow Pb_3(PO_4)_2(s)$ (white)	$3Zn^{2+} + 2PO_4^{3-} \rightarrow Zn_3(PO_4)(s)$ (white)

*Because of the acidity of Al^{3+} and Fe^{3+}, the carbonates of these cations do not exist. Hydroxides are produced instead.
** $AgOH(s)$ does not exist. The reaction is $2Ag^+ + 2OH^- \rightarrow Ag_2O(s) + H_2O$.

NOW IT'S YOUR TURN!

1. Repeat the reaction between silver nitrate ($AgNO_3$) and sodium hydroxide (NaOH). This mixture produces water, sodium nitrate, and silver oxide rather than silver hydroxide. Write and balance a chemical equation to describe this reaction. What is the distinctive color of silver oxide?

   $2AgNO_3 + 2NaOH \rightarrow Ag_2O(s) + H_2O + 2NaNO_3$. Dark brown.

2. Repeat the reaction between calcium chloride ($CaCl_2$) and sodium sulfate (Na_2SO_4). Write and balance a chemical equation to describe this reaction. What did you observe that is distinctive about this reaction?

   $CaCl_2 + Na_2SO_4 \rightarrow CaSO_4(s) + 2NaCl$. The precipitate forms slowly.

3. Repeat the reaction between aluminum chloride ($AlCl_3$) and sodium hydroxide (NaOH). Write and balance a chemical equation to describe this reaction. Now add several more drops of NaOH. What did you observe that is distinctive about this reaction?

   $AlCl_3 + 3NaOH \rightarrow Al(OH)_3(s) + 3NaCl$. The precipitate dissolves in excess NaOH.

4. Repeat the reaction between zinc chloride ($ZnCl_2$) and sodium hydroxide (NaOH). Write and balance a chemical equation to describe this reaction. Now add several more drops of NaOH. What did you observe that is distinctive about this reaction?

$ZnCl_2 + 2NaOH \rightarrow Zn(OH)_2(s) + 2NaCl.$ The precipitate dissolves

in excess NaOH.

5. Repeat the reaction between lead(II) nitrate ($Pb(NO_3)_2$) and sodium hydroxide (NaOH). Write and balance a chemical equation to describe this reaction. Now add several more drops of NaOH. What did you observe that is distinctive about this reaction?

$Pb(NO_3)_2 + 2NaOH \rightarrow Pb(OH)_2(s) + 2NaNO_3.$ The precipitate dissolves in

excess NaOH.

Chapter 17 • *Thermochemistry*   **SMALL-SCALE EXPERIMENT**

27 HEAT OF FUSION OF ICE

Small-Scale Experiment for text Section 17.3

OBJECTIVES

- **Measure** temperature changes when ice melts in water.
- **Calculate** heat changes from experimental data.
- **Calculate** the heat of fusion of ice from experimental data.

INTRODUCTION

Consider this. You pop the top on the can of your favorite soft drink and pour it over ice. Does the soft drink become cold simply because the ice is cold or is there more to it than that? You know that heat always flows from a warm object to a cooler one. For example, when you place your hand on a cold window, your hand gets cold. Heat flows from your hand to the window, giving your hand a cooling sensation. Similarly, when you touch a hot stove, heat flows from the stove to your hand, and your hand feels hot. It makes sense then that when a warm drink comes into contact with cold ice, heat will flow from the drink to the ice, and the drink will become cooler.

Something very important also happens: The ice melts! Melting ice is an endothermic process. That is, the melting process absorbs heat from the surroundings, causing the surroundings to cool off. It's the melting ice, not its cold temperature, that is most responsible for cooling the drink. The ability of ice to cool objects is largely due to the fact that some of the ice melts when it comes into contact with warm objects.

The heat change associated with melting ice or any other solid can be expressed quantitatively. The amount of heat absorbed from the surroundings when a specific amount of solid melts is called the *heat of fusion*. Heats of fusion are usually expressed in the SI units of kilojoules per mole (kJ/mol). The heat of fusion of ice is also commonly expressed in units of calories per gram (cal/g).

PURPOSE

In this experiment, you will use the technique of calorimetry to measure the heat of fusion of ice, the amount of heat absorbed when ice melts. You will place a piece of ice into some hot water and record the temperature change of the system as the ice melts when energy flows from the hot water to the ice. You will first measure the mass and temperature of the hot water. You will also need to know the mass and temperature of the ice but, because of possible significant heat losses, you will determine these quantities indirectly. Because ice melts at 0°C, it will suffice to assume that the temperature of the ice is 0°C. To minimize heat loss, the best way to measure the mass of the ice is to measure the difference in mass of the hot water before and after you place the ice into it. You will carry out the experiment in an insulated plastic-foam coffee cup.

Name _____ Date _____ Class _____

SAFETY

- Wear your safety goggles.

MATERIALS

hot water from the tap
crushed ice

EQUIPMENT

balance
plastic-foam coffee cup
1-ounce plastic cup
alcohol thermometer

EXPERIMENTAL PROCEDURE

1. Tare a plastic-foam coffee cup.

2. Fill a 1-ounce plastic cup 1/4 full with hot water from the tap. Transfer it to the tared coffee cup and measure the mass. Record the mass in Table 27.1.

3. Measure the temperature of the water and record it in Table 27.1.

4. Place a small ice chip into the water, stir, and record in Table 27.1 the lowest temperature reached after the ice melts completely.

5. Measure the mass of the entire system and record your results in Table 27.1

6. Work through the calculations on the Experimental Data page and then repeat the experiment until your calculated heat of fusion of ice is consistent.

EXPERIMENTAL DATA

Record your results in Tables 27.1 and 27.2 or in copies of the tables in your notebook.

Table 27.1   Experimental Data

Quantity	Trial 1	Trial 2	Trial 3
a. Mass of hot water (g)	4.735	5.013	28.129
b. Hot water temperature (°C)	44	49	49
c. Final temperature (°C)	16	23	10
d. Total mass, hot water and ice (g)	6.097	6.138	40.830
e. Ice temperature (°C)	0	0	0

Table 27.2   Calculated Data

Quantity	Calculation:	Trial 1	Trial 2	Trial 3
f. Mass of ice (g)	d − a	1.362	1.125	11.674
g. ΔT for hot water (°C)	c − b	−28	−26	−39
h. Heat lost by water (cal)	a × (c − b) × 1	−132.6	−130.3	−1097
i. ΔT for ice (°C)	c − e	16	23	10
j. Heat gained by ice (cal)	f × (c − e) × 1	21.8	25.9	127.01
k. Heat lost + heat gained (cal)	h + j	−110.8	−104.4	−970.0
l. Heat of fusion of ice (cal/g)	−k/f	81.4	92.8	76.4

CLEANING UP

Pour the water and ice down the drain. Recycle the cups. Put the thermometer away.

Name _____ Date _____ Class _____

QUESTIONS FOR ANALYSES

Use what you learned in this experiment to answer the following questions.

1. Without directly measuring the mass of the ice, how can you determine the mass of the ice from your data?

   Measure the mass of the water before and after adding the ice. The difference is the

   mass of the ice.

2. Why is ΔT for the hot water negative? What does the negative sign mean?

   ΔT is defined as the final temperature minus the initial temperature. The

   final temperature is lower than the initial temperature, so the sign is

   negative. The negative sign indicates the direction of the temperature

   change in the process. The temperature decreased.

3. What does the negative sign of the heat lost by the water signify?

   The negative sign indicates the direction of energy flow; heat was lost by

   the water.

4. Why can you assume the initial temperature of the ice is 0°C?

   The melting point of ice is 0°C. Ice and liquid water are in equilibrium at 0°C.

5. What is the sign of the heat absorbed by the ice? Explain.

   The positive sign means that energy flowed into the ice.

6. The law of conservation of energy requires that the heat gained by the ice should balance the heat lost by the water, assuming no losses of energy to the surroundings. Does item **k** in Table 27.2 of the calculated data equal zero? Explain.

   It's much less than zero. The heat gained by the ice takes into account only the

   temperature change, not the phase change. The difference is the amount of

   heat required to melt the ice.

7. Why does the heat required to melt the ice divided by the mass of the ice equal the heat of fusion of ice (heat of fusion = −k/f)? Why is the negative sign necessary?

   The units for heat of fusion are calories per gram. The heat calculated

   was for a certain mass of ice not equal to one gram so it was divided by the

   mass. The negative sign is necessary to convert the heat lost by the water

   to heat gained by the ice.

8. Given that one calorie equals 4.18 joules, use your experimental data to calculate the heat of fusion of ice in joules per gram.

   x J/g = 81.4 c̶a̶l̶/g × 4.18 J/c̶a̶l̶ = 340 J/g.

9. Use your experimental data to calculate the molar heat of fusion of ice in kJ/mol.

   x J/mol = 340 J̶/g̶ × 18 g̶/mol × 1 kJ/1000 J̶ = 6.12 kJ/mol.

10. Find the accepted value for the heat of fusion of ice in your textbook and compare your calculated values with the accepted value. Calculate the % error.

$$\% \text{ error} = \frac{|\text{experimental value} - \text{accepted value}|}{\text{accepted value}} \times 100$$

   % error = (81.4 − 80.0)(100)/80.0 = 1.75%.

NOW IT'S YOUR TURN!

1. Try doing the experiment, using a larger sample of hot water and ice. Use one ounce of hot water and about five times as much ice. Are your results similar? Explain.

   There is a larger error presumably because there are more heat losses from

   a larger sample.

2. Heat losses to the environment are an obvious source of error in this experiment. For example, significant heat losses can occur between the time you measure the temperature of the hot water and add the ice. Any cooling of the hot water during this period will result in an error. Analyze the experimental procedure and try to identify where it can be improved. Repeat the experiment, using a modified method to optimize your results.

Chapter 18 • *Reaction Rates and Equilibrium* **SMALL-SCALE EXPERIMENT**

28 FACTORS AFFECTING THE RATE OF A CHEMICAL REACTION

Small-Scale Experiment for text Section 18.1

OBJECTIVES

- **Define** *rate of reaction* in terms of bubble formation.
- **Observe** and **record** the effect of temperature, concentration, and surface area on rate of reaction.

INTRODUCTION

You know that energy is required to cook food. The energy may come from boiling water or from the heating elements of a microwave or a conventional oven. Whatever the case, the warmer the temperature, the faster food cooks. On the other hand, in order to preserve food, it's common to place it in a refrigerator or a freezer. The cool temperature in the refrigerator helps to retard spoiling. The warmer the temperature, the faster food spoils. Temperature has an effect on the rate at which food cooks and also on the rate at which it spoils, but temperature is just one factor that affects the speed at which chemical reactions occur.

If you've ever started a campfire, you know that small wood shavings are more easily lit than large logs. Given equal volumes of wood in the forms of shavings and a single log, the wood shavings have more exposed surface area than does the log. The wood in the form of shavings makes more surfaces available for ignition. Thus, increased surface area has an effect on how fast a given chemical reaction occurs.

Combustion is a rapid reaction of a fuel with oxygen that gives off a lot of heat. The more oxygen there is available to the reaction, the faster the reaction will go. That is, the greater the concentration of oxygen, the faster the reaction will go. A camp fire burns at a certain rate in air where the concentration of oxygen is about 20 percent by volume. If that concentration is cut down by the smothering effect of a fire extinguisher, the fire dies down or goes out; the reaction slows or stops. Thus, concentration affects reaction rate.

PURPOSE

In this experiment, you will explore these and other factors that affect the rates of chemical reactions. You will examine reactions of hydrochloric acid with magnesium metal, with solid calcium carbonate, and with aqueous sodium hydrogen carbonate. Careful observations will enable you to derive a working definition of *rate of reaction* in terms of the products evolved. You will then examine how temperature, surface area, and concentration affect rate of reaction.

Name _____ Date _____ Class _____

SAFETY ⬡ 🔳 ☠ ⚠ ⚗

- Wear safety goggles, an apron, and gloves when working with corrosive chemicals.
- Use full small-scale pipets only for the controlled delivery of liquids.
- Don't chew gum, drink, or eat in the laboratory. Never taste a chemical in the laboratory.
- Avoid inhaling substances that can irritate your respiratory system.

MATERIALS

Small-scale pipets of the following solutions:
hydrochloric acid (HCl)
sodium hydrogen carbonate (NaHCO$_3$)
water

Solids:
magnesium (Mg)
calcium carbonate(CaCO$_3$)

EQUIPMENT

small-scale reaction surface
ice
hot water
2 plastic cups

Name _____ Date _____ Class _____

EXPERIMENTAL PAGE

1. What is rate of reaction? Make the following mixings and record your results in Table 28.1.

	1 piece Mg	1 piece CaCO$_3$	1 drop NaHCO$_3$
6 drops HCl			

2. What is the effect of temperature on rate of reaction? Cool one HCl pipet in ice water; warm another in hot water from the tap; and mix the following, one pair at a time. Record your results in Table 28.2.

	1 piece Mg	1 piece CaCO$_3$	1 drop NaHCO$_3$
6 drops cold HCl			
6 drops warm HCl			

3. What is the effect of surface area of Mg or CaCO$_3$ on rate of reaction? Choose two equal-size pieces of Mg, and break or cut one. Repeat for CaCO$_3$. Make the following mixings and record your results in Table 28.3.

	1 piece Mg	Cut or crushed Mg*	1 piece CaCO$_3$	Crushed CaCO$_3$
6 drops HCl		*Cut Mg ribbon or turnings into fine pieces with scissors.		

4. What is the effect of concentration of HCl on rate of reaction? Make the following mixings and record your results in Table 28.4.

	1 piece Mg	1 piece CaCO$_3$	1 drop NaHCO$_3$
10 drops HCl			
5 drops HCl + 5 drops H$_2$O			
1 drop HCl + 9 drops H$_2$O			

Place this side of the Experimental Page facedown. Use the other side under your small-scale reaction surface.

EXPERIMENTAL DATA

Record your results in Tables 28.1, 28.2, 28.3, and 28.4 or in copies of the tables in your notebook.

Table 28.1   Exploring Rate of Reaction

	1 piece Mg	1 piece CaCO₃	1 drop NaHCO₃
6 drops HCl	bubbles	bubbles All bubbles start off fast and taper off.	bubbles

Table 28.2   Effect of Temperature

	1 piece Mg	1 piece CaCO₃	1 drop NaHCO₃
6 drops cold HCl	slow bubbles	slow bubbles	slow bubbles
6 drops warm HCl	fast bubbles	fast bubbles	fast bubbles

Table 28.3   Effect of Surface Area

	1 piece Mg	Cut or crushed Mg	1 piece CaCO₃	Crushed CaCO₃
6 drops HCl	bubbles	more bubbles	bubbles	more bubbles

Table 28.4   Effect of Concentration

	1 piece Mg	1 piece CaCO₃	1 drop NaHCO₃
10 drops HCl	fast bubbles	fast bubbles	fast bubbles
5 drops HCl + 5 drops H₂O	slower	slower	slower
1 drop HCl + 9 drops H₂O	very slow	very slow	very slow

Name _____ Date _____ Class _____

CLEANING UP

Avoid contamination by cleaning up in a way that protects you and your environment. Carefully isolate any unreacted solids and place them in the proper recycling container. Clean the small-scale reaction surface by absorbing the contents onto a paper towel. Rinse the small-scale reaction surface with a damp paper towel and dry it. Dispose of the paper towels in the waste bin. Wash your hands thoroughly with soap and water.

QUESTIONS FOR ANALYSES

Use what you learned in this experiment to answer the following questions.

1. Define rate of reaction in terms of bubble formation. How does rate of reaction change with time?

   Rate of reaction is how fast bubbles appear. The rate slows down with time.

2. What is the effect of temperature on rate of reaction?

   Higher temperature increases rate.

3. What is the effect of the surface area of Mg or $CaCO_3$ on rate of reaction?

   Increasing the surface area speeds up reactions.

4. What is the effect of concentration of HCl on rate of reaction?

   Higher concentrations increase rate.

5. Magnesium reacts with acid to yield hydrogen gas and a salt. Write the balanced chemical equation for the reaction of hydrochloric acid with magnesium.

   $2HCl + Mg \rightarrow H_2(g) + MgCl_2$.

6. An acid reacts with a carbonate or hydrogen carbonate to yield carbon dioxide gas, water, and a salt. Write the balanced chemical equations for the reactions of hydrochloric acid with calcium carbonate and with sodium hydrogen carbonate.

   $2HCl + CaCO_3 \rightarrow CO_2(g) + H_2O + CaCl_2$.

   $HCl + NaHCO_3 \rightarrow CO_2(g) + H_2O + NaCl$.

NOW IT'S YOUR TURN!

1. Carry out the following reactions. What happens in each case? Write chemical equations to describe each reaction.

   a. $Pb(NO_3)_2 + KI \rightarrow$ Immediate bright yellow ppt.

   $Pb(NO_3)_2 + 2KI \rightarrow PbI_2(s) + 2KNO_3$.

   b. $H_2SO_4 + CaCl_2 \rightarrow$ Slow-forming white ppt.

   $H_2SO_4 + CaCl_2 \rightarrow CaSO_4(s) + 2HCl$.

29 LE CHÂTELIER'S PRINCIPLE AND CHEMICAL EQUILIBRIUM

Small-Scale Experiment for text Section 18.2

OBJECTIVES

- **Observe** and **record** how a chemical system at equilibrium responds to changes in concentration of reactants or products.
- **Describe** shifts in equilibrium in terms of Le Châtelier's principle.

INTRODUCTION

If you've ever watched a game of football, you know that it has become very specialized. Coaches design special offenses and defenses for various down and distance situations, as well as for positions of the ball on the field, the score, and the time remaining in the game. For example, offensive and defensive strategies are quite different for a third down and one situation than for a first down and ten. As a result, several offensive and defensive players often run on and off the field after each play. One thing remains constant: only 11 players per team are on the field for any given play. This is an example of a dynamic equilibrium. A dynamic equilibrium is one in which forward reactions (players running on the field) take place at the same rate as reverse reactions (players running off the field). There is no net change in the number of players on the field.

You learned in Section 18.2 that chemical systems often reach a state of dynamic equilibrium. In a system at chemical equilibrium, the rate of the forward reaction equals the rate of the reverse reaction. As a result, the amounts of the reactants and products of equilibrium remain constant as long as no stress is placed on the system.

Le Châtelier's principle says that if a system at equilibrium is stressed, the equilibrium balance will shift in a direction that will relieve the stress. For example, if you add a reactant, the equilibrium will shift toward products (to the right) so that there is a different balance of reactants and products. Similarly, if you add a product, the equilibrium will shift toward reactants (to the left).

PURPOSE

In this experiment, you will investigate chemical systems at equilibrium. You will disturb them by adding or subtracting reactants or products and observe how the equilibrium system responds. You will explain those changes in terms of Le Châtelier's principle.

SAFETY 🫁 🧍 ☠️ 🧪 ⚗️

- Wear safety goggles, an apron, and gloves when working with corrosive chemicals.
- Use full small-scale pipets only for the controlled delivery of liquids.
- Don't chew gum, drink, or eat in the laboratory. Never taste a chemical in the laboratory.
- Avoid inhaling substances that can irritate your respiratory system.

MATERIALS

Small-scale pipets of the following solutions:

bromthymol blue (BTB)

hydrochloric acid (HCl)

sodium hydroxide (NaOH)

ammonia (NH_3)

copper(II) sulfate ($CuSO_4$)

lead(II) nitrate ($Pb(NO_3)_2$)

potassium iodide (KI)

nitric acid (HNO_3)

silver nitrate ($AgNO_3$)

sodium carbonate (Na_2CO_3)

sodium thiosulfate ($Na_2S_2O_3$)

sodium phosphate (Na_3PO_4)

EQUIPMENT

small-scale reaction surface

empty pipet for stirring

plastic cup

EXPERIMENTAL PAGE

Mix the following. Stir each mixture thoroughly by blowing air through a pipet. The chemical equations describe the changes you observe.

1. Mix one drop BTB and one drop HCl (H^+). Record your observations in Table 29.1. Now add just enough NaOH to induce another change. Alternately add more HCl and NaOH.

$$HBTB \rightleftharpoons H^+ + BTB^-$$
$$\text{yellow} \qquad \text{blue}$$

2. Mix one drop BTB and one drop NH_3. Record your observations in Table 29.1. Now add just enough HCl (H^+) to effect a change.

$$NH_3 + HOH \rightleftharpoons NH_4^+ + OH^- \qquad NH_3 + H^+ \rightleftharpoons NH_4^+$$

3. Mix one drop NH_3 and two drops $CuSO_4$ (Cu^{2+}). Record your observations in Table 29.1. Now add, with stirring, just enough NH_3 to effect a change. Add HCl, with stirring, until the light blue precipitate returns. Add more HCl until the precipitate disappears. Repeat this procedure until you are sure of what you see.

$$Cu^{2+} + 2OH^- \rightleftharpoons Cu(OH)_2(s) \text{ (light blue precipitate)}$$
$$Cu^{2+} + 4NH_3 \rightleftharpoons Cu(NH_3)_4^{2+} \text{ (royal blue solution)}$$
$$H^+ + OH^- \rightleftharpoons HOH$$

4. Mix one drop $Pb(NO_3)_2$ (Pb^{2+}) and one drop KI (I^-). Record your observations in Table 29.1. Now add, with stirring, enough NaOH to effect a change. Now add HNO_3.

$$Pb^{2+} + 2I^- \rightleftharpoons PbI_2(s) \text{ (bright yellow precipitate)}$$
$$Pb^{2+} + 2OH^- \rightleftharpoons Pb(OH)_2(s) \text{ (milky white precipitate)}$$

5. Mix one drop $Pb(NO_3)_2$ and one drop NaOH with stirring. Record your observations in Table 29.1. Now add more NaOH, drop by drop with stirring, until a change occurs. Finally, add nitric acid, HNO_3 (H^+), drop by drop, slowly, with stirring, until a change occurs.

$$Pb^{2+} + 2OH^- \rightleftharpoons Pb(OH)_2(s) \qquad Pb^{2+} + 3OH^- \rightleftharpoons Pb(OH)_3^-$$
$$H^+ + OH^- \rightleftharpoons HOH$$

6. Add two drops $AgNO_3$ to a plastic cup. Now add one drop of each of the chemicals in the left column, one at a time. Stir and observe after each addition. When a change occurs, record your observations in Table 29.1. Go on to the next chemical. Near the last addition, you may need to add a few more drops of $AgNO_3$.

Add these chemicals in this order	Equations that account for changes
a. 1 drop Na_2CO_3	**a.** $2Ag^+ + CO_3^{2-} \rightleftharpoons Ag_2CO_3(s)$
b. HNO_3	**b.** $CO_3^{2-} + 2H^+ \rightleftharpoons HOH + CO_2(g)$
c. NaOH	**c.** $2Ag^+ + 2OH^- \rightleftharpoons Ag_2O(s) + H_2O$
d. HCl	**d.** $H^+ + OH^- \rightleftharpoons HOH$
	$Ag^+ + Cl^- \rightleftharpoons AgCl$
e. NH_3	**e.** $Ag^+ + 2NH_3 \rightleftharpoons Ag(NH_3)_2^+$
f. KI	**f.** $Ag^+ + I^- \rightleftharpoons AgI(s)$
g. $Na_2S_2O_3$	**g.** $Ag^+ + S_2O_3^{2-} \rightleftharpoons AgS_2O_3^-$
h. Na_3PO_4	**h.** $3Ag^+ + PO_4^{3-} \rightleftharpoons Ag_3PO_4(s)$

Place this side of the Experimental Page facedown. Use the other side under your small-scale reaction surface.

Name _____ Date _____ Class _____

EXPERIMENTAL DATA

Record your results in Table 29.1 or in a copy of the table in your notebook.

Table 29.1 Dynamic Equilibria

1. BTB + HCl | Green to yellow.
+ NaOH: | Yellow to blue.
| Yellow with acid, blue with base.

2. BTB + NH_3 | Green to blue.
+ HCl | Blue to yellow.

3. NH_3 + $CuSO_4$ | Clear light blue to milky light blue.
More NH_3 | Turns clear to dark blue.
+ HCl | Light blue ppt.
More HCl | Ppt disappears.

4. $Pb(NO_3)_2$ + KI | Bright yellow ppt.
+ NaOH | Milky white ppt replaces yellow ppt.
+ HNO_3 | Yellow ppt reappears.

5. $Pb(NO_3)_2$ + NaOH | Milky white ppt.
More NaOH | Ppt dissolves.
+ HNO_3 | Ppt reappears and dissolves.

6. $AgNO_3$ + Na_2CO_3 | Milky white ppt.
+ HNO_3 | Ppt dissolves.
+ NaOH | Muddy brown ppt.
+ HCl | Grainy white ppt.
+ NH_3 | Ppt dissolves.
+ KI | Lime green ppt.
+ $Na_2S_2O_3$ | Ppt dissolves.
+ Na_3PO_4 | Milky white ppt.

CLEANING UP

Avoid contamination by cleaning up in a way that protects you and your environment. Carefully clean the small-scale reaction surface by absorbing the contents onto a paper towel. Rinse the small-scale reaction surface with a damp paper towel and dry it. Dispose of the paper towels in the waste bin. Wash your hands thoroughly with soap and water.

QUESTIONS FOR ANALYSES

Use what you learned in this experiment to answer the following questions.

1. Bromthymol blue (BTB) is an acid, so it has a hydrogen ion (H^+). For the purposes of this question, you will write it HBTB. HBTB ionizes in water to produce hydrogen ion (H^+) and bromthymol blue ion (BTB^-).

$$HBTB \rightleftharpoons H^+ + BTB^-$$

$$\text{yellow} \qquad \qquad \text{blue}$$

   a. What color appeared when you added HCl to BTB? What color is HBTB? Explain the shift in equilibrium in terms of Le Châtelier's principle.

   Yellow; Yellow; The equilibrium shifts to the left to consume some of the

   added hydrogen ion.

   b. What color appeared when you added NaOH to the mixture? What color is BTB^-? Explain the shift in equilibrium in terms of Le Châtelier's principle.

   Blue. Blue. Hydroxide ion neutralizes hydrogen ion, reducing its

   concentration and causing the reaction to shift to the right to

   replace the hydrogen ion. $H^+ + OH^- \rightleftharpoons HOH$.

2. Ammonia reacts with water to produce hydroxide ion. Ammonia is neutralized by hydrogen ion:

$$NH_3 + HOH \rightleftharpoons NH_4^+ + OH^-$$

$$NH_3 + H^+ \rightleftharpoons NH_4^+$$

   a. What color did BTB change in the presence of ammonia (NH_3)? Explain the color change in terms of Le Châtelier's principle. Include an equation in your explanation.

   Blue. Ammonia produces hydroxide ion in solution. This hydroxide ion

   neutralizes hydrogen ion, causing the BTB equilibrium to shift to the right

   to replace it. $HBTB \rightleftharpoons H^+ + BTB^-$.

   b. What happened when HCl was added? Explain in terms of Le Châtelier's principle.

   The solution turned yellow. The hydrogen ion from HCl neutralizes the

   hydroxide ion, causing the BTB equilibrium to shift to the left.

3. Copper ions react differently in the presence of varying amounts of ammonia (NH_3). The hydroxide produced from a small amount of ammonia produces a precipitate. Excess ammonia produces a highly colored solution:

$$Cu^{2+} + 2OH^- \rightleftharpoons Cu(OH)_2(s) \text{ (precipitation equilibrium)}$$

$$Cu^{2+} + 4NH_3 \rightleftharpoons Cu(NH_3)_4^{2+} \text{ (complex ion in solution)}$$

a. What color is the *precipitate* when only a little ammonia is added? What color is the *solution* in the presence of excess ammonia?

Light blue. Dark blue.

b. Explain in terms of Le Châtelier's principle the disappearance of the precipitate when excess ammonia is added.

Excess ammonia consumes copper(II) ion from the left side of the

precipitation equilibrium, shifting the equilibrium to the right and thus

causing the precipitate to dissolve.

c. What is the effect of the HCl? Explain in terms of Le Châtelier's principle.

A lesser amount of HCl causes the complex ion to break up and the

precipitate to form again. More HCl dissolves the precipitate. Hydrogen

ion from a little HCl neutralizes ammonia, shifting the complex ion

equilibrium to the left and causing the dark blue complex ion to disappear.

The available copper(II) ions react with hydroxide to form the precipitate.

More HCl neutralizes hydroxide and causes the precipitate to dissolve.

4. Lead(II) ion reacts with iodide ion to produce a bright yellow precipitate, and with hydroxide ion to form a milky white precipitate.

$$Pb^{2+} + 2I^- \rightleftharpoons PbI_2(s) \qquad \text{bright yellow}$$

$$Pb^{2+} + 2OH^- \rightleftharpoons Pb(OH)_2(s) \qquad \text{milky white}$$

a. Why does the yellow precipitate disappear when sodium hydroxide is added? Explain in terms of Le Châtelier's principle.

Hydroxide ion uses up lead(II) ion, a reactant in the yellow precipitation

equilibrium. This shifts the lead(II) iodide precipitation equilibrium to the

left, causing the yellow precipitate to dissolve.

b. Why does the yellow precipitate reappear when nitric acid is added?

Nitric acid neutralizes hydroxide ion in the lead(II) hydroxide precipitation

equilibrium, driving the equilibrium to the left. This provides more lead ion

for the lead(II) iodide precipitation reaction.

5. Lead(II) ion reacts with varying amounts of hydroxide ions in different ways. A small amount of hydroxide produces a precipitate; an excess of hydroxide ion produces a complex ion:

$$Pb^{2+} + 2OH^- \rightleftharpoons Pb(OH)_2(s)$$

$$Pb^{2+} + 3OH^- \rightleftharpoons Pb(OH)_3^- \text{ (complex ion in solution)}$$

a. Why does the precipitate disappear when excess NaOH is added? Explain in terms of Le Châtelier's principle.

Excess hydroxide ion uses up lead(II) ion, a reactant in the precipitation

reaction (the first equation). This shifts the equilibrium to the left, causing

the precipitate to dissolve.

b. Why does the precipitate reappear when a little nitric acid is added?

Hydrogen ion from nitric acid neutralizes excess hydroxide ion, causing

the complex ion equilibrium to shift to the left. This provides lead(II) ion for

the precipitation reaction, causing it to shift to the right.

c. Why does the precipitate disappear when excess nitric acid is added?

More hydrogen ion neutralizes the rest of the hydroxide ion, causing the

precipitation reaction to shift to the left.

6. Explain the observations in Step 6 by writing net ionic equations to describe each reaction of silver ion (Ag⁺) you observed.

a. $2Ag^+ + CO_3^{2-} \rightleftharpoons Ag_2CO_3(s)$.

b. $CO_3^{2-} + 2H^+ \rightleftharpoons H_2O + CO_2(g)$.

c. $2Ag^+ + 2OH^- \rightleftharpoons Ag_2O(s) + H_2O$.

d. $H^+ + OH^- \rightleftharpoons HOH$ and $Ag^+ + Cl^- \rightleftharpoons AgCl(s)$.

e. $Ag^+ + 2NH_3 \rightleftharpoons Ag(NH_3)_2^+$.

f. $Ag^+ + I^- \rightleftharpoons AgI(s)$.

g. $Ag^+ + S_2O_3^{2-} \rightleftharpoons AgS_2O_3^-$.

h. $3Ag^+ + PO_4^{3-} \rightleftharpoons Ag_3PO_4(s)$.

7. Explain why BTB is green in neutral water solution. In terms of Le Châtelier's principle, why does it turn yellow when acid is added, and blue when base is added?

It's green because there is a roughly equal amount of both HBTB (yellow)

and BTB⁻ (blue). Hydrogen ion shifts the equilibrium to the left, resulting in

more yellow and less blue. Hydroxide ion shifts the equilibrium toward the

right, resulting in more blue and less yellow.

Name _____ Date _____ Class _____

NOW IT'S YOUR TURN!

1. Repeat Step 1 with other indicators such as phenolphthalein (HPhen); bromphenyl blue (HBPB); methyl red (HMR); alizarine yellow R (HAYR); and thymol blue (HTB). Explain in terms of Le Châletier's principle what happens with each when HCl and NaOH are added. Write net ionic equations to describe their reactions in water.

HCl drives the equilibrium to the left. NaOH drives the equilibrium to the right.

$HPhen \rightleftharpoons H^+ + Phen^-$ $HAYR \rightleftharpoons H^+ + AYR^-$

colorless   pink   yellow   red

$HBPB \rightleftharpoons H^+ + BPB^-$ $HTB \rightleftharpoons H^+ + TB^-$

yellow   blue   pink   yellow

$HMR \rightleftharpoons H^+ + MR^-$

red   yellow

2. Repeat the precipitation reaction of lead nitrate with potassium iodide, as in Step 4. Can you alternately add NaOH and HNO_3 to change the precipitates? Explain.

Yes. NaOH produces a milky white precipitate and HNO_3 produces a yellow

precipitate.

3. Repeat the precipitation reaction of lead nitrate with sodium hydroxide, as in Step 5. Name two ways you can make the precipitate disappear. Prove your answer by carrying out the experiments.

Add HNO_3. Add NaOH.

4. Perform the following experiment and explain your results in terms of Le Châtelier's principle.

$$Fe^{3+} + SCN^- \rightleftharpoons FeSCN^{2+}$$
yellow   blood red
One drop $FeCl_3$ One drop KSCN

One drop NaOH   One drop $AgNO_3$
$Fe^{3+} + OH^- \rightleftharpoons Fe(OH)_3(s)$ $Ag^+ + 2SCN^- \rightleftharpoons Ag(SCN)_2^-$

a. Mix one drop FeCl$_3$ with one drop KSCN. What happened? Write an equation to explain.

A dark red solution formed. Fe^{3+} + SCN$^-$ ⇌ FeSCN^{2+}.

b. Add 10 drops water, separate into four parts with a soda straw, and add the indicated solutions. Tell what happens in each case. Explain in terms of the respective equilibria.

c. Upon the addition of FeCl$_3$, the solution also turned darker red,

pushing the following equilibrium right, Fe^{3+} + SCN$^-$ ⇌ FeSCN^{2+}.

d. Upon the addition of KSCN, the solution also turned darker red,

pushing the following equilibrium right, Fe^{3+} + SCN$^-$ ⇌ FeSCN^{2+}.

e. Upon the addition of NaOH, an orange precipitate was formed,

pushing the following equilibrium right, Fe^{3+} + OH$^-$ ⇌ Fe(OH)$_3$(s).

f. Upon the addition of AgNO$_3$, the solution turned clear, pushing the

following equilibrium right, Ag$^+$ + 2SCN$^-$ ⇌ Ag(SCN)$_2^-$.

Chapter 19 • *Acids, Bases, and Salts*   **SMALL-SCALE EXPERIMENT**

30 A SMALL-SCALE COLORIMETRIC pH METER

Small-Scale Experiment for text Section 19.2

OBJECTIVES

- **Construct** and **calibrate** a colorimetric pH meter.
- **Measure** and **record** the pH of various household solutions, using the colorimetric pH meter.
- **Calculate** pOH from pH and [H⁺] and [OH⁻] from pH and pOH.

INTRODUCTION

pH is a way of expressing how acidic or how basic a solution is. The more acidic a solution is, the lower its pH. The less acidic a solution is, the higher its pH. A pH of 7 represents a neutral solution. A pH lower than 7 is acidic, and a pH higher than 7 is basic.

pH is used to express the molar concentration of the acid content of a solution. The relationship between pH and the molar concentration of H^+ or $[H^+]$ is shown below.

pH	[H+]	Solution Acidity/Basicity
14*	10^{-14}	very basic
13	10^{-13}	
12	10^{-12}	
11	10^{-11}	basic
10	10^{-10}	
9	10^{-9}	
8	10^{-8}	slightly basic
7	10^{-7}	neutral
6	10^{-6}	slightly acidic
5	10^{-5}	
4	10^{-4}	
3	10^{-3}	acidic
2	10^{-2}	
1	10^{-1}	
0*	$10^{-0} = 1$	very acidic

*At these pH's, solutions are not ideal and pH $\neq -\log[H+]$.

In summary: If pH > 7, the solution is basic.

           If pH = 7, the solution is neutral.

           If pH < 7, the solution is acidic.

A pH meter is an instrument used to measure the pH of a solution rapidly and accurately. Most pH meters consist of a pair of electrodes connected to an electronic metering device. A reference electrode has a constant voltage, while a glass electrode changes voltage depending on the pH of the solution being measured. The pH meter compares the difference in voltage between the two electrodes, and this difference is calibrated to read out as a pH. Because pH meters consist of fragile glass electrodes and sensitive electronic parts, they are usually very expensive and often temperamental.

PURPOSE

In this experiment, you will make a very reliable *calorimetric pH meter*. The colorimetric pH meter uses a *universal indicator*, one that changes color with pH. You will mix the universal indicator with a series of 12 standard pH solutions called *buffers*. Each buffer solution has an integer pH between 1 and 12. In the presence of 12 different buffers, the universal indicator will change to 12 distinctly different colors. You can use these colors as standards by comparing other solutions to them. To measure the pH of an unknown solution, for example, you can add the universal indicator to the solution and match the resulting color with the color of one of the buffers. The pH of the matching buffer is the pH of the unknown solution.

SAFETY

- Wear safety goggles.
- Use full small-scale pipets only for the controlled delivery of liquids.
- Don't chew gum, drink, or eat in the laboratory. Never taste a chemical in the laboratory.

MATERIALS

Small-scale pipets of the following solutions:
universal indicator (UI)
buffer solutions (pH 1–12)
Household products: baking soda, vinegar, window cleaner, baking powder, lemon juice, tea, a soft drink, laundry detergent, milk, orange juice, etc.

EQUIPMENT

small-scale reaction surface
empty pipet for stirring

EXPERIMENTAL PAGE

Part A. Constructing a pH Meter

1. Add one drop of UI to each space.

2. Add five drops of the buffer corresponding to each pH. Stir. Each integer pH should now have a unique and distinguishing color. If not, add more buffer.

pH 1	pH 2	pH 3	pH 4
pH 8	pH 7	pH 6	pH 5
pH 9	pH 10	pH 11	pH 12

Part B. Measuring pH

3. Measure the pH's of various household solutions by placing five drops of each liquid to be tested in one drop of UI. Stir, and match the color to one of the pH's above.

4. Measure the pH's of various household solids by adding five drops of water and one drop of UI to a few grains of each solid. Stir, and match the color to one of the pH's above.

Place this side of the Experimental Page facedown. Use the other side under your small-scale reaction surface.

EXPERIMENTAL DATA

Record your results in Tables 30.1 and 30.2 or in copies of tables in your notebook.

Table 30.1   Colorimetric pH Meter

pH 1	bright red	pH 2	red	pH 3	red-orange	pH 4	orange
pH 8	blue-green	pH 7	green	pH 6	yellow-green	pH 5	yellow
pH 9	blue	pH 10	dark blue	pH 11	blue-violet	pH 12	violet

Table 30.2   pH's of Household Products

Household Product	pH	$pH + pOH = 14$ pOH	$[H^+] = 10^{-pH}$ $[H^+]$	$[OH^-] = 10^{-pOH}$ $[OH^-]$
vinegar	4	10	10^{-4}	10^{-10}
window cleaner	9	5	10^{-9}	10^{-5}
soft drink	3	11	10^{-3}	10^{-11}
baking soda	10	4	10^{-10}	10^{-4}
washing soda	11	3	10^{-11}	10^{-3}

Calculate the pOH, $[H^+]$, and $[OH^-]$ of each household product you tested, and record your results in Table 30.2.

CLEANING UP

Avoid contamination by cleaning up in a way that protects you and your environment. Carefully clean the small-scale reaction surface by absorbing the contents onto a paper towel. Rinse the small-scale reaction surface with a damp paper towel and dry it. Dispose of the paper towels in the waste bin. Wash your hands thoroughly with soap and water.

QUESTIONS FOR ANALYSES

Use what you learned in this experiment to answer the following questions.

1. The relationship between pH and pOH is: pH + pOH = 14. List the pOH's of all the household products you tested.

   Subtract pH from 14. Vinegar = 10, window cleaner = 5, soft drink = 11,

   baking soda = 4, washing soda = 3.

2. The relationship between pH and $[H^+]$ is: $[H^+] = 10^{-pH}$. List the $[H^+]$ of each product you tested.

   Place negative pH as an exponent of 10. Vinegar = 10^{-4}, window

   cleaner = 10^{-9}, soft drink = 10^{-3}, baking soda = 10^{-10}, washing soda = 10^{-11}.

3. The relationship between pOH and $[OH^-]$ is: $[OH^-] = 10^{-pOH}$. List the $[OH^-]$ of each product you tested.

   Place negative pOH as an exponent of 10. Vinegar = 10^{-10}, window

   cleaner = 10^{-5}, soft drink = 10^{-11}, baking soda = 10^{-4}, washing soda = 10^{-3}.

4. What limitations does your pH meter have?

   It measures pH only to an integer pH unit. Highly colored substances

   interfere with the measurement of pH.

NOW IT'S YOUR TURN!

1. Search for any other naturally colored substances that can serve as universal indicators. Try flower petals, grape and berry juices, etc.

2. Design an experiment to determine colors of common indicator solutions at various pH's.

   Add a drop of indicator to five drops of each buffer with pH 1 to 12.

Chapter 19 • *Acids, Bases, and Salts*   **SMALL-SCALE EXPERIMENT**

31 TITRATION CURVES

Small-Scale Experiment for text Section 19.4

OBJECTIVES

- **Observe** and **record** pH changes during various acid–base titrations.
- **Construct** titration curves from experimental data for these titrations.
- **Interpret** titration curves and identify suitable indicators for the titrations.
- **Estimate** the pKs of various weak acids and bases.

INTRODUCTION

You have already learned that acid–base indicators are weak acids or bases that change color near their pK's. Because the accuracy of a titration depends in part on how closely the end point coincides with the equivalence point, the indicator used should change color very near the equivalence point. Phenolphthalein changes from colorless to pink in basic solution at about pH 9, yet we used this indicator to detect the end points of acid–base titrations that have equivalence points at exactly pH 7. How can you tell if phenolphthalein is a suitable indicator for the titrations of strong acids with strong bases? You can answer this question by examining the nature of titration curves.

A *titration curve* is a graph showing how the pH changes as a function of the amount of added titrant in a titration. You obtain data for a titration curve by titrating a solution and measuring the pH after every drop of added titrant. For example, you can construct a titration curve for the titration of hydrochloric acid with sodium hydroxide, NaOH, by measuring the pH after every drop of NaOH. A plot of the pH on the *y*-axis versus drops of NaOH on the *x*-axis will tell us how the pH changes as the titration proceeds.

A titration curve gives you a lot of information about a titration. For example, you can use the curve to identify the pH of the *equivalence point* of the titration. The equivalence point is the point on the titration curve where the moles of acid equal the moles of base. The midpoint of the steepest part of the curve (the most abrupt change in pH) is a good approximation of the equivalence point.

You can use knowledge of the equivalence point to choose a suitable indicator for a given titration. The indicator must change color at a pH that corresponds to the equivalence point. Because all titrations of weak acids and bases are different, it is important to construct titration curves and choose suitable indicators before you try to determine the concentrations of weak acids and bases.

Finally, you can use your titration curves to approximate the pK's of various weak acids and bases. Ethanoic acid, for example, ionizes in water to a small extent according to the following equation:

$$CH_3COOH + H_2O \rightleftharpoons CH_3COO^- + H_3O^+$$

The acid ionization constant, K_a, is expressed as:

$$K_a = \frac{[CH_3COO^-][H_3O^+]}{[CH_3COOH]}$$

When the acid is exactly half neutralized (half the number of drops of NaOH to the equivalence point), $[CH_3COOH] = [CH_3COO^-]$. So $K_a = [H_3O^+]$ or $pK_a = pH$. This means that the pH of the solution halfway to the equivalence point represents a good approximation of the pK_a.

PURPOSE

In this experiment, you will use your colorimetric pH meter from Small-Scale Experiment 29 to generate data to construct the titration curves for various acid–base titrations. You will use the information obtained from the graphs to estimate the pK's of various weak acids and bases and to choose the appropriate indicator for each titration.

SAFETY 🗱 🗱 🗱 🗱 🗱

- Wear safety goggles, an apron, and gloves when working with corrosive chemicals.
- Use full small-scale pipets only for the controlled delivery of liquids.
- Don't chew gum, drink, or eat in the laboratory. Never taste a chemical in the laboratory.
- Avoid inhaling substances that can irritate your respiratory system.

MATERIALS

Small-scale pipets of the following solutions:
universal indicator (UI)
buffer solutions (pH 1–12)
hydrochloric acid (HCl)
sodium hydroxide (NaOH)
ethanoic acid (CH_3COOH)

EQUIPMENT

small-scale reaction surface
empty pipet for stirring
plastic cups

EXPERIMENTAL PAGE

1. Construct a pH meter for use in this experiment: Place one drop of UI in each space below, then add five drops of each indicated pH solution. Record your data in Table 31.1.

pH 1	pH 2	pH 3	pH 4
pH 8	pH 7	pH 6	pH 5
pH 9	pH 10	pH 11	pH 12

2. Add one drop of UI and four drops of HCl to each of the following spaces. Then add the indicated number of drops of NaOH while stirring. Record the pH of each mixture in Table 31.2.

1 drop NaOH	2 drops NaOH	3 drops NaOH	4 drops NaOH
8 drops NaOH	7 drops NaOH	6 drops NaOH	5 drops NaOH
9 drops NaOH	10 drops NaOH	11 drops NaOH	12 drops NaOH

3. Repeat Step 2 on a larger scale in a cup. Add one drop of UI and 10 drops of HCl to a clean, dry cup. Add NaOH drop by drop, and record the pH after each drop in Table 31.1. Continue for 25 to 30 drops of NaOH.

4. Repeat Step 3, using CH$_3$COOH. Add one drop of UI and 10 drops of CH$_3$COOH to a clean, dry cup. Add NaOH drop by drop, and record the pH after each drop in Table 31.1. Continue for 25 to 30 drops of NaOH.

Place this side of the Experimental Page facedown. Use the other side under your small-scale reaction surface.

Name _____ Date _____ Class _____

EXPERIMENTAL DATA

Record your results in Tables 31.1 and 31.2 or in copies of the tables in your notebook.

Table 31.1   Colorimetric pH Meter

pH 1	bright red	pH 2	red	pH 3	red orange	pH 4	orange
pH 8	blue green	pH 7	green	pH 6	yellow green	pH 5	yellow
pH 9	blue	pH 10	dark blue	pH 11	blue violet	pH 12	violet

Table 31.2   Titration

Drops of NaOH and corresponding pH's

HCl/NaOH (reaction surface)

Drops	1	2	3	4	5	6	7	8	9	10	11	12
pH	1	1	1	1	1	1	1	1	2	7	10	12

HCl/NaOH (cup)

Drops	1	2	3	4	5	6	7	8	9	10	11	12
pH	1	1	1	1	1	1	1	1	1	1	1	1
Drops	13	14	15	16	17	18	19	20	21	22	23	24
pH	1	1	1	1	1	1	3	7	10	12	12	12
Drops	25	26	27	28	29	30						
pH	12	12	12	12	12	12						

CH₃COOH/NaOH (cup)

Drops	1	2	3	4	5	6	7	8	9	10	11	12
pH	3	4	4	4	4	4	5	5	5	5	5	5
Drops	13	14	15	16	17	18	19	20	21	22	23	24
pH	6	6	6	6	6	7	8	9	10	11	12	12
Drops	25	26	27	28	29	30						
pH	12	12	12	12	12	12						

Use graph paper to construct a titration curve for both titrations, HCl and CH$_3$COOH, by plotting the pH (*y*-axis) versus the number of drops of NaOH added (*x*-axis). Connect the points with a smooth "S" curve.

CLEANING UP

Avoid contamination by cleaning up in a way that protects you and your environment. Carefully clean the small-scale reaction surface by absorbing the contents onto a paper towel, wipe it with a damp paper towel, and dry it. Clean the plastic cup by disposing of the liquid contents and rinsing it thoroughly with water. Dry it with a paper towel. Dispose of the paper towels in the waste bin. Wash your hands thoroughly with soap and water.

QUESTIONS FOR ANALYSES

Use what you learned in this experiment to answer the following questions.

1. Write and balance a chemical equation to describe the reaction between HCl and NaOH. What is the mole ratio between HCl and NaOH?

   HCl + NaOH → H$_2$O + NaCl. 1:1 ratio.

2. Write and balance a chemical equation to describe the reaction between CH$_3$COOH and NaOH. What is the mole ratio between CH$_3$COOH and NaOH?

   CH$_3$COOH + NaOH → H$_2$O + CH$_3$COONa. 1:1 ratio.

3. The equivalence point is the point on the titration curve where the moles of acid equal the moles of base. The pH of the equivalence point of the titration can be approximated by finding the midpoint of the steepest part of the graph (where the pH changes most rapidly). Examine your titration curve for the titration of HCl with NaOH in the cup. What is the pH at the equivalence point for the titration?

   About 7.

4. Examine your titration curve for the titration of CH_3COOH with NaOH. What is the pH at the equivalence point for the titration?

   About 9.

5. You can use your knowledge of the equivalence point to choose a suitable indicator for any acid–base titration. The indicator must change color at a pH that is at the steepest part of the titration curve. Examine your titration curve of HCl with NaOH, and explain why a large number of indicators would be suitable for this titration.

   In one or two drops, the pH jumps from about 3 to about 11. Any indicator

   that changes color between about 4 and 10 would be suitable.

6. Compare the general shape of the curve for the weak acid (CH_3COOH) with the one for the strong acid (HCl).

   a. Which curve has a higher initial pH?

   Ethanoic acid.

   b. Which curve rises faster near the equivalence point?

   HCl.

   c. Is the pH at the equivalence point the same for both?

   No.

   d. Will the same group of indicators detect both equivalence points?

   No. Only phenolphthalein will detect both.

9. You can use your titration curve to approximate the pK_a of ethanoic acid (CH_3COOH). Ethanoic acid ionizes in water to a small extent, according to the following equation:

$$CH_3COOH + H_2O \rightleftharpoons CH_3COO^- + H_3O^+$$

The acid ionization constant, K_a, is expressed as:

$$K_a = \frac{[CH_3COO^-][H_3O^+]}{[CH_3COOH]}$$

When the acid is exactly half-neutralized (half the number of drops of NaOH to the equivalence point), then half of the ethanoic acid has been converted to acetate ion. This means that the amount of ethanoic acid left equals the amount of acetate ion produced, or $[CH_3COOH] = [CH_3COO^-]$. These values cancel in the above expression, resulting in $K_a = [H_3O^+]$ or $pK_a = pH$. This means that the pH of the solution halfway to the equivalence point represents a good approximation of the pK_a. At the equivalence point, how many drops of NaOH are required?

About 15 to 19.

10. What is the pH of the solution when half that many drops have been added? Estimate the pK_a of ethanoic acid.

pH = 4.5, pK_a = 4.5.

11. If NaOH is 0.5M, use your titration data to calculate the approximate molar concentration of HCl and CH_3COOH. Assume that the drop sizes are the same and that they are proportional to liters.

$$\frac{x \text{ mol HCl}}{L} = \frac{20 \text{ L NaOH}}{10 \text{ L HCl}} \times \frac{0.5 \text{ mol NaOH}}{L} \times \frac{1 \text{ mol HCl}}{1 \text{ mol NaOH}} = 1.0M \text{ HCl}$$

$$\frac{x \text{ mol } CH_3COOH}{L} \times \frac{18 \text{ L NaOH}}{10 \text{ L } CH_3COOH} \times \frac{0.5 \text{ mol NaOH}}{L} \times \frac{1 \text{ mol } CH_3COOH}{1 \text{ mol NaOH}} = 0.9M \text{ } CH_3COOH$$

NOW IT'S YOUR TURN!

1. Repeat Step 3 on the Experimental Page, using HNO_3 instead of HCl. Add one drop of UI and 10 drops of HNO_3 to a clean, dry cup. Add NaOH drop by drop, and record the pH after each drop. Continue for 25 to 30 drops of NaOH. Record your observations. Construct a titration curve.

2. Design experiments to construct titration curves for the titrations of the following: H_2SO_4 with NaOH, H_3PO_4 with NaOH, Na_2CO_3 with HCl, and NH_3 with HCl.

3. Repeat all four titrations, but this time do them "backwards." For HCl, HNO_3, and CH_3COOH, add 20 drops of NaOH first and then titrate with the acid. Record the pH after each drop, and construct titration curves. For NH_3, add 10 drops of HCl and titrate with NH_3.

32 STRONG AND WEAK ACIDS AND BASES

Small-Scale Experiment for text Section 19.5

OBJECTIVES

- **Identify** and **distinguish between** strong and weak acids and strong and weak bases.
- **Identify** acids and bases as hydrogen-ion acceptors and hydrogen-ion donors.
- **Identify** conjugate acid–base pairs in acid–base reactions.
- **Describe** acid–base reactions by using hydrogen-ion transfer equations.
- **Explain** the differences between strong and weak acids and bases by using equilibrium principles.

INTRODUCTION

You have seen that acids are substances that react with water to produce H_3O^+ ions in solutions. Similarly, bases are chemicals that react with water to produce OH^- ions. For example, you have already seen that when an acid like HCl dissolves in water, it reacts by transferring a hydrogen ion to water according to the following equation:

$$HCl + H_2O \rightarrow H_3O^+ + Cl^-$$

To what degree does this reaction proceed? Do all the molecules of HCl react, or do only some of them transfer hydrogen ions while others remain intact?

PURPOSE

In this experiment, you will take a new look at acids and bases and classify them according to the Brønsted–Lowry theory. You have already acquired working definitions of acids and bases. Acids turn BTB yellow and produce hydrogen ions in solution. Bases turn BTB blue and produce hydroxide ions in solution. You will use BTB (bromthymol blue) and UI (universal indicator) as probes to classify solutions as acids and bases. You will review how to write net ionic equations to show how each substance transfers a hydrogen ion to or from water. You will learn to identify the acid–base conjugate pairs in hydrogen-ion transfer equations. You will then use the hydrogen carbonate ion, HCO_3^-, to investigate acid–base reactions and group acid solutions according to relative strengths. You will use your data to formulate the concept that acids and bases can be classified as both strong and weak, depending on their behavior.

SAFETY

- Wear safety goggles, an apron, and gloves when working with corrosive chemicals.
- Use full small-scale pipets only for the controlled delivery of liquids.
- Don't chew gum, drink, or eat in the laboratory. Never taste a chemical in the laboratory.
- Avoid inhaling substances that can irritate your respiratory system.

MATERIALS

Small-scale pipets of the following solutions:
hydrochloric acid (HCl)
nitric acid (HNO_3)
sulfuric acid (H_2SO_4)
ethanoic acid (CH_3COOH)
citric acid ($C_6H_8O_7$)
boric acid (H_3BO_3)
bromthymol blue (BTB)
universal indicator (UI)
sodium carbonate (Na_2CO_3)
sodium hydrogen sulfate ($NaHSO_4$)
sodium hydroxide ($NaOH$)
sodium dihydrogen phosphate (NaH_2PO_4)
sodium monohydrogen phosphate (Na_2HPO_4)
potassium hydroxide (KOH)
sodium hydrogen carbonate ($NaHCO_3$)
sodium hydrogen sulfite ($NaHSO_3$)
calcium hydroxide ($Ca(OH)_2$)
sodium ethanoate (CH_3COONa)
sodium phosphate (Na_3PO_4)
ammonia (NH_3)
ammonium chloride (NH_4Cl)

EQUIPMENT

small-scale reaction surface
empty pipet for stirring
conductivity apparatus

EXPERIMENTAL PAGE

Part A. Acids and Indicators

1. Mix one drop of each indicated solution. Look carefully for similarities and differences to distinguish strong acids from weak acids.

2. Test each acid for conductivity. Be sure to rinse the leads of the conductivity apparatus between tests. Record your results in Table 32.1.

1 drop of each acid

	HCl	HNO$_3$	H$_2$SO$_4$	2 drops HCl + 9 drops H$_2$O	CH$_3$COOH	citric acid C$_6$H$_8$O$_7$	boric acid H$_3$BO$_3$
1 drop each BTB							
UI							
Na$_2$CO$_3$							
Test for conductivity							

Part B. Acids, Bases, and Indicators

3. Mix one drop of indicator with 5 drops of each of the indicated solutions. Record your results in Table 32.2.

	1 drop each			1 drop each			1 drop each	
	BTB	UI		BTB	UI		BTB	UI
5 drops each NaHSO$_4$ (HSO$_4^-$)			NaHCO$_3$ (HCO$_3^-$)			Ca(OH)$_2$ (OH$^-$)		
NaOH (OH$^-$)			Na$_2$CO$_3$ (CO$_3^{2-}$)			CH$_3$COONa (CH$_3$COO$^-$)		
Na$_2$HPO$_4$ (HPO$_4^{2-}$)			NaH$_2$PO$_4$ (H$_2$PO$_4^-$)			Na$_3$PO$_4$ (PO$_4^{3-}$)		
KOH (OH$^-$)			NaHSO$_3$ (HSO$_3^-$)			NH$_3$		

Place this side of the Experimental Page facedown. Use the other side under your small-scale reaction surface.

Name _____ Date _____ Class _____

EXPERIMENTAL DATA

Record your results in Tables 32.1 and 32.2 or in copies of the tables in your notebook.

Table 32.1   Acids and Indicators

	HCl	HNO$_3$	H$_2$SO$_4$	2 drops HCl + 9 drops H$_2$O	CH$_3$COOH	citric acid C$_6$H$_8$O$_7$	boric acid H$_3$BO$_3$
BTB	yellow	yellow	yellow	yellow	yellow	yellow	yellow
UI	red	red	red	red	orange	yellow	yellow
Na$_2$CO$_3$	bubbles	bubbles	bubbles	slow bubbles	slow bubbles	slow bubbles	slow bubbles
Test for conductivity	bright light	bright light	bright light	dim light	dim light	dim light	dim light

Table 32.2   Acids, Bases, and Indicators

	1 drop each			1 drop each			1 drop each	
	BTB	UI		BTB	UI		BTB	UI
NaHSO$_4$ (HSO$_4{}^-$)	yellow	red	NaHCO$_3$ (HCO$_3{}^-$)	blue	blue	Ca(OH)$_2$ (OH$^-$)	blue	violet
NaOH (OH$^-$)	blue	violet	Na$_2$CO$_3$ (CO$_3{}^{2-}$)	blue	blue	CH$_3$COONa (CH$_3$COO$^-$)	blue	blue green
Na$_2$HPO$_4$ (HPO$_4{}^{2-}$)	blue	blue	NaH$_2$PO$_4$ (H$_2$PO$_4{}^-$)	yellow	yellow	Na$_3$PO$_4$ (PO$_4{}^{3-}$)	blue	blue
KOH (OH$^-$)	blue	violet	NaHSO$_3$ (HSO$_3{}^-$)	yellow	orange	NH$_3$	blue	blue

CLEANING UP

Avoid contamination by cleaning up in a way that protects you and your environment. Carefully clean the small-scale reaction surface by absorbing the contents onto a paper towel, wipe the small-scale reaction surface with a damp paper towel, and dry it. Dispose of the paper towels in the waste bin. Wash your hands thoroughly with soap and water.

QUESTIONS FOR ANALYSES

Use what you learned in this experiment to answer the following questions.

1. What does BTB indicate that all solutions in Part A can be classified as?

   Acids.

2. What is the chemical behavior of all the solutions with Na_2CO_3? Is this typical of acids or bases?

   They all form bubbles of $CO_2(g)$. Acids.

3. Suggest a reason that the acids give different colors with universal indicator.

   HCl, HNO_3, and H_2SO_4 are red with UI, thus showing they have lower pH's

   than the other acids. These acids deliver more hydrogen ions to solution

   than do the other acids.

4. Which HCl reaction does the ethanoic acid reaction more closely resemble? Why does the undiluted HCl seem to be a "stronger" acid than ethanoic acid?

   The diluted one. The undiluted HCl has a lower pH and reacts faster than

   ethanoic acid.

5. To account for the different rates of reaction with Na_2CO_3, predict which acid, HCl or ethanoic, probably has the greater amount of hydrogen ions present in solution. Do both acids transfer hydrogen ions to water to the same degree? Which ionizes to the greater degree?

   HCl. No. HCl.

6. Classify each solution in Part B as an acid or a base. Estimate the pH of each solution and classify each as strong or weak. For all the weak acids and bases, write a net ionic equation to describe the hydrogen-ion transfer reaction of each acid or base with water. (Show each acid as a hydrogen-ion donor and each base as a hydrogen-ion acceptor.)
   For example:

   An acid is a *hydrogen-ion donor:* $CH_3COOH + HOH \rightleftharpoons H_3O^+ + CH_3COO^-$

   A base is a *hydrogen-ion acceptor:* $NH_3 + HOH \rightleftharpoons NH_4^+ + OH^-$

Notice that water acts as a base in the first equation and as an acid in the second. Water is said to be *amphoteric* because it can act as an acid or base, depending on the conditions. As always, when writing net ionic equations, you can ignore Na^+ ions because they are spectator ions.

weak acid: $HSO_4^- + H_2O \rightleftharpoons SO_4^{2-} + H_3O^+$.

strong base: NaOH.

weak base: $HPO_4^{2-} + HOH \rightleftharpoons H_2PO_4^- + OH^-$.

strong base: KOH.

weak base: $HCO_3^- + HOH \rightleftharpoons H_2CO_3 + OH^-$.

weak base: $CO_3^{2-} + HOH \rightleftharpoons HCO_3^- + OH^-$.

weak acid: $H_2PO_4^- + HOH \rightleftharpoons HPO_4^{2-} + H_3O^+$.

weak acid: $HSO_3^- + HOH \rightleftharpoons SO_3^{2-} + H_3O^+$.

strong base: $Ca(OH)_2$.

weak base: $CH_3COO^- + HOH \rightleftharpoons CH_3COOH + OH^-$.

weak base: $PO_4^{3-} + HOH \rightleftharpoons HPO_4^{2-} + OH^-$.

weak base: $NH_3 + HOH \rightleftharpoons NH_4^+ + OH^-$.

7. Identify each pair of species in your net ionic equations (both reactants and products) as a conjugate acid–base pair. For example:

The first reactant and the first product listed above are conjugate acid–

base pairs. The second reactant and the second product are also conjugate

acid–base pairs.

NOW IT'S YOUR TURN!

1. Investigate the common chemical solutions in this lab for use in a colorimetric pH meter in place of pH buffer standards. Set up the pH meter as in Small-Scale Experiment 30, and match the colors that various solutions produce with UI.

2. Design an experiment to use hydrogen carbonate ion, HCO_3^-, as a probe for weak acids. For example, you have seen that carbonates react with acids to produce carbon dioxide and water:

$$CO_3^{2-} + 2H^+ \rightleftharpoons CO_2(g) + H_2O$$

Notice that the stoichiometry of the reaction requires two moles of hydrogen ions for every one mole of carbonate. If the amount of available hydrogen ion were limited, for example, by the presence of a weak acid, the reaction might produce hydrogen carbonate ion rather than carbon dioxide:

$$CO_3^{2-} + H^+ \rightleftharpoons HCO_3^-$$

An additional equivalent of hydrogen ion is needed to carry the reaction to completion:

$$HCO_3^- + H^+ \rightleftharpoons CO_2(g) + H_2O$$

33 BUFFERS

Small-Scale Experiment for text Section 19.5

OBJECTIVES

- **Measure** and **record** the pHs of various buffer solutions.
- **Determine** the resistance of various buffers to changes in pH.

INTRODUCTION

A *buffer solution* is a solution that resists a change in pH when small amounts of acid or base are added to it. Buffer solutions are usually composed of a conjugate acid–base pair—either a weak acid and the salt of its conjugate base or a weak base and the salt of its conjugate acid. For example, a buffer that maintains a pH of about 4.5 can be prepared by making a solution of ethanoic acid and sodium acetate.

$$CH_3COOH + H_2O \rightleftharpoons H_3O^+ + CH_3COO^-$$

acid   base
                                     (from sodium acetate)

$$CH_3COO^- + H_2O \rightleftharpoons CH_3COOH + OH^-$$

base   acid
(from sodium acetate)

Such a mixture resists a change in pH because the weak acid, CH_3COOH, will react with any added base. Similarly, the base, CH_3COO^-, will react with added acid.

A buffer can also be made of a weak base and the salt of its conjugate acid. Ammonia and ammonium chloride, for example, make up a buffer that maintains a pH of about 10.

$$NH_3 + H_2O \rightleftharpoons NH_4^+ + OH^-$$

base   acid

This buffer also has an acid and a base that are capable of reacting with added hydronium or hydroxide ions to maintain the pH at a nearly constant value.

PURPOSE

In this experiment, you will prepare several buffer solutions. You will add small amounts of both acid and base to each buffer to test their resistance to change in pH. You will then design other buffer solutions from weak acids and weak bases and test their behavior toward added acid and base.

SAFETY 🧪 🏭 ☠️ ⚗️ 🧫

- Wear safety goggles, an apron, and gloves when working with corrosive chemicals.
- Use full small-scale pipets only for the controlled delivery of liquids.
- Don't chew gum, drink, or eat in the laboratory. Never taste a chemical in the laboratory.
- Avoid inhaling substances that can irritate your respiratory system.

MATERIALS

Small-scale pipets of the following solutions:
universal indicator (UI)
buffer solution (pH 1–12)
water
sodium hydroxide (NaOH)
hydrochloric acid (HCl)
ethanoic acid (CH_3COOH)
sodium ethanoate (CH_3COONa)
phosphoric acid (H_3PO_4)
sodium dihydrogen phosphate (NaH_2PO_4)
sodium hydrogen carbonate ($NaHCO_3$)
sodium carbonate (Na_2CO_3)
ammonium chloride (NH_4Cl)
ammonia (NH_3)
sodium chloride (NaCl)
sodium nitrate ($NaNO_3$)
sodium sulfate (Na_2SO_4)
potassium iodide (KI)

EQUIPMENT

3 plastic cups
small-scale reaction surface

EXPERIMENTAL PAGE

1. Construct a pH meter for use in this experiment: Place one drop of UI in each space below, then five drops of each indicated pH solution.

pH 1	pH 2	pH 3	pH 4
pH 8	pH 7	pH 6	pH 5
pH 9	pH 10	pH 11	pH 12

2. Place three cups in the designated places, and add one drop of UI and 10 drops of distilled water to each.

1 drop UI

cup

Count the number of drops of NaOH to a distinct color change.

1 drop UI

cup

Count the number of drops of HCl to a distinct color change.

1 drop UI

cup

Use a control to compare colors.

3. Place three cups in the designated places and add one drop of UI, 10 drops of CH_3COOH, and 10 drops of CH_3COONa to each.

1 drop UI

cup

Count the number of drops of NaOH to a distinct color change.

1 drop UI

cup

Count the number of drops of HCl to a distinct color change.

1 drop UI

cup

Use a control to compare colors.

4. Repeat Step 3, replacing the CH_3COOH and CH_3COONa, in turn, with the following combinations.

    a. $H_3PO_4 + NaH_2PO_4$ b. $NaHCO_3 + Na_2CO_3$ c. $NH_4Cl + NH_3$

    d. $NaCl + NaNO_3$ e. $Na_2SO_4 + KI$ f. $H_3PO_4 + NaOH$

  g. Try mixing various combinations and test their buffer capacities.

Place this side of the Experimental Page facedown. Use
the other side under your small-scale reaction surface.

EXPERIMENTAL DATA

Record your results in Tables 33.1 and 33.2 or in copies of the tables in your notebook.

Table 33.1   Colorimetric pH Meter

pH 1 bright red	pH 2 red	pH 3 red-orange	pH 4 orange
pH 8 blue-green	pH 7 green	pH 6 yellow-green	pH 5 yellow
pH 9 blue	pH 10 dark blue	pH 11 blue-violet	pH 12 violet

Table 33.2   Buffers

Mixture	Initial pH	Drops NaOH to change	Drops HCl to change
water	5–7	1	1
$CH_3COOH + CH_3COONa$	5	10–20	10–20
$H_3PO_4 + NaH_2PO_4$	4	10–20	10–20
$NaHCO_3 + Na_2CO_3$	9	10–20	10–20
$NH_4Cl + NH_3$	9	10–20	10–20
$NaCl + NaNO_3$	7	1–2	1–2
$Na_2SO_4 + KI$	7	1–2	1–2
$H_3PO_4 + NaOH$	5	10–20	10–20

CLEANING UP

Avoid contamination by cleaning up in a way that protects you and your environment. Carefully clean the small-scale reaction surface by absorbing the contents onto a paper towel, wipe it with a damp paper towel, and dry it. Clean the plastic cups by disposing of the liquid contents and rinsing them thoroughly with water. Dry them with a paper towel. Dispose of the paper towels in the waste bin. Wash your hands thoroughly with soap and water.

QUESTIONS FOR ANALYSES

Use what you learned in this experiment to answer the following questions.

1. What is a buffer?

   A solution that resists change in pH.

2. How do you know which mixtures are buffers?

   They do not change pH with small amounts of added acid or base.

3. How do you know which mixtures are not buffers?

   They change pH immediately upon addition of acid or base.

4. Buffer capacity is a measure of the amount of acid or base a buffer will absorb before it changes pH significantly. A crude measure of buffer capacity is the number of drops of acid or base that is added before a pH change is shown by an indicator color change. What is the buffer capacity of each solution you measured in this experiment?

   In each case, equal to the number of drops of acid or base added before the

   pH changed significantly.

NOW IT'S YOUR TURN!

1. Use the chemicals in this experiment to explore other possible buffer combinations. Mix 10 drops each of various solutions, two at a time, and test the buffer capacity of each resulting solution. Tell what you mix and what happens in each case.

   Carry out Step 3 of the experiment with different combinations of the

   chemicals available in this experiment.

2. Buffers are mixtures of weak acids and bases. Because of their formulations, some common household products are potential buffers. Design and carry out experiments to test household products for buffer capacity. Tell what you do and what the results are. Whenever possible, read the label of each product to try to determine the chemicals that give the substance its buffer capacity.

   Try seltzer tablets, baking soda, baking powder, cream of tartar, aspirin,

   vitamin C formula (a mixture of ascorbic acid and sodium ascorbate), liquid

   and solid antacids, and other household items. Students may have to dilute

   the acids and bases depending on the sample size they use. Note: Do not

   make bleach and ammonia available to students, as these solutions are

   incompatible.

Chapter 20 • *Oxidation–Reduction Reactions*   **SMALL-SCALE EXPERIMENT**

34 DETERMINATION OF AN ACTIVITY SERIES

Small-Scale Experiment for text Section 20.1

OBJECTIVES

- **Derive** an activity series from experimental data.
- **Describe** oxidation–reduction reactions by writing net ionic equations and half-reactions.
- **Formulate** a functional definition for *oxidation* and *reduction*.

INTRODUCTION

You have seen that magnesium reacts with HCl much more readily than does zinc. Copper appears not to react at all with hydrochloric acid. The half-reactions that describe these processes reveal that electrons are lost by the metals and gained by the hydrogen ions. For example, the half-reactions for the reaction of magnesium with hydrochloric acid are

$$2H^+ + 2e^- \rightarrow H_2(g) \qquad \text{reduction}$$

$$Mg(s) \rightarrow Mg^{2+} + 2e^- \qquad \text{oxidation}$$

The relative ease with which a metal loses electrons is called its *oxidation potential*. You have seen, for example, that magnesium is more reactive toward acids than is zinc. This means that magnesium loses electrons more readily than zinc does. In other words, magnesium has a higher oxidation potential.

Conversely, the relative ease with which a metal cation gains electrons is called its *reduction potential*. For example, we have seen that copper ions react with zinc metal according to the following half-reactions and net ionic equation:

Reduction	$Cu^{2+} + 2e^- \rightarrow Cu(s)$
Oxidation	$Zn(s) \rightarrow Zn^{2+} + 2e^-$
Net ionic	$Cu^{2+} + Zn(s) \rightarrow Cu(s) + Zn^{2+}$

Because copper ions react with zinc metal by taking away its electrons, we can say that copper has the greater reduction potential and zinc has the greater oxidation potential.

PURPOSE

In this experiment, you will carry out a series of reactions in which electrons are gained and lost between metals and metal ions. You will organize the experiments so that metals actually compete for one another's electrons. You will observe which metals lose electrons more readily and which metal ions gain electrons more readily. You can compare the relative tendencies of metals to gain and lose electrons by counting the number of reactions each metal and each metal ion undergoes. The metal involved in the most reactions is the one that loses electrons (is oxidized) the most readily. It has the highest oxidation potential. The metal involved in the least number of reactions loses electrons the least readily. It has the lowest oxidation potential. A list of metals ranging from those most easily oxidized to those least easily oxidized is called an activity series. From this data, you will derive an activity series for common metals.

SAFETY

- Wear safety goggles.
- Use full small-scale pipets only for the controlled delivery of liquids.
- Don't chew gum, drink, or eat in the laboratory. Never taste a chemical in the laboratory.

MATERIALS

Small-scale pipets of the following solutions:
copper(II) sulfate ($CuSO_4$)
iron(II) sulfate ($FeSO_4$)
magnesium sulfate ($MgSO_4$)
silver nitrate ($AgNO_3$)
zinc chloride ($ZnCl_2$)

Four pieces each of the following solid metals:
zinc (Zn)
silver (Ag)
magnesium (Mg)
iron (Fe)
copper (Cu)

EQUIPMENT

small-scale reaction surface

EXPERIMENTAL PAGE

Add two drops of each salt solution to one piece of each of the indicated metals.

	$CuSO_4$ (Cu^{2+})	$FeSO_4$ (Fe^{2+})	$MgSO_4$ (Mg^{2+})	$AgNO_3$ (Ag^+)	$ZnCl_2$ (Zn^{2+})
One piece each Zn(s)					■
Ag(s)				■	
Mg(s)			■		
Fe(s)		■			
Cu(s)	■				

Place this side of the Experimental Page facedown. Use the other side under your small-scale reaction surface.

Name _____ Date _____ Class _____

EXPERIMENTAL DATA

Record your results in Table 34.1 or in a copy of the table in your notebook.

Table 34.1   Metal Activity

	$CuSO_4$ (Cu^{2+})	$FeSO_4$ (Fe^{2+})	$MgSO_4$ (Mg^{2+})	$AgNO_3$ (Ag^+)	$ZnCl_2$ (Zn^{2+})	
$Zn(s)$	Rxn	Rxn	NVR*	Rxn	■	$Zn(s) \rightarrow Zn^{2+} + 2e^-$ <hr> $Zn^{2+} + 2e^- \rightarrow Zn(s)$
$Ag(s)$	NVR	NVR	NVR	■	NVR	$Ag(s) \rightarrow Ag^+ + e^-$ <hr> $Ag^+ + e^- \rightarrow Ag(s)$
$Mg(s)$	Rxn	Rxn	■	Rxn	Rxn	$Mg(s) \rightarrow Mg^{2+} + 2e^-$ <hr> $Mg^{2+} + 2e^- \rightarrow Mg(s)$
$Fe(s)$	Rxn	■	NVR	Rxn	NVR	$Fe(s) \rightarrow Fe^{2+} + 2e^-$ <hr> $Fe^{2+} + 2e^- \rightarrow Fe(s)$
$Cu(s)$	■	NVR	NVR	Rxn	NVR	$Cu(s) \rightarrow Cu^{2+} + 2e^-$ <hr> $Cu^{2+} + 2e^- \rightarrow Cu(s)$

*NVR = No Visible Reaction

Write oxidation and reduction half-reactions for each metal in the spaces provided next to the table.

CLEANING UP

Avoid contamination by cleaning up in a way that protects you and your environment. Carefully clean and dry each piece of leftover metal and place it in the appropriate recycling container. Clean the small-scale reaction surface by absorbing the contents onto a paper towel, rinse it with a damp paper towel, and dry it. Dispose of the paper towels in the waste bin. Wash your hands thoroughly with soap and water.

QUESTIONS FOR ANALYSES

Use what you learned in this experiment to answer the following questions.

1. Read across each row of Table 34.1. Count the number of reactions that each metal undergoes with the metal salts. Order them according to reactivity. This order is called an activity series.

   Mg > Zn > Fe > Cu > Ag.

2. Reading down the rows of Table 34.1, count the number of reactions that each metal ion undergoes. Order them according to reactivity.

   $Ag^+ > Cu^{2+} > Fe^{2+} > Zn^{2+} > Mg^{2+}$.

3. Compare the reactivity of the metal ions to that of the metals. What are the similarities and differences?

   The activity series for the metal ions is in the reverse order of that of

   the metals.

4. For each reaction you observe, a metal is oxidized; that is, it gives away its electrons. In doing so, the metal becomes a metal ion. Write an oxidation half-reaction for each reaction you observed. Write them in order of reactivity, with the most reactive first.

   Oxidations: $Mg(s) \rightarrow Mg^{2+} + 2e^-$

   $Zn(s) \rightarrow Zn^{2+} + 2e^-$

   $Fe(s) \rightarrow Fe^{2+} + 2e^-$

   $Cu(s) \rightarrow Cu^{2+} + 2e^-$

   $Ag(s) \rightarrow Ag^+ + e^-$

5. For each reaction you observe, a metal ion is reduced; that is, the metal ion gains electrons. In doing so, the metal ion becomes a metal atom. Write a reduction half-reaction for each reaction you observed. Write them in order of reactivity, with the most reactive first.

   Reductions: $Ag^+ + e^- \rightarrow Ag(s)$

   $Cu^{2+} + 2e^- \rightarrow Cu(s)$

   $Fe^{2+} + 2e^- \rightarrow Fe(s)$

   $Zn^{2+} + 2e^- \rightarrow Zn(s)$

   $Mg^{2+} + 2e^- \rightarrow Mg(s)$

6. Examine your two lists of half-reactions and describe how each list can be used to predict whether a reaction will occur between a metal and a metal ion.

   Each metal on the list will react with a metal ion below it but not above it.

   Likewise, each metal ion on the list will react with a metal below it but not

   above it.

7. Add the half-reactions to obtain the net ionic equations for each of the reactions you observed. Use either list and choose two half-reactions. Reverse the one lower on the list and add them together. Make sure the number of electrons gained equals the number of electrons lost. For example,

Oxidation	$Mg(s) \rightarrow Mg^{2+} + 2e^-$
Reduction	$2\,[Ag^+ + e^- \rightarrow Ag(s)]$
Net Ionic Equation	$Mg(s) + 2Ag^+ \rightarrow Mg^{2+} + 2Ag(s)$

Notice that silver metal does not give its electrons to a zinc ion:

$Ag^0(s) + Zn^{2+} \rightarrow$ No Visible Reaction

$Zn(s) + 2Ag^+ \rightarrow Zn^{2+} + 2Ag(s).$

$Fe(s) + 2Ag^+ \rightarrow Fe^{2+} + 2Ag(s).$

$Cu(s) + 2Ag^+ \rightarrow Cu^{2+} + 2Ag(s).$

$Mg(s) + Cu^{2+} \rightarrow Mg^{2+} + Cu(s).$

$Zn(s) + Cu^{2+} \rightarrow Zn^{2+} + Cu(s).$

$Fe(s) + Cu^{2+} \rightarrow Fe^{2+} + Cu(s).$

$Zn(s) + Fe^{2+} \rightarrow Zn^{2+} + Fe(s).$

$Mg(s) + Fe^{2+} \rightarrow Mg^{2+} + Fe(s).$

$Mg(s) + Zn^{2+} \rightarrow Mg^{2+} + Zn(s).$

NOW IT'S YOUR TURN!

1. Repeat the experiment, using common household objects in place of the metals. For example, use galvanized nails or zinc-plated washers for zinc, silverware for silver, staples for iron, and pennies for copper. How do your results compare with the original experiment?

They are about the same.

35 OXIDATION–REDUCTION REACTIONS

Small-Scale Experiment for text Section 20.3

OBJECTIVES

- **Observe** and **record** oxidation–reduction reactions between aqueous ions.
- **Describe** oxidation and reduction processes by writing half-reactions.
- **Write** and balance redox equations by balancing half-reactions.
- **Identify** reactants as oxidizing agents and reducing agents.

INTRODUCTION

You saw in the last two labs that oxidation–reduction reactions commonly occur when metals react with either acids or metal ions. Redox reactions also occur between ions, one ion being oxidized and the other being reduced. For example, permanganate ions, MnO_4^-, undergo a redox reaction with iodide ions, I^-, in the presence of acid:

$$16H^+ + 2MnO_4^- + 10I^- \rightarrow 2Mn^{2+} + 5I_2 + 8H_2O$$

This reaction is easily seen in the laboratory because permanganate has a distinctive purple color that disappears upon formation of the nearly colorless Mn^{2+} ion. Similarly, the colorless iodide ion reacts to form the iodine molecule, which appears yellow in aqueous solution. The reaction mixture turns from purple to yellow as the reaction proceeds.

In this reaction, permanganate is reduced and iodide is oxidized. In other words, manganese gains electrons and iodine loses electrons. Because permanganate accepts electrons from iodide and causes iodide to be oxidized, permanganate, the reduced reactant, is also called the oxidizing agent. Similarly, because iodide donates electrons to permanganate and causes permanganate to be reduced, iodide, the oxidized reactant, is also called a reducing agent.

PURPOSE

In this experiment, you will carry out a number of redox reactions involving ions in aqueous solution and write balanced equations to describe the reactions. You will also identify the oxidizing and reducing agents in each case and become familiar with which substances usually act as oxidizing agents and which are most often reducing agents.

Name _____ Date _____ Class _____

SAFETY 🫧 🎽 ☠ 🧪 ♨

- Wear safety goggles, an apron, and gloves when working with corrosive chemicals.
- Use full small-scale pipets only for the controlled delivery of liquids.
- Don't chew gum, drink, or eat in the laboratory. Never taste a chemical in the laboratory.
- Avoid inhaling substances that can irritate your respiratory system.

MATERIALS

Small-scale pipets of the following solutions:
potassium iodide (KI)
sodium hypochlorite (NaOCl)
potassium permanganate ($KMnO_4$)
hydrogen peroxide (H_2O_2)
potassium iodate (KIO_3)
potassium dichromate ($K_2Cr_2O_7$)
sodium nitrite ($NaNO_2$)
copper(II) sulfate ($CuSO_4$)
iron(III) chloride ($FeCl_3$)
starch solution
hydrochloric acid (HCl)
sodium hydrogen sulfite ($NaHSO_3$)
sodium thiosulfate (Na_2S_2O3)
sodium hydrogen sulfate ($NaHSO_4$)

EQUIPMENT

small-scale reaction surface

EXPERIMENTAL PAGE

1. Mix one drop each of the indicated solutions in the spaces below. If no reaction is visible, add starch, an indicator for I_2. If no reaction occurs still, add HCl. Record your results in Table 35.1.

KI
(I^-)

a. NaClO (ClO^-) $ClO^- + I^- \rightarrow Cl^- + I_2$

b. $KMnO_4$ (MnO_4^-) $MnO_4^- + I^- \rightarrow Mn^{2+} + I_2$

c. H_2O_2 $H_2O_2 + I^- \rightarrow H_2O + I_2$

d. KIO_3 (IO_3^-) $IO_3^- + I^- \rightarrow I^- + I_2$

e. $K_2Cr_2O_7$ ($Cr_2O_7^{2-}$) $Cr_2O_7^{2-} + I^- \rightarrow Cr^{3+} + I_2$

f. $NaNO_2$ (NO_2^-) $NO_2^- + I^- \rightarrow NO(g) + I_2$

g. $CuSO_4$ (Cu^{2+}) $Cu^{2+} + I^- \rightarrow CuI(s) + I_2$

h. $FeCl_3$ (Fe^{3+}) $Fe^{3+} + I^- \rightarrow Fe^{2+} + I_2$

2. Add a few drops of $NaHSO_3$ to each of the mixtures in Step 1, **a–d**. Record your results in Table 35.1.

$$HSO_3^- + I_2 \rightarrow SO_4^{2-} + I^-$$

3. Add a few drops of $Na_2S_2O_3$ to each of the mixtures in Step 1, **e–h**. Record your results in Table 35.1.

$$S_2O_3^{2-} + I_2 \rightarrow S_4O_6^{2-} + I^-$$

Place this side of the Experimental Page facedown. Use
the other side under your small-scale reaction surface.

EXPERIMENTAL DATA

Record your results in Table 35.1 or in a copy of the table in your notebook.

Table 35.1 Redox Reactions and Indicators

	KI	Starch	HCl	NaHSO$_3$	Na$_2$S$_2$O$_3$
a. NaClO	yellow	NA*	NA	colorless	NA
b. KMnO$_4$	pink to yellow	NA	NA	colorless	NA
c. H$_2$O$_2$	NVR**	NVR	black	colorless	NA
d. KIO$_3$	NVR	NVR	black	colorless	NA
e. K$_2$Cr$_2$O$_7$	NVR	NVR	black	NA	colorless
f. NaNO$_2$	NVR	NVR	black	NA	colorless
g. CuSO$_4$	brown	NA	NA	NA	colorless
h. FeCl$_3$	dark orange	NA	NA	NA	light yellow

*NA = Not Applicable
**NVR = No Visible Reaction

CLEANING UP

Avoid contamination by cleaning up in a way that protects you and your environment. Carefully clean the small-scale reaction surface by absorbing the contents onto a paper towel, wipe it with a damp paper towel, and dry it. Dispose of the paper towels in the waste bin. Wash your hands thoroughly with soap and water.

QUESTIONS FOR ANALYSES

Use what you learned in this experiment to answer the following questions.

1. What color is aqueous I_2? What color is I_2 in the presence of starch?

   Yellow. Black.

2. Listed below are the reactants and products for each mixing. Assign oxidation numbers to each chemical species that changes oxidation number and then write half-reactions for each reaction.

   $$+1 \quad -1 \quad\quad -1 \quad\quad 0$$

   a. $ClO^- + I^- \rightarrow Cl^- + I_2$

   $ClO^- + 2e^- \rightarrow Cl^-$.

   $2I^- \rightarrow I_2 + 2e^-$.

   $$+7 \quad\quad -1 \quad\quad +2 \quad\quad 0$$

   b. $MnO_4^- + I^- \rightarrow Mn^{2+} + I_2$

   $MnO_4^- + 5e^- \rightarrow Mn^{2+}$.

   $2I^- \rightarrow I_2 + 2e^-$.

   $$-1 \quad\quad -1 \quad\quad -2 \quad\quad 0$$

   c. $H_2O_2 + I^- \rightarrow H_2O + I_2$

   $H_2O_2 + 2e^- \rightarrow H_2O$.

   $2I^- \rightarrow I_2 + 2e^-$.

   $$+5 \quad -1 \quad\quad -1 \quad\quad 0$$

   d. $IO_3^- + I^- \rightarrow I^- + I_2$

   $IO_3^- + 6e^- \rightarrow I^-$.

   $2I^- \rightarrow I_2 + 2e^-$.

   $$+6 \quad\quad -1 \quad\quad +3 \quad\quad 0$$

   e. $Cr_2O_7^{2-} + I^- \rightarrow Cr^{3+} + I_2$

   $Cr_2O_7^{2-} + 6e^- \rightarrow 2Cr^{3+}$.

   $2I^- \rightarrow I_2 + 2e^-$.

   $$+3 \quad\quad -1 \quad\quad -2 \quad\quad 0$$

   f. $NO_2^- + I^- \rightarrow NO(g) + I_2$

   $NO_2^- + e^- \rightarrow NO(g)$.

   $2I^- \rightarrow I_2 + 2e^-$.

   $$+2 \quad\quad -1 \quad\quad +1 \quad\quad\quad 0$$

   g. $Cu^{2+} + I^- \rightarrow CuI(s) + I_2$

   $Cu^{2+} + 1e^- \rightarrow CuI(s)$.

   $2I^- \rightarrow I_2 + 2e^-$.

   $$+3 \quad\quad -1 \quad\quad +2 \quad\quad\quad 0$$

   h. $Fe^{3+} + I^- \rightarrow Fe^{2+} + I_2$

   $Fe^{3+} + e^- \rightarrow Fe^{2+}$.

   $2I^- \rightarrow I_2 + 2e^-$.

   (Remember that half-reactions must be balanced only for the chemical species that gains or loses electrons.)

3. What color did the mixtures turn upon addition of $NaHSO_3$? $Na_2S_2O_3$? What does each indicate?

   All turned back to the original color or colorless, indicating the

   disappearance of I_2.

4. Given the reactants and products for Steps 2 and 3, write half-reactions for each:

   $HSO_3^- + I_2 \rightarrow SO_4^{2-} + I^-$

   $HSO_3^- \rightarrow SO_4^{2-} + 2e^-$

   $I_2 + 2e^- \rightarrow 2I^-$

   $S_2O_3^{2-} + I_2 \rightarrow S_4O_6^{2-} + I^-$

   $2S_2O_3^{2-} \rightarrow S_4O_6^{2-} + 2e^-$

   $I_2 + 2e^- \rightarrow 2I^-$

5. Fill in the table below with all of the oxidizing agents and reducing agents that you observed in this experiment.

Oxidizing agents	Reducing agents	Oxidizing agents	Reducing agents
OCl^-	I^-	$Cr_2O_7^{2-}$	I^-
MnO_4^-	I^-	NO_2^-	I^-
IH_2O_2	I^-	Cu^{2+}	I^-
IO_3^-	I^-	Fe^{3+}	I^-
I_2	HSO_3^-	I_2	$S_2O_3^{2-}$

6. Complete and balance redox equations for each reaction you observed. Multiply each half-reaction by coefficients that balance the electrons gained and lost, and add the half-reactions. For example,

$$2 \, [MnO_4^- + 5e^- \rightarrow Mn^{2+}]$$

$$\underline{5 \, [2I^- \rightarrow I_2 + 2e^-]}$$

$$2MnO_4^- + 10I^- \rightarrow 2Mn^{2+} + 5I_2$$

Add water to one side of the equation to balance the oxygens, and add H^+ to the other side to balance the hydrogens:

$$16H^+ + 2MnO_4^- + 10I^- \rightarrow 2Mn^{2+} + 5I_2 + 8H_2O$$

Check to see that all atoms are balanced and that the total charge is balanced.

a. $2H^+ + ClO^- + 2I^- \rightarrow Cl^- + I_2 + H_2O.$ _____

b. $16H^+ + 2MnO_4^- + 10I^- \rightarrow 2Mn^{2+} + 5I_2 + 8H_2O.$ _____

c. $2H^+ + H_2O_2 + 2I^- \rightarrow 2H_2O + I_2.$ _____

d. $6H^+ + IO_3^- + 5I^- \rightarrow 3I_2 + 3H_2O.$ _____

e. $14H^+ + Cr_2O_7^{2-} + 6I^- \rightarrow 2Cr^{3+} + 3I_2 + 7H_2O.$ _____

f. $4H^+ + 2NO_2^- + 2I^- \rightarrow 2NO(g) + I_2 + 2H_2O.$ _____

g. $2Cu^{2+} + 4I^- \rightarrow 2CuI(s) + I_2.$ _____

h. $2Fe^{3+} + 2I^- \rightarrow 2Fe^{2+} + I_2.$ _____

NOW IT'S YOUR TURN!

1. Recall that an *oxidizing agent* is a chemical that causes another chemical to be oxidized, and in the process, the oxidizing agent is reduced (gains electrons). Similarly, a *reducing agent* is a chemical that causes another chemical to be reduced, and in the process, the reducing agent is oxidized (loses electrons). For example, in this experiment, you observed that ClO^- is an oxidizing agent because each Cl atom is reduced from an oxidation number of $+1$ to -1. Also, I^- is a reducing agent because each I atom is oxidized from an oxidation number of -1 to 0.

$$ClO^- + 2e^- \rightarrow Cl^- \qquad 2I^- \rightarrow I_2 + 2e^-$$

Name _____ Date _____ Class _____

Add one drop of each solution to the indicated space. Add HCl if no reaction occurs. Then write half-reactions and a redox equation, and identify the oxidizing agent and the reducing agent for each. If no reaction occurs, indicate no visible reaction by writing "NVR."

	$MnO_4^- \rightarrow Mn^{2+}$ $KMnO_4$	$Cr_2O_7^{2-} \rightarrow Cr^{3+}$ $K_2Cr_2O_7$	$I_2 \rightarrow I^-$ KI + Starch + NaClO	$Fe^{3+} \rightarrow Fe^{2+}$ $FeCl_3$
$NaHSO_3$ $HSO_3^- \rightarrow SO_4^{2-}$	colorless	NVR	colorless	colorless
H_2O_2 $H_2O_2 \rightarrow O_2$	colorless, bubbles	black to blue to green, bubbles	NVR	colorless, bubbles
$Na_2S_2O_3$ *$S_2O_3^{2-} \rightarrow SO_4^{2-}$	colorless	green	colorless	colorless
$NaNO_2$ **$NO_2^- \rightarrow NO(g) + NO_3^-$	colorless	NVR	NVR	NVR

What gas produces the bubbles you saw? In which mixtures did you see bubbles?

O_2 gas. H_2O_2 + $KMnO_4$, H_2O_2 + $K_2Cr_2O_7$, and H_2O_2 + $FeCl_3$.

Describe what happens with each mixing. Make a table of your results.

*In the presence of I_2, thiosulfate undergoes this reaction: $2S_2O_3^{2-} + I \rightarrow S_4O_6^{2-} + 2I^-$
**In the presence of acid, the nitrite ion reacts to form nitrogen oxide gas: $3NO_2^- + 2H^+ \rightarrow 2NO(g) + H_2O + NO_3^-$

Chapter 21 • *Electrochemistry*   **SMALL-SCALE EXPERIMENT**

36 SMALL-SCALE VOLTAIC CELLS

Small-Scale Experiment for text Section 21.1

OBJECTIVES

- **Build** and **test** simple voltaic cells.
- **Measure** and **compare** the voltages of commercial cells with the ones you build.
- **Describe** the chemistry of voltaic cells by writing half-reactions.
- **Construct** an electrochemical series from experimental data.

INTRODUCTION

Americans own some 900 million battery-operated devices and spend 2.5 billion dollars a year feeding the devices batteries. Batteries (voltaic dry cells) are simple devices that transform chemical energy into electrical energy. They operate on the principle of oxidation–reduction chemistry. One chemical inside the battery is a reducing agent and gives up electrons. Another chemical is an oxidizing agent and accepts the electrons given up by the former. The flow of electrons from one chemical to another constitutes an electric current. The device is designed to tap the electric current that flows from reducing agent to oxidizing agent. As the chemical reaction progresses, less and less current is produced. Eventually the current diminishes to the extent that the battery is essentially "dead." At this point, you usually throw it away and replace it with a new one.

Which materials make the best batteries? In previous experiments, you discovered that some metals lose electrons more readily than others. The metal cations that are formed as a result do not gain electrons as readily as do metal cations formed from less reactive metals.

The following list of half-reactions shows the reduction of metal ions to metal atoms. The reverse of each half-reaction is the oxidation half-reaction of the metal. Any metal on the list will react only with a metal ion that is below it in the list. For example, magnesium metal, Mg(*s*), will react with all of the other metal ions in the list. Iron, Fe(*s*), will react only with Cu^{2+} and Ag^+. Silver, Ag(*s*), will not react with any of the metal ions in the list.

$$Mg^{2+} + 2e^- \rightarrow Mg(s)$$
$$Zn^{2+} + 2e^- \rightarrow Zn(s)$$
$$Fe^{3+} + 3e^- \rightarrow Fe(s)$$
$$Cu^{2+} + 2e^- \rightarrow Cu(s)$$
$$Ag^+ + e^- \rightarrow Ag(s)$$

Name _____ Date _____ Class _____

PURPOSE

In this experiment, you will build some small-scale batteries (voltaic cells) from metals and solutions of metal ions. You will use a volt meter to measure and compare the voltages they produce. You will relate this information to the redox chemistry involved and to the activity series you developed in Small-Scale Experiment 34.

SAFETY ☣ ☠ ✂

- Wear safety goggles.
- Use full small-scale pipets only for the controlled delivery of liquids.
- Don't chew gum, drink, or eat in the laboratory. Never taste a chemical in the laboratory.
- To avoid a puncture wound, use scissors or other sharp objects only as intended.

MATERIALS

Small-scale pipets of the following solutions:
copper(II) sulfate ($CuSO_4$)
zinc chloride ($ZnCl_2$)
sodium nitrate ($NaNO_3$)
silver nitrate ($AgNO_3$)
lead(II) nitrate [$Pb(NO_3)_2$]
magnesium sulfate ($MgSO_4$)

Solids:
copper (Cu)
zinc (Zn)
silver (Ag)
lead (Pb)
magnesium (Mg)

EQUIPMENT

volt meter
various commercial batteries (dry cells)
small-scale reaction surface
scissors
9-cm filter paper

EXPERIMENTAL PAGE

1. Measure the voltage of these commercial cells: standard carbon, heavy duty, alkaline, rechargeable. (A positive meter reading means the electrons flow into the meter at the connector labeled "−".) Reverse the leads and measure the voltage again. Record your results in Table 36.1.

2. Test copper and zinc in the spaces below. Record your results in Table 36.2.

    a. Mix two drops of each of the indicated solutions with one piece of each metal.

<table>
<tr><td></td><td>2 drops $CuSO_4$</td><td>2 drops $ZnCl_2$</td><td></td></tr>
<tr><td>1 piece Zn</td><td></td><td></td><td>1 piece Cu</td></tr>
</table>

    b. Cut and place a rectangular piece of filter paper on the template below, and add three drops of each solution so the center solution barely overlaps the other two solutions. Then add one piece of each metal and measure the positive (+) voltage of the cell you just made. Reverse the leads and measure it again. Record your results in Table 36.2.

<table>
<tr><td>$CuSO_4$</td><td>$NaNO_3$</td><td>$ZnCl_2$</td></tr>
<tr><td>Cu(s)</td><td></td><td>Zn(s)</td></tr>
</table>

3. Cut a piece of filter paper as shown below, and add a few drops of each solution so that each "arm" is wet. The $NaNO_3$ solution should touch the other solutions. Place a piece of the indicated metal on each arm and measure the voltages of each lead (Pb) cell with the black, negative (−) connector on "Pb." Press firmly. Record the voltages in Table 36.3.

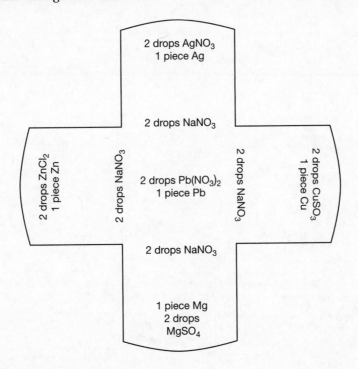

EXPERIMENTAL DATA

Record your results in Tables 36.1, 36.2, and 36.3 or in copies of the tables in your notebook.

Table 36.1   Commercial Dry Cell Voltages

Name of commercial cell	Voltage	Voltage(with leads reversed)
standard carbon	1.5	−1.5
heavy duty	1.5	−1.5
alkaline	1.5	−1.5
rechargeable	1.25	−1.25

Values may be lower if "dead" batteries are used.

Table 36.2   Copper-Zinc Cell

a. $CuSO_4$ + Zn(s)	$ZnCl_2$ + Cu(s)	b. Voltage of Cu–Zn cell
black ppt	NVR	+0.95

Table 36.3   Lead Cells

Ag	Cu	Mg	Zn
0.84	0.42	−1.25	−0.53

Electrons flow away from:

Pb	Pb	Mg	Zn

CLEANING UP

Avoid contamination by cleaning up in a way that protects you and your environment. Carefully clean and dry the pieces of metal and place them in the proper recycling containers. Clean the small-scale reaction surface by absorbing the contents onto a paper towel, wipe it with a damp paper towel, and dry it. Dispose of the paper towels in the waste bin. Wash your hands thoroughly with soap and water.

QUESTIONS FOR ANALYSES

Use what you learned in this experiment to answer the following questions.

1. When measuring voltages, what happens when you reverse the red, positive (+) and black, negative (−) leads of the volt meter?

   The sign of the voltage changes, but the absolute value does not.

2. When the meter reads a positive voltage, into which connector do the electrons flow?

   The black, negative (−) one.

3. Which reaction occurs in Step 2a? Write half-reactions for the reaction.

   Zinc reacts with copper sulfate:

   $Zn(s) \rightarrow Zn^{2+} + 2e^-$.

   $Cu^{2+} + 2e^- \rightarrow Cu(s)$.

4. Based on the sign of the voltage, which metal loses electrons, Cu or Zn? Explain.

   Zn. The voltage is positive when the black (−) connector is on zinc. Electrons

   flow from Zn into the meter.

5. Write the half-reactions for the Cu–Zn cell you constructed in Step 2b. How do these compare to those you wrote for Step 2a?

   $Zn(s) \rightarrow Zn^{2+} + 2e^-$.

   $Cu^{2+} + 2e^- \rightarrow Cu(s)$.

   The reactions are the same.

6. Construct a set of reduction potentials by writing *reduction* half-reactions for all five metals, including lead, from Step 3. Assign 0.00 volts to Pb, and list the half-reactions in order of increasing voltages (most negative value first).

Half-reaction	Voltage
$Mg^{2+} + 2e^- \rightarrow Mg(s)$	−1.25
$Zn^{2+} + 2e^- \rightarrow Zn(s)$	−0.53
$Pb^{2+} + 2e^- \rightarrow Pb(s)$	0.00
$Cu^{2+} + 2e^- \rightarrow Cu(s)$	+0.42
$Ag^+ + e^- \rightarrow Ag(s)$	+0.84

7. Compare your ordered list of half-reactions to the activity series you developed in Small-Scale Experiment 34. What conclusions can you draw?

   It's similar, but lead is in place of iron.

8. Draw a simple cross-sectional diagram of the Zn–Cu cell you made showing the direction of electron flow. Mark the cathode, the anode, and the salt bridge.

9. The table of reduction potentials you constructed in Question 8 can be used to predict the voltages of a cell made from any two metals on the table. Simply find the difference between the two voltages in question. For example, the voltage of an Ag–Zn cell will probably be about 1.37 volts [0.84 − (−0.53) = 1.37]. Use your reduction potential table above to predict the voltages of the following cells: Ag–Cu, Ag–Zn, Ag–Mg, Cu–Zn, Cu–Mg, Zn–Mg.

0.42, 1.37, 2.1, 0.95, 1.7, 0.72.

NOW IT'S YOUR TURN!

1. Design an experiment to measure the cell voltages of each cell for which you predicted values in Question 9, and compare your results with your predicted values.

Red (+) connector on:

Black (−) connector on:	Ag	Cu	Pb	Zn	Pb
Ag		−0.40	−0.86	−1.42	−2.13
Cu	+0.40		−0.42	−0.98	−1.75
Pb	+0.89	+0.42		−0.53	−1.25
Zn	+1.40	+0.96	+0.56		−0.59
Mg	+2.17	+1.75	+1.30	+0.61	

2. Make a good guess as to what the metals are in such common metal objects as nickels, dimes, food cans, soft-drink cans, nails, washers, and galvanized nails. Test each of your predictions by replacing one of the metal electrodes in Step 3 of the experiment with the common metal object in question. What common metal is each object made from? Are your results conclusive? Suggest an explanation.

3. Go shopping and record the prices of various types of the same sizes of commercial voltaic cells (batteries). The following table compares the lifetimes of various commercial batteries. Use your data and the table to decide which type of battery is the most cost-effective.

Type of cell	Expected lifetime (hours)*	Price
General purpose (zinc-carbon)	1–7	_____
Heavy duty (zinc-chloride)	1.5–15	_____
Alkaline	5–27	_____
Rechargeable (nickel-cadmium)**	2–7	_____

*The expected lifetime varies with the size of the battery, the device in which it is used, and whether it is used continuously or intermittently.
**Can be recharged up to 1000 times with a recharger.

37 MOLECULAR STRUCTURE OF HYDROCARBONS

Small-Scale Experiment for text Section 22.3

OBJECTIVES

- **Construct** models of hydrocarbon molecules.
- **Compare** the structures of hydrocarbons with their chemical formulas.
- **Compare** the structures of alkanes, alkenes, and alkynes.

INTRODUCTION

Chemical formulas give you information about the composition of substances as well as their structures. Organic chemistry uses many different kinds of formulas and models to describe the composition and structure of molecules.

A molecular formula shows only the number and kinds of atoms in a molecule. A *structural formula* is more useful for studying organic compounds because it shows the arrangement of atoms in a molecule and the types of bonds. Compounds with the same molecular formula but different structural formulas are called isomers. In a *complete structural formula,* every atom and every bond is shown. In a *condensed structural formula,* either none of the bonds are shown or only the bonds between carbon atoms are shown. In a *line-angle formula,* a straight line is used to represent each carbon-carbon bond. A carbon atom is understood to be at each corner where lines meet. The hydrogen atoms are not shown at all. It is understood that there are enough hydrogen atoms attached to each carbon atom so that each carbon atom forms four bonds. A *ball-and-stick model* shows how the atoms and bonds are arranged in space. It is does not show the relative distances between the atoms.

	Molecular and line-angle formula	Complete structural formula	Condensed structural formulas	Ball-and-stick model
Butane	C_4H_{10}		$CH_3CH_2CH_2CH_3$	
2-methylpropane	C_4H_{10}		CH_3CHCH_3 CH_3	

PURPOSE

In this experiment, you will make models of hydrocarbons to help you visualize their three-dimensional structures. You will use pipe cleaners to represent the bonds; polystyrene spheres to represent the carbon atoms; and pop beads to represent the hydrogen atoms. Black pipe cleaners will represent carbon-carbon bonds and white pipe cleaners will represent carbon-hydrogen bonds. You will bend the pipe cleaners to better represent the three-dimensional geometry of molecules.

SAFETY ✂

- Behave in a way that is consistent with a safe laboratory.
- To avoid a puncture wound, use scissors or other sharp objects only as intended.

EQUIPMENT

12 pop beads
3 black and 3 white pipe cleaners
6 one-inch-diameter polystyrene spheres
scissors
ruler

EXPERIMENTAL PROCEDURE

Make a model of each hydrocarbon listed in Table 37.1, and fill in Table 37.1.

1. Construct a ball-and-stick model of methane, CH_4.

   a. Insert four 2-cm-long pieces of white pipe cleaner into a polystyrene sphere, arranging them so they form a tetrahedron. (The bond angles in methane are all 109.5°, which is lightly larger than a right angle.)

   b. Place a pop bead on the end of each pipe cleaner.

2. Construct a ball-and-stick model of ethane, CH_3CH_3.

   a. Connect two polystyrene spheres with a 5-cm piece of black pipe cleaner.

   b. Insert three 2-cm-long pieces of white pipe cleaner into each polystyrene sphere, arranging the pieces so they form a tetrahedron. (The bond angles in ethane are all 109.5°.)

   c. Place a pop bead on the end of each pipe cleaner.

3. Construct a ball-and-stick model of propane, $CH_3CH_2CH_3$.

   a. Connect three polystyrene spheres with two 5-cm pieces of black pipe cleaner, adjusting the angles formed by the pipe cleaners to be slightly greater than a right angle.

   b. Insert two 2-cm long pieces of white pipe cleaner into the center sphere and three in each of the end spheres. Adjust all the angles so they are slightly greater than right angles.

   c. Place a pop bead on the end of each pipe cleaner.

4. Use the same techniques to construct models of the following hydrocarbons. Be sure each carbon has four bonds.

   a. butane, $CH_3CH_2CH_2CH_3$ (See p. 261.)

   b. 2-methylpropane (See p. 261.)

   c. pentane, $CH_3CH_2CH_2CH_2CH_3$

5. Ethene is an alkene. All six carbon atoms lie in the same plane with bond angles between the carbon atoms of 120°.

   a. Construct a model of ethene, $CH_2{=}CH_2$.

   b. Construct a model of propene, $CH_3CH{=}CH_2$.

6. Ethyne is an alkyne. All four atoms lie in a straight line.

   a. Construct a model of ethyne, $CH{\equiv}CH$.

   b. Construct a model of propyne, $CH_3C{\equiv}CH$.

Name _____ Date _____ Class _____

EXPERIMENTAL DATA

Record your results in Table 37.1 or in a copy of the table in your notebook.

Table 37.1   Models of Hydrocarbons

Name	Molecular Formula	Structural Formula	Ball-and-Stick Diagram	Bond Angles
1. methane	CH_4	CH_4		109°
2. ethane	C_2H_6	CH_3CH_3		109°
3. propane	C_3H_3	$CH_3CH_2CH_3$		109°
4a. butane	C_4H_{10}	$CH_3CH_2CH_2CH_3$		109°
4b. 2-methylbutane	C_5H_{12}	$\begin{array}{c} CH_3CHCH_2CH_3 \\ \mid \\ CH_3 \end{array}$		109°
4c. pentane	C_5H_{12}	$CH_3CH_2CH_2CH_2CH_3$		109°
5a. ethene	C_2H_4	$CH_2{=}CH_2$		120°
5b. propene	C_3H_6	$CH_3CH_2{=}CH_2$		109° and 120°
6a. ethyne	C_2H_2	$CH{\equiv}CH$		180°
6b. propyne	C_3H_4	$CH_3C{\equiv}CH$		180° and 109°

Name _____ Date _____ Class _____

CLEANING UP

When you finish, take apart your models, straighten out each piece of pipe cleaner, and put them away as directed by your teacher.

QUESTIONS FOR ANALYSES

Use what you learned in this experiment to answer the following questions.

1. What information does a molecular formula provide? Give an example.

It shows the number of each kind of atom in a compound. The formula C_2H_6 shows

that a molecule of ethane consists of two carbon atoms and six hydrogen atoms.

2. What information does a structural formula provide? Give an example.

It shows the arrangement of atoms in a molecule and the types of bonds.

CH_3CH_3, ethane.

3. What is the difference between a complete structural formula and a condensed structural formula?

The complete structural formula shows each atom and each bond. The condensed

structural formula shows either only the atoms or the atoms and only the

carbon-carbon bonds.

4. What additional information does a ball-and-stick model provide?

The ball-and-stick model shows how the atoms in a molecule are arranged in space.

5. What is the bond angle of a carbon-carbon single bond?

109.5°.

6. What is the bond angle of a carbon-carbon double bond?

120°.

7. What is the bond angle of a carbon-carbon triple bond?

180°.

NOW IT'S YOUR TURN!

1. Construct models of the following cyclic hydrocarbons. Recall that in a cyclic hydrocarbon, there is a ring of carbon atoms.

    a. cyclopropane (**Hint:** You can use your propane model to begin to construct this model.)

    b. cyclobutane

2. A branched-chain alkene may have *cis* and *trans* geometric isomers. Construct models of 1-butene (CH_2=$CHCH_2CH_3$) and 2-butene (CH_3CH=$CHCH_3$). Which compound has geometric isomers? Construct models of each geometric isomer.

   2-butene has geometric isomers.

3. Construct models of 1-butyne, C≡CCH_2CH_3, and 2-butyne, CH_3C≡CCH_3. Use the models to determine if either of these alkynes have geometric isomers.

   Alkynes have no geometric isomers because each of the carbons on either side of

   the triple bond are bonded to only one other atom, and the carbon atoms are bonded

   at a 180° angle.

4. Benzene, C_6H_6, is an aromatic hydrocarbon. All 12 of its atoms lie in the same plane. Its six carbon atoms form a ring. Construct a model of benzene.

5. Construct a line-angle model of methane, CH_4, without using spheres as atoms. Compare it to your ball-and-stick model.

   a. Fold two 4-cm-long pieces of white pipe cleaner in half, making a bend in the center of each piece.

   b. Interlock the pipe cleaners and pinch them together at the bends.

   c. Unfold the four ends so they form angles slightly larger than right angles.

6. Construct a line-angle model of ethane, CH_3CH_3, without using spheres as atoms. Compare it to your ball-and-stick model.

   a. Make another model of methane.

   b. Cut a 5-cm-long piece of black pipe cleaner and bend the piece so that there is a small hook at each end.

   c. Attach a methane molecule to each end of the black pipe cleaner by pinching a hook around each methane molecule's center. (How many bonds does each carbon have in your model?)

   d. Eliminate a hydrogen from each end by twisting together any two of the white pipe cleaners.

   e. Arrange all the angles so they are slightly larger than right angles.

7. Construct a model of propane, $CH_3CH_2CH_3$.

   a. Cut a 10-cm-long piece of black pipe cleaner and fold it in half.

   b. Fold a 4-cm-long piece of white pipe cleaner in half, and pinch together the black and white pipe cleaners at their folds.

   c. Attach a methane molecule to each end, as with ethane, and twist together two hydrogens at each end.

   d. Make all the angles slightly larger than right angles.

38 VITAMIN C IN TABLETS

Small-Scale Experiment for text Section 23.3

OBJECTIVES

- **Determine** the vitamin C content of vitamin C tablets by iodometric titration.
- **Observe** the oxidation of vitamin C in aqueous solution.

INTRODUCTION

Vitamins regulate biochemical reactions that take place within living cells. The human body requires vitamins only in tiny amounts. For a compound to be classified as a vitamin, its absence in the diet must cause a specific disease that is cured when the vitamin is resupplied. Vitamin C deficiency, for example, causes scurvy, a disease common to sailors until the latter part of the eighteenth century.

PURPOSE

In this experiment, you will use an iodometric titration to measure the amount of vitamin C in vitamin supplements. This method takes advantage of the fact that vitamin C is a water-soluble organic compound that is easily oxidized and is therefore a good reducing agent. Iodine oxidizes vitamin C according to the following equation:

$$CH_2OH \quad H \quad \cdots \quad + I_2 \rightarrow 2H^+ + 2I^- + \quad CH_2OH \quad H \quad \cdots$$

$C_6H_8O_6$
Vitamin C
(Ascorbic acid)

$C_6H_6O_6$
Oxidized form of vitamin C
(Dehydroascorbic acid)

Because aqueous iodine solutions are unstable and inconvenient to work with, you will titrate vitamin C samples in this lab with potassium iodate, KIO_3, in the presence of an acidic iodide solution. The iodate ion oxidizes iodide to iodine.

$$IO_3^- + 5I^- + 6H^+ \rightleftharpoons 3I_2 + 3H_2O$$

Notice that an equilibrium is established. To ensure that the reaction goes to completion, it is necessary to use excess iodide and to make the solution acidic.

The iodine formed in this reaction immediately oxidizes the vitamin C according to the previous equation. Once all the vitamin C is oxidized, there will be an excess of I_2 that will react with starch to form the distinctive blue-black complex. This change serves as a good end point.

Name _____ Date _____ Class _____

SAFETY ⬛ ⬛ ⬛ ⬛ ⬛

- Wear safety goggles, an apron, and gloves when working with corrosive chemicals.
- Use full small-scale pipets only for the controlled delivery of liquids.
- Don't chew gum, drink, or eat in the laboratory. Never taste a chemical in the laboratory.
- Avoid inhaling substances that can irritate your respiratory system.

MATERIALS

various vitamin C tablets (100 mg)
Small-scale pipets of the following solutions:
0.1M potassium iodate (KIO_3)   starch
potassium iodide (KI)   vitamin C (ascorbic acid)
hydrochloric acid (HCl)

EQUIPMENT

small-scale reaction surface, plastic cup, balance

EXPERIMENTAL PROCEDURE

Part A. The Chemistry of the Titration

1. Place two drops of KIO_3 on a small-scale reaction surface, and add the following solutions. Stir each mixture and record your results in Table 38.1.

   a. Add two drops of KI and two drops of HCl. In acid solution, iodate ion oxidizes iodide ion to iodine: $IO_3^- + 5I^- + 6H^+ \rightleftharpoons 3I_2 + 3H_2O$

   b. Add a few more drops of KI to the above mixture. Excess iodide ion reacts with iodine to form triodide ion: $I^- + I_2 \rightarrow I_3^-$

   c. Now add one drop of starch. Starch reacts with triodide ion to form a starch iodine complex: $I_3^- + starch \rightarrow starch\text{-}iodine\ complex$

   d. Now add vitamin C, stirring until the black color disappears. Vitamin C reduces iodine to iodide ion: $C_6H_8O_6 + I_2 \rightarrow 2H^- + 2I^- + C_6H_6O_6$

   e. Finally, add KIO_3 until the black color reappears. At this point, all the vitamin C has reacted and the excess iodate reacts to form iodine, which gives the black end point in the presence of starch.

Part B. Titration of Vitamin C in Tablets

2. Crush a vitamin C tablet on a piece of paper, and transfer *all* of it to a clean, dry cup.

3. Add 10 drops KI, two drops HCl, and three drops starch.

4. Tare a full KIO_3 pipet.

   a. Place a full KIO_3 pipet in a clean, dry small-scale balance pan.

   b. Adjust the beam until the small-scale pointer indicates the zero point.

5. Titrate the vitamin C with KIO_3 to a jet black end point.

6. Determine the mass loss of the KIO_3. Record your findings in Table 38.2.

   a. Replace the pipet on the small-scale balance.

   b. Add weights to zero the small-scale balance again. The sum of the added weights is the mass loss of the KIO_3.

7. Repeat until your results are consistent.

EXPERIMENTAL DATA

Record your results in Tables 38.1 and 38.2 or in copies of the tables in your notebook.

Table 38.1   The Chemistry of the Titration

	KIO_3	KI + HCl	Excess KI	Starch	Vitamin C	KIO_3
Color	colorless	yellow	dark yellow	black	colorless	black

Table 38.2   Titration of Vitamin C in Tablets

Tablet	1	2	3	4
Mass loss of KIO_3 (mg)	1932	1855		
Vitamin C per tablet (mg)	102	98		

Calculate the milligrams of vitamin C in each tablet you titrated. Record your results in Table 38.2. To do the calculation, you will need the following pieces of information:

a. The mass loss of KIO_3 used in the titration in mg.

b. The density of the KIO_3 solution = 1 mL/1000 mg.

c. The concentration of KIO_3 = 0.1 mmol/mL.

d. 3 mmol vitamin C/1 mmol of KIO_3.

e. The molecular mass of vitamin C = 176 mg/mmol.

   mg Vitamin C = $\mathbf{a} \times \mathbf{b} \times \mathbf{c} \times \mathbf{d} \times \mathbf{e}$

To be sure you understand the calculation, substitute each quantity (number and units) into the equation and cancel the units. For subsequent calculations, simplify the equation by combining terms that are always constant.

CLEANING UP

Avoid contamination by cleaning up in a way that protects you and your environment. Carefully clean the plastic cup by pouring the liquid contents down the drain and rinsing it thoroughly with water. Dry it with a paper towel. Clean the small-scale reaction surface by absorbing the contents onto a paper towel, wipe it with a damp paper towel, and dry it. Dispose of the paper towels in the waste bin. Wash your hands thoroughly with soap and water.

QUESTIONS FOR ANALYSES

Use what you learned in this experiment to answer the following questions.

1. When you mix KI, KIO$_3$, and HCl, what is produced? How can you tell? Write the net ionic equation.

   I$_2$. Starch turns black. IO$_3^-$ + 5I$^-$ + 6H$^+$ ⇌ 3I$_2$ + 3H$_2$O.

2. When you add vitamin C to the black I$_2$ mixture, why does the color disappear? Write a net ionic equation.

   Vitamin C reduces I$_2$ to I$^-$. C$_6$H$_8$O$_6$ + I$_2$ → 2H$^+$ + 2I$^-$ + C$_6$H$_6$O$_6$.

3. Compare the values for the amount of vitamin C you calculated with the values you find on the product label by calculating the absolute error and the relative error.

   absolute error = |mg measured experimentally − mg on label|

   |102 mg measured − 100 mg on label| = 2 mg absolute error
   |98 mg measured − 100 mg on label| = 2 mg absolute error

   $$\text{relative (\%) error} = \frac{\text{absolute error}}{\text{mg on label}} \times 100$$

   $\dfrac{2 \text{ mg}}{100 \text{ mg}} \times 100 = 2\%$ relative error

4. Why can the density of the KIO$_3$ solution be taken as 1000 mg/mL?

   Dilute aqueous solutions have very nearly the same density as pure water.

NOW IT'S YOUR TURN!

1. Design and carry out an experiment to determine the amount of vitamin C in tablets containing amounts of vitamin C larger than 100 mg. Tell what you do, what your results are, and what they mean.

   The major problem is the sample size. Either students must use fractions

   of tablets and account for the differences, or they must use more

   concentrated KIO$_3$.

2. Design an experiment to measure the amount of vitamin C in a tablet by using volumetric techniques. Compare your results to those obtained from the weight titration in this lab. (**Hint:** Dissolve the vitamin C tablet in a known amount of water, and titrate a measured amount of the resulting solution. You will have to calibrate your pipets by using a balance or a well strip.)

3. Dissolve a vitamin C tablet in water, and design an experiment to measure the amount of vitamin C that remains as a function of time. How does temperature affect your results?

Chapter 23 • *Functional Groups*   **SMALL-SCALE EXPERIMENT**

39 VITAMIN C IN DRINKS

Small-Scale Experiment for text Section 23.3

OBJECTIVE

- **Measure** and **compare** the amounts of vitamin C in various kinds of fruit juices and fruit-drink mixes.

INTRODUCTION

If you have decided to obtain your vitamin C from a well-balanced diet, you may be wondering, "What is the best source of vitamin C, and how much of it do I need to eat or drink?" Orange juice is well-known for its vitamin C content, but many other foods, especially fresh fruits and vegetables, provide substantial amounts of the nutrient. Most noteworthy are other citrus fruits such as lemons, tangerines, and grapefruits. Other good sources of vitamin C are asparagus, broccoli, Brussels sprouts, cauliflower, cabbage, cantaloupe, green peppers, parsley, spinach, rutabagas, and turnip greens. However, prolonged cooking of fresh vegetables in water destroys much of the existing vitamin C.

PURPOSE

In this experiment, you will use the iodometric titration technique you learned in Small-Scale Experiment 38 to determine the vitamin C content of various foods. You will compare the vitamin C content of fresh-squeezed orange juice, frozen orange juice concentrate, and grapefruit juice. You will also measure and compare the vitamin C content of other juices and fruit-drink mixes.

SAFETY 🫁 🧍 ☠️ 🜋 🜍

- Wear safety goggles, an apron, and gloves when working with corrosive chemicals.
- Use full small-scale pipets only for the controlled delivery of liquids.
- Consider all foods used in this experiment to be contaminated. Do not taste any samples or eat or drink anything in the laboratory.
- Avoid inhaling substances that can irritate your respiratory system.

MATERIALS

various samples of fruit juices and fruit drinks
Small-scale pipets of the following solutions:
potassium iodide (KI)
hydrochloric acid (HCl)
0.01M potassium iodate (KIO$_3$)
starch

EQUIPMENT

plastic cup

EXPERIMENTAL PROCEDURE

1. Measure approximately 5000 mg of juice. Record the mass in Table 39.1.

   a. Place a nickel (or two pennies) of known mass in the plastic cup on the balance pan.

   b. Adjust the balance to zero.

   c. Remove the nickel, and add juice to the cup until the balance again reads zero.

2. Add 10 drops of KI, 20 drops of HCl, and five drops of starch to the juice.

3. Tare a full KIO$_3$ pipet.

   a. Place a full KIO$_3$ pipet in a second clean, dry balance pan.

   b. Adjust the beam until the pointer indicates the zero point.

4. Titrate the juice with KIO$_3$ to a jet black end point.

5. Determine the mass loss of the KIO$_3$. Record your results in Table 39.1.

   a. Replace the KIO$_3$ pipet in the balance.

   b. Add weights to zero the balance. The sum of the added weights is the mass loss of KIO$_3$.

6. Repeat until your results are consistent.

7. Repeat for several other juice samples as directed by your teacher.

EXPERIMENTAL DATA

Record your results in Table 39.1 or in a copy of the table in your notebook.

Table 39.1 Vitamin C in Drinks

	Mass of juice (mg)	Mass loss of KIO_3 (mg)	Vitamin C per 6-oz glass (mg)
Fresh orange juice	5000	305	57
Frozen orange juice	5000	250	47
Fresh grapefruit juice	5000	150	28

Calculate the milligrams of vitamin C in a 6-oz glass for each sample you titrated. Record your results in Table 39.1. To do the calculation, you will need the following pieces of information:

   a. The mass loss of the KIO_3 you used in the titration in mg.

   b. The mass of the juice you used in the titration in mg.

   c. Density of juice = 1000 mg/mL.

   d. Density of KIO_3 solution = 1000 mg/mL.

   e. Concentration of KIO_3 = 0.01 mmol/mL.

   f. Molecular mass of vitamin C = 176 mg/mmol.

   g. 3 mmol vitamin C/1 mmol KIO_3.

   h. 29.6 mL/1 oz.

   i. 6 oz/1 glass.

$$\frac{x \text{ mg vitamin C}}{1 \text{ glass}} = \frac{a}{b} \times \frac{c}{d} \times e \times f \times g \times h \times i$$

To be sure you understand the calculation, substitute each quantity (number and units) into the equation and cancel the units. For subsequent calculations, simplify the equation by combining terms that are always constant.

CLEANING UP

Avoid contamination by cleaning up in a way that protects you and your environment. Carefully clean the plastic balance pan by pouring the liquid contents down the drain and rinsing it thoroughly with water. Dry it with a paper towel. Dispose of the paper towels in the waste bin. Wash your hands thoroughly with soap and water.

Name _____ Date _____ Class _____

QUESTIONS FOR ANALYSES

Use your Experimental Data and what you learned in this experiment to answer the following questions.

1. Write a net ionic equation for the reaction of iodate ion with iodide ion in the presence of acid. (See Small-Scale Experiment 38.)

$$IO_3^- + 5I^- + 6H^+ \rightleftharpoons 3I_2 + 3H_2O.$$

2. Given the two half-reactions for the reaction of vitamin C with iodine, identify the oxidation and the reduction, and write and balance an equation in acid solution:

oxidation: $C_6H_8O_6 \rightarrow C_6H_6O_6 + 2e^-$

reduction: $I_2 + 2e^- \rightarrow 2I^-$

net ionic: $C_6H_8O_6 + I_2 \rightarrow 2H^+ + 2I^- + C_6H_6O_6$

3. The recommended dietary allowance (RDA) is the amount of any vitamin or mineral your daily diet should supply to maintain a general standard of good health. The RDA of vitamin C is 60 mg. Calculate how many ounces of each of the various fruit juices you need to consume to receive the RDA of vitamin C.

$$\text{oz of juice} = 60 \text{ mg} \times \frac{6 \text{ oz of juice}}{\text{mg vitamin C}}$$

Fresh orange juice = 60 × 6/57 = 6.3 oz, frozen orange juice =

60 × 6/47 = 7.7 oz, fresh grapefruit juice = 60 × 6/28 = 12.9 oz.

4. Go on a shopping trip and record the prices of the various sources of vitamin C you titrated (orange juice, grapefruit juice, fruit drinks, and tablets). Determine the cost of 60 mg of vitamin C from each source. Which source is least expensive? Which source is most expensive?

NOW IT'S YOUR TURN!

1. Design and carry out experiments that will give you data to compare the amount of vitamin C in various packages of orange juice (cartons, cans, fresh-squeezed).

2. Design and carry out experiments to determine the amount of vitamin C in powdered flavored fruit drinks.

   Use a 200-mg sample of the powder and titrate with 0.01 M KIO₃. Read the

   label on the powdered product to determine what fraction 200 mg is

   of the total contents. Use this fraction to calculate the total amount of

   vitamin C in the original package.

3. Determine the amount of vitamin C in the water used to boil a fresh vegetable that is known to be high in vitamin C.

   Boil the vegetable and titrate a sample of the water.

40 REACTIONS OF BIOMOLECULES

Small-Scale Experiment for text Sections 24.2, 24.3, and 24.4

OBJECTIVES

- **Observe** and **record** reactions of important classes of biological molecules.
- **Identify** classes of biological compounds in foods from experimental data.

INTRODUCTION

The food you eat can be classified into five different chemical categories: carbohydrates, proteins, fats, vitamins, and minerals. Carbohydrates are monomers and polymers of aldehydes and ketones with numerous hydroxyl groups attached. One of the simplest carbohydrates is glucose, a monosaccharide, or simple sugar. The chemical structure of glucose looks like this:

Starch is a polysaccharide composed of many repeating glucose subunits. Its structure looks like this:

Proteins are long, continuous chains of simpler molecules called amino acids. Amino acids are compounds containing amino ($-NH_2$) and carboxylic acid ($-COOH$) groups in the same molecule. Linked together, two or more amino acids constitute a peptide. A peptide with more than 100 amino acids is called a protein.

Fats are long-chain carboxylic acids, or esters. Triglycerides are triesters of long-chain fatty acids. The R-groups represent a long saturated or unsaturated hydrocarbon chain.

$$R-\overset{\overset{\displaystyle O}{\|}}{C}-O-R$$

A fat

$$CH_2-OCR$$
$$CH-OCR$$
$$CH_2-OCR$$

A triglyceride

PURPOSE

In this experiment, you will test various foods for the presence of starch, protein, and fat. You will do this by carrying out some common chemical tests for these kinds of molecules.

SAFETY

- Wear safety goggles.
- Use full small-scale pipets only for the controlled delivery of liquids.
- Consider all foods used in this experiment to be contaminated. Do not taste any samples or eat or drink anything in the laboratory.
- To avoid a puncture wound, use scissors or other sharp objects only as intended.
- Do not touch hot glassware or equipment.

MATERIALS

Small-scale pipets of the following solutions:
potassium iodide (KI)
sodium hypochlorite (NaClO)
starch
Small samples of various foods including dry cereal, milk, powdered milk, pasta, sugar, potato chips, crackers, peanut butter, margarine, corn oil, yeast, gelatin, and flour.
copper(II) sulfate ($CuSO_4$)
sodium hydroxide (NaOH)
water
Sudan III

EQUIPMENT

small-scale reaction surface
white paper
toothpick
scissors

EXPERIMENTAL PAGE

1. To test for starch, mix one drop each of KI and NaClO in each square below with a small sample of the indicated substance. Record your results in Table 40.1.

starch	pasta	cracker	bread	cereal	flour

2. To test for protein, mix one drop each of $CuSO_4$ and NaOH in each square below with a small sample of the indicated substance. Record your results in Table 40.2.

milk	powdered milk	yeast	gelatin	bread	water

3. To test for fat, place a small white scrap of paper over each square below, and use a toothpick to stir one drop of Sudan III thoroughly with a small sample of the indicated substance. Record your results in Table 40.3.

corn oil	margarine	peanut butter	milk	flour	water

Place this side of the Experimental Page facedown. Use the other side under your small-scale reaction surface.

EXPERIMENTAL DATA

Record your results in Tables 40.1, 40.2, or 40.3 or in copies of the tables in your notebook.

Table 40.1 Test for Starch

starch	pasta	cracker	bread	cereal	flour
black	black	black	black	black	black

Table 40.2 Test for Protein

milk	powdered milk	yeast	gelatin	bread	water
blue-violet	blue-violet	blue-violet	blue-violet	no change	no change

Table 40.3 Test for Fat

corn oil	margarine	peanut butter	milk	flour	water
dark red	dark red	dark red	dark red	no change	no change

CLEANING UP

Avoid contamination by cleaning up in a way that protects you and your environment. Carefully clean the small-scale reaction surface by absorbing the contents onto a paper towel, wipe it with a damp paper towel, and dry it. Dispose of the paper towels, scraps of paper, and toothpicks in the waste bin. Wash your hands thoroughly with soap and water.

QUESTIONS FOR ANALYSES

Use what you learned in this experiment to answer the following questions.

1. Describe a positive test for starch. Which samples gave a positive test for starch?

   KI + NaClO added to the sample produces a blue-black color. Pasta,

   crackers, bread, cereal, and flour.

2. Describe a positive test for protein. Which samples gave positive tests?

CuSO₄ + NaOH added to the sample produces a blue-violet color. Milk,

powdered milk, yeast, and gelatin.

3. Describe a positive test for fat. Which samples gave positive tests?

Sudan III mixed into the sample with a toothpick causes the red color to

intensify as it is absorbed into the sample. Corn oil, margarine, peanut

butter, and milk.

4. Which substance contained more than one classification of food?

Milk.

5. The positive test for starch works because potassium iodide reacts with sodium hypochlorite to produce I₂. The presence of iodine is detected by starch, which turns blue-black according to the following unbalanced chemical equations.

$$\underline{1}\ \ ClO^- + \underline{2}\ \ I^- + \underline{2}\ \ H^+ \rightarrow \underline{1}\ \ I_2 + \underline{1}\ \ H_2O + \underline{1}\ \ Cl^-$$

I_2 + starch → blue-black starch-iodine complex.

a. Balance the first equation above.

b. Write half-reactions to show the oxidation and the reduction for the first equation above.

$ClO^- + 2e^- \rightarrow Cl^-$ $2I^- \rightarrow I_2 + 2e^-$

reduction   oxidation

6. Sodium hydroxide breaks protein chains into individual amino acids, which bond to copper(II) ions to form a distinguishing deep blue-violet color. Draw the structural formula of an amino acid.

$$H_2N - \underset{\underset{H}{|}}{\overset{\overset{R}{|}}{C}} - \overset{\overset{O}{\|}}{C} - OH$$

7. Sudan III is a fat-soluble dye that imparts a red orange stain to the long-chain fat molecules. Do you expect Sudan III to be very soluble in water? Why?

No. Fat-soluble dyes dissolve in nonpolar molecules. Water is very polar.

("Like dissolves like.")

8. Why do you suppose the dye color of Sudan III intensifies when it is mixed with fats?

As Sudan III is absorbed into the fat, it becomes more concentrated.

NOW IT'S YOUR TURN!

1. Try testing the various foods in this lab for all three classes of biological molecules—starch, protein, and fat.

2. So-called reducing sugars have structural properties that will give electrons to copper(II) ion and reduce it.

$$Cu^{2+} + e^- \rightarrow Cu^+$$

Reducing sugars can be identified by using Benedict's solution, which contains copper(II) ions, or Cu^{2+}. When heated, a mixture of Benedict's solution and a reducing sugar turns from blue to green or yellow.

Carry out a positive Benedict's test for reducing sugars in the following way:

a. Combine the chemicals shown below on a glass slide.

b. Place the glass slide on a hot plate. **CAUTION:** *The glass will be hot. Handle with a plastic spatula.*

c. Note the change with time. A distinct color change indicates a reducing sugar.

```
2 drops Benedict's solution
           +
      1 drop glucose
```

3. Test one drop of various other samples with two drops of Benedict's solution. Try water, galactose, milk, honey, etc.

4. Add a drop of HCl to sucrose, a nonreducing sugar. What happens when you add Benedict's solution? What can you conclude?

The solution turns from blue to green or yellow. HCl has hydrolyzed the

sucrose to produce glucose, a reducing sugar.

Chapter 25 • *Nuclear Chemistry*   **SMALL-SCALE EXPERIMENT**

HALF-LIVES AND REACTION RATES

Small-Scale Experiment for text Section 25.2

OBJECTIVES

- **Measure** and **record** the rate at which hydrochloric acid (HCl) reacts with magnesium (Mg).
- **Identify** the half-life of the reaction by interpreting a graph of the experimental data.
- **Determine** the order of the reaction by plotting the experimental data.

INTRODUCTION

A half-life is the time required for one half of the atoms of a radioisotope to emit radiation and to decay to products. After one half-life, half of the radioactive atoms have decayed into atoms of another element. After another half-life, only a quarter of the original sample remains. After another half-life, only an eighth remains, and so on.

Because the concept of half-life is probably unfamiliar to you, you may conclude intuitively that if it takes one hour for half of a radioactive sample to decay, then it should take only another hour for the other half to decay. This conclusion is based on the false assumption that the rate of decay is linear (constant over time). In fact, radioisotopes decay in a nonlinear fashion. The rate of decay slows over time so that the more time that has elapsed, the more slowly the decay proceeds. The reactants of many chemical reactions that involve no radioactivity at all react to form products at an easily measurable half-life.

PURPOSE

In this experiment, you will make a quantitative study of the rate of reaction between hydrochloric acid and magnesium and determine the half-life of the reaction.

$$2HCl + Mg \rightarrow MgCl_2 + H_2(g)$$

As time progresses, the reactants will be consumed. You will stop the reaction after various time intervals by removing the magnesium. You will then measure the amount of HCl consumed in reacting with Mg by titrating the unreacted HCl with potassium hydroxide, KOH. The number of drops of KOH required in the titration is proportional to the amount of HCl consumed by the magnesium. You will then begin the reaction again, stop it after a longer period of time, and titrate the HCl again. By doing this several times, you will have measured the number of drops of KOH required for the titration at various times during the reaction. The same piece of magnesium can be used because the thin ribbon has nearly the same surface area exposed in each run. For this reason, the amount of magnesium exposed to the acid in each run will not change. This is important because you will be measuring the disappearance of HCl over time, and you do not want it to be affected by the different sizes of magnesium pieces. Finally, after several runs, the ribbon will become so thin that it will no longer be useful, and you can stop the experiment. You will determine the half-life of the reaction by plotting the drops of KOH used in the titration versus time.

SAFETY 🦺 👓 ⚗️ 🧪

- Wear safety goggles, an apron, and gloves when working with corrosive chemicals.
- Use full small-scale pipets only for the controlled delivery of liquids.
- Avoid inhaling substances that can irritate your respiratory system.

MATERIALS

Small-scale pipets of the following solutions:
hydrochloric acid (HCl)   potassium hydroxide (KOH)
phenolphthalein (phen)   water
Solid: magnesium ribbon

EQUIPMENT

watch or clock
1-ounce plastic cup

EXPERIMENTAL PROCEDURE

1. Add 10 drops of HCl to a clean, dry one-ounce plastic cup.

2. Add one drop of phenolphthalein and titrate with KOH, counting the drops to the pink end point. Record your results in Table 41.1. Clean and dry the cup for the next run. (**Note:** This run for time 0 is a titration of the HCl before any magnesium is added.)

3. Add 10 more drops of HCl to a clean, dry cup.

4. Cut 3 cm of Mg ribbon. Dip the piece of Mg in a few drops of HCl for a few seconds to dissolve the tarnish. Dry the ribbon.

5. Tilt the cup at an angle and dip the piece of Mg into the HCl for 10 seconds. Hold the Mg ribbon vertically, moving it constantly to dislodge the forming gas bubbles. Keep the magnesium submerged at a constant depth. At the end of 10 seconds, remove the Mg and wash it quickly with water, making sure the wash water enters the HCl in the cup. Dry the Mg for the next run.

6. Add one drop of phenolphthalein and titrate and record your data in Step 2.

7. Repeat Steps 5 and 6 for time intervals of 20, 30, 40, 50, 60, and 70 seconds or until all the magnesium is used up. Record your results in Table 41.1.

EXPERIMENTAL DATA

Record your results in Table 41.1 or in a copy of the table in your notebook.

Table 41.1 Reaction-Rate Data

Run	0	1	2	3	4	5	6	7
Drops of HCl	10	10	10	10	10	10	10	10
Time (s)	0	10	20	30	40	50	60	70
Drops of KOH to pink	43	25	15	7	5	4	Mg depleted	Mg depleted
1/drops of KOH	0.023	0.040	0.067	0.14	0.10	0.25	—	—
Log drops of KOH	1.6	1.4	1.2	0.85	0.70	0.60	—	—

1. Calculate the reciprocal of the number of drops of KOH (1/drops of KOH) for each time you measured. Record your results in Table 41.1.

2. Calculate the log of the number of drops of KOH, log (drops of KOH), for each time you measured. Record your results in Table 41.1.

3. Make a plot of drops of KOH (y-axis) versus time in seconds (x-axis).

Drops of KOH versus Time

Name _____ Date _____ Class _____

CLEANING UP

Avoid contamination by cleaning up in a way that protects you and your environment. Carefully clean the plastic cup by flooding it with water and rinsing its contents down the drain. Shake excess water out, and allow it to dry upside down on a paper towel. Dispose of any remaining magnesium by placing it in the appropriate recycling container. Wash your hands thoroughly with soap and water.

QUESTIONS FOR ANALYSES

Use what you learned in this experiment to answer the following questions.

1. What do you see when Mg reacts with HCl? Write a complete chemical equation and a net ionic equation for the reaction between Mg and HCl.

   Bubbles. $2HCl + Mg(s) \rightarrow MgCl_2 + H_2(g)$. $2H^+ + Mg(s) \rightarrow Mg^{2+} + H_2(g)$.

2. Look at your plot of drops KOH versus time. What happens to the rate of reaction as time progresses? Why?

   It slows down because the concentration of the HCl decreases over time.

3. How many drops of KOH were required to titrate the HCl after 0 seconds? What is half this value?

   43. 21.5.

4. Using your plot of drops KOH versus time, determine the half-life of the reaction. To do this, find the time required for the HCl to drop to half its value by finding the time that corresponds to half the number of drops of KOH in Question 3.

   Approximately 12 seconds.

5. Find the time required for the number of drops to fall to one fourth of the original value and one eighth of the original value. Explain how these values also represent the half-life of the reaction.

   11 drops after 24 seconds, 6 drops after 36 seconds. The amount of HCl

   falls to half of its value after each 12-second time interval.

6. Use your data in Table 41.1 to make the following plots:

   a. 1/drops of KOH versus time in seconds

b. log (drops KOH) versus time in seconds.

7. The "order" of the reaction gives us information about the number of hydrogen ions involved up to and including the rate-determining step. The rate of a zero-order reaction is independent of the concentration of HCl. In a first-order reaction, the rate varies directly with the concentration of HCl. The rate of a second-order reaction varies with the square of the concentration of HCl. The order of the reaction of HCl and Mg with respect to the HCl concentration can be determined from the plot that most closely resembles a straight line.

Straight-Line Plot	Order of Reaction
drops KOH versus time	zero order
log (drops KOH) versus time	first order
1/drops KOH versus time	second order

What is the "order" of the reaction with respect to the HCl concentration? How do you know?

First order. The plot of log (drops KOH) versus time is a straight line.

8. The rate law for the reaction takes the form: rate = k[HCl]^n where n = the order of the reaction. What is the rate law for this reaction?

Rate = k[HCl]^1.

NOW IT'S YOUR TURN!

1. Design and carry out a similar experiment for the reaction of $CaCO_3(s)$ + HCl.

2. Design and carry out an experiment to measure the rate of reaction in a different way. For example, measure the amount of hydrogen gas produced over time or the weight loss of magnesium over time.